Nucleus and Cytopla:

Nucleus and Cytoplasm

HENRY HARRIS

FELLOW OF LINCOLN COLLEGE
PROFESSOR OF PATHOLOGY IN THE UNIVERSITY OF OXFORD

THIRD EDITION

CLARENDON PRESS · OXFORD
1974

Oxford University Press, Ely House, London W.1

GLASGOW NEW YORK TORONTO MELBOURNE WELLINGTON
CAPE TOWN SALISBURY IBADAN NAIROBI DAR ES SALAAM LUSAKA ADDIS ABABA
BOMBAY CALCUTTA MADRAS KARACHI LAHORE DACCA
KUALA LUMPUR SINGAPORE HONG KONG TOKYO

CASEBOUND ISBN O 19 854124 4
PAPERBACK ISBN O 19 854125 2

© OXFORD UNIVERSITY PRESS 1968, 1970, 1974

FIRST EDITION 1968
SECOND EDITION 1970
THIRD EDITION 1974

MADE AND PRINTED IN GREAT BRITAIN
BY WILLIAM CLOWES & SONS, LIMITED
LONDON, BECCLES AND COLCHESTER

Two roads diverged in a wood, and I—
I took the one less traveled by,
And that has made all the difference.

Robert Frost
from *The Road Not Taken*

Preface to the First Edition

THE object of this book, originally delivered as a series of lectures at the Sir William Dunn School of Pathology, University of Oxford, is to provide an introduction to some of the salient problems in the field of nucleo-cytoplasmic relationships. The approach is analytical rather than didactic, but it is intended to stimulate enthusiasm, not stifle it. I spend most of my time doing experiments with animal cells, but I have also worked with *Acetabularia* and *Vicia* on the one hand, and with *Escherichia coli* and *Bacillus cereus* on the other; and if I tend to view the simple diagram and the attractive generalization with a critical eye, it is because a very varied experience has made it clear to me that, with rare exceptions, information comes slowly and accompanied, more often than not, by a great deal of misinformation. But in this book I also describe many of my own experiments, and I give my own interpretations of them, and I make theories on the strength of them; so there is more than enough to attract the attention of other critical eyes. I do not, of course, imagine that all the conclusions which I have reached will be universally popular, but I like to think that many of them will now be regarded as a closer approximation to the truth than might have been the case a few years ago. I hope that the student who reads these pages will come away with the conviction that some of the most important problems in modern biology are far from solved; for then, if he is lucky, he may later find that he can have many hours of simple pleasure in attempting to solve them.

Oxford   HENRY HARRIS
Michaelmas 1967

Preface to the Second Edition

In the field of nucleo-cytoplasmic relationships, in which dozens of journals publish hundred of papers each month, perhaps no apology is needed for the production of a second edition of this book so soon after the first. None the less, reliable information still comes slowly; and although some evidence that appeared strong in 1967 appears less strong in 1970, and some arguments then tenuous now appear to be correct, nothing has happened that seems to me to necessitate a fundamental revision of the main conclusions that I reached three years ago. I have done what I can to incorporate important new developments and hope that the book will continue to be of use to those who find the analytical approach attractive.

Oxford
Hilary 1970

HENRY HARRIS

Preface to the Third Edition

THIS edition of *Nucleus and Cytoplasm* has been more extensively revised than the last. The long-awaited development of assays for the biological activity of messenger ribonucleic acids, the analysis of transcriptional and translational controls in terms of real molecules, the continued progress in the field of cell fusion have enabled me to replace a good deal of speculation by a little of what begins to look increasingly like hard fact. That has given me pleasure. It has given me even greater pleasure to find, in a time when scientific books have largely become compilations of specialist articles by many different hands, that there are readers who continue to take an interest in one man's view of the cell, however imperfect it might be.

Oxford   HENRY HARRIS
Trinity 1973

Acknowledgements

PLATE 4a is reproduced by courtesy of Professors J.-E. Edström and W. Beermann and the editors of *Journal of Cell Biology*; Plate 4b by courtesy of the late Dr. U. Clever and the editors of *Chromosoma*; Plate 5 by courtesy of Drs. M. Lezzi and M. Robert and the editors of *Chromosoma*; Plate 18a by courtesy of Dr. W. Gehring and the editors of *Developmental Biology*; and Plate 18b by courtesy of Drs. G. Eguichi and T. S. Okada and the editors of *Proceedings of the National Academy of Sciences* (U.S.A.). Plate 3 was kindly supplied by Dr. D. Kay of the Sir William Dunn School of Pathology. I wish to thank the editors of *Bacteriological Reviews* for permission to reproduce Fig. 3; the editor of *Nature* for permission to reproduce Fig. 4; the editors of *Biochimica et Biophysica Acta* for permission to reproduce Fig. 5; the editors of *Journal of Biological Chemistry* for permission to reproduce Fig. 7; and the editors of *Biochemical Journal, Journal of Cell Science, Proceedings of the Royal Society* and *Biochimica et Biophysica Acta* for permission to reproduce many plates and figures originally published by my colleagues and myself in these journals.

Contents

List of Plates   xii

1. The expression of genetic information   1

2. The genetic operator model   21

3. The search for the messenger   46

4. Regulation in higher cells   77

5. Cell fusion   109

6. Differentiation   142

Author Index   167

Subject Index   176

List of Plates

(Plates 1–8 appear between pages 82 and 83)

PLATE 1. Two species of the giant unicellular alga *Acetabularia* showing differences in the morphology of the caps. These structures provide a mechanism for the formation and dissemination of the spores. (a) *Acetabularia mediterranea*. (b) *Acetabularia crenulata*. C, cap; W, whorls, which are formed shortly before the development of the cap; S, stalk; R, rhizoid containing the single nucleus.

2. The formation of a fruiting body in a culture of the slime mould *Dictyostelium discoideum*. The motile amoebae aggregate to form the fruiting body which is thus composed of many cells. Its function is essentially equivalent to that of the cap in *Acetabularia*. Some earlier stages in the process of fruiting body formation are shown on the left.

3. Spore formation in *Bacillus subtilis*. The spore is formed intracellularly. The cell contains a vegetative nucleus and a spore nucleus. (By courtesy of Dr. D. Kay.)

4a. The polytene salivary gland chromosomes (I, II, III, IV) of *Chironomus tentans*. The nucleoli (N) and a large puff (Balbiani ring) (BR) are shown. (By courtesy of Prof. J.-E. Edström and Prof. W. Beermann.)

4b. Two large puffs (Balbiani rings) on chromosome IV of the salivary gland of *Chironomus tentans*. (By courtesy of the late Dr. U. Clever.)

5. Formation of specific puffs in isolated polytene chromosomes. (a) Chromosome II of *Chironomus thummi* isolated in the condensed state. (b) Differential dispersion of the same chromosome induced by changes in the electrolyte composition of the medium. Arrows show puffs formed at specific loci. L, left arm of chromosome; R, right arm; C, centromere. (By courtesy of Drs. M. Lezzi and M. Robert.)

6a. A multinucleate cell formed by the fusion of several HeLa cells.

6b. Autoradiograph of a binucleate cell containing one HeLa nucleus and one Ehrlich nucleus. The HeLa cells had been grown in [3H] thymidine before the heterokaryons were produced. The HeLa nucleus is labelled and the Ehrlich nucleus is not.

7. Four frames from a cinematographic sequence showing a HeLa-Ehrlich heterokaryon undergoing mitosis and giving rise to two hybrid mononucleate daughter cells.

8a. A HeLa-Ehrlich hybrid cell at metaphase. This cell contains 181 chromosomes in proportions very close to those expected from the fusion of one modal Ehrlich cell and two modal HeLa cells. Arrows indicate two HeLa (H) and one Ehrlich (E) marker chromosomes.

8b. A heterokaryon containing one HeLa nucleus and a number of rabbit macrophage nuclei.

(Plates 9–12 appear between pages 114 and 115)

9a. A heterokaryon containing three HeLa nuclei and two rat lymphocyte nuclei.

9b. A heterokaryon containing one HeLa nucleus and two chick erythrocyte nuclei.

10a. A heterokaryon containing three rabbit macrophage nuclei and two rat lymphocyte nuclei, which are smaller and stain more deeply. Note the peripheral distribution of the nuclei in the cell.

10b. A heterokaryon containing four rabbit macrophage nuclei and three hen erythrocyte nuclei. Note the peripheral distribution of the nuclei in the cell.

11a. An erythrocyte ghost (EG) adherent to a HeLa cell (H). The arrow shows a virus particle wedged between the two cell membranes.

11b. Tenuous cytoplasmic bridges, shown by arrows, formed between an erythrocyte ghost (EG) and a HeLa cell (H). The cytoplasm of the HeLa cell, which can be distinguished by its characteristic array of ribosomes, has flowed into the erythrocyte ghost.

12a. An erythrocyte nucleus passing into the cytoplasm of a HeLa cell.

12b. A heterokaryon containing one HeLa nucleus and one hen erythrocyte nucleus. The erythrocyte nucleus is highly contracted and its chromatin is condensed. 'Nuclear bodies', which are areas of extreme condensation in the chromatin, are seen.

Plates 13–16 appear between pages 130 and 131

13a. A heterokaryon containing one HeLa nucleus and one hen erythrocyte nucleus 24 h after cell fusion. The erythrocyte nucleus has undergone enlargement, the chromatin has become more dispersed and the 'nuclear bodies' are no longer visible.

13b. Autoradiograph of a heterokaryon exposed for 20 min to [3H] uridine. The cell contains one HeLa nucleus and three hen erythrocyte nuclei in various stages of enlargement. All the nuclei are synthesizing RNA. Note that the labelling of the erythrocyte nuclei increases as they enlarge.

14a. A heterokaryon containing two mouse nuclei and one hen erythrocyte nucleus, 18 h after fusion. The haemadsorption reaction reveals the presence of hen-specific antigens on the surface of the cell.

14b. A heterokaryon containing two mouse nuclei and one hen erythrocyte nucleus, 5 days after cell fusion. The erythrocyte nucleus has been reactivated, but the absence of any haemadsorption shows that the hen-specific antigens are no longer present on the surface of the cell. The erythrocyte nucleus shows a small nucleolus.

15. A heterokaryon containing two irradiated mouse nuclei and one hen erythrocyte nucleus, 11 days after cell fusion. This is now a typical radiation giant cell. The reactivated erythrocyte nucleus has a prominent nucleolus, and hen-specific antigens have reappeared on the surface of the cell.

16a. Autoradiograph of an A9-chick erythrocyte heterokaryon in which the erythrocyte nucleus has been reactivated but has not yet developed a nucleolus. The cell has been exposed for 4 h to tritiated hypoxanthine, but there is very little incorporation of label.

16*b*. Autoradiograph of an A$_9$-chick erythrocyte heterokaryon in which the erythrocyte nucleus shows early development of the nucleolus. The cell has been exposed for 4 h to tritiated hypoxanthine. Both the A$_9$ and the erythrocyte nucleus are now clearly labelled. The cell has acquired the ability to incorporate hypoxanthine into nucleic acid.

Plates 17–18 appear between pages 158 and 159

17*a*. Autoradiograph of a heterokaryon containing a mouse nucleus and 2 chick erythrocyte nuclei, exposed for 6 h to a tritiated RNA precursor. The mouse nucleus and the 2 erythrocyte nuclei are very heavily labelled, and there is substantial cytoplasmic labelling.

17*b*. Autoradiograph of another heterokaryon from the same preparation as the cell shown in Plate 17*a*. The mouse nucleus has been inactivated by a microbeam of ultraviolet light. The erythrocyte nuclei, which have not yet developed nucleoli, are heavily labelled, but the cytoplasm contains almost no radioactivity.

18*a*. Transdetermination in an imaginal disc. A culture of antennal imaginal disc cells has given rise to a wing. Most of the antennal components (A) have normal wild type coloration (w), but two areas (the palpus and rostral membrane) have mutant coloration (m). These regions represent a clone of mutant cells. From this clone transdetermination has given rise to a wing (W) which also has mutant coloration. (By courtesy of Dr. W. Gehring.)

18*b*. 'Transdifferentiation' in cell culture. A clonal population of pigmented retinal cells has given rise to a subcolony of cells that produce lens proteins and organize themselves into a 'lentoid' body. (By courtesy of Drs. G. Eguchi and T. S. Okada.)

1

The expression of genetic information

1. Introduction

THESE days, when a biologist talks about genetic information he has
in mind ordered sequences of nucleotides in DNA. When he talks
about transfer of information he is probably thinking about the mechanism by which the instructions encoded in a sequence of DNA nucleotides are transported to some other site in the cell; and when he
talks about expression of genetic information he usually means the
mechanisms by which the biological significance of a particular sequence of DNA nucleotides becomes apparent in some aspect of cell
behaviour. In the case of eukaryotic cells we still know very little about
the mechanisms by which information is transferred from the genes to
specific sites in the cytoplasm, and still less about the mechanisms
that determine whether and when this information is ultimately
expressed. We know, of course, that the sequence of nucleotides in
DNA is transcribed into some form of homologous sequence of
nucleotides in RNA, and that this RNA forms a template for the
synthesis of a corresponding sequence of amino acids in a polypeptide. But if, like the hedgehog, we can take comfort in the knowledge of this one big thing,[1] we should not blind ourselves to the fact
that almost no part of the process is understood in precise chemical
detail, and that the bare outline on which we are agreed does not
provide us with satisfactory explanations for many of the most
fundamental properties of higher cells. We do not, for example,
know:

(1) How the transcription of DNA in eukaryotic cells is regulated
and how precise this regulation is.

(2) Whether the genes are transcribed in any particular order, and
if so, what determines this order.

(3) Whether the amount of a particular protein synthesized in the

cell is determined by the number of RNA copies that have been produced from the corresponding gene.

(4) Whether there is wide variation in the amount of RNA produced by different structural genes, and if so, what determines this variation.

(5) Whether there is any predictable relationship between the time at which a particular gene is transcribed and the time at which the corresponding protein is synthesized.

(6) In what form the RNA carrying the genetic instructions is transported to the cytoplasm of the cell, and whether this transport is itself regulated.

(7) Whether there are great differences in the lifetimes of different RNA templates in the cytoplasm of the cell and, if there are, what determines these differences.

(8) Whether there is any close relationship between the lifetime of an RNA template and the facility with which the synthesis of the corresponding protein can be initiated or suppressed.

(9) How the synthesis of a specific protein on a particular RNA template is switched on and off.

(10) Whether the rate of protein synthesis varies from template to template, and if so, what determines this variation.

When I say that we do not know the answers to these questions, I do not wish to imply that no attempts have been made to answer them. I mean simply that I do not find the evidence on these points compelling enough to permit me to feel confident that decisive answers have been obtained. But, in looking at this evidence, I cannot avoid the impression that some answers are very much more probable than others; and, in a sense, this work is an acknowledgement of the obligation to justify one's point of view.

3. Lessons from an enucleate cell

In 1926 Joachim Hämmerling, initially in collaboration with his teacher, Max Hartmann, began a series of investigations on the behaviour of the giant unicellular alga, *Acetabularia*, a member of the class *Dasycladaceae*. This plant, which is between 3 and 5 cm long when mature, contains a single nucleus located in the tip of one of the rhizoids at the base of its stalk. The giant cell develops from a small zygote: it forms first a stalk with rhizoids at its base and later a cap that has a characteristic shape for each species (Plates 1*a* and 1*b*). The nucleus of the cell can be removed simply by cutting off the rhizoid in which it is located; and the nucleus from one cell can readily be transplanted to another. Taking advantage of these features, Hämmerling carried out some simple experiments that proved to be decisive for our understanding of certain aspects of nucleo-cytoplasmic relationships. Hämmerling's original experiments were analysed in essentially descriptive terms;[2,3] but they have, over the last decade or so, been extensively elaborated by his pupils and others, using the more sophisticated methodology of contemporary biochemistry.[4,5] In some respects, the experiments that have been done on *Acetabularia* constitute the most precise analysis of nucleo-cytoplasmic interactions that has so far been made. I have no desire to belittle the enormous value of the work that has been done in recent years on *Escherichia coli* and other micro-organisms, especially in expanding the range and the power of genetical methods; but, on certain crucial questions, the evidence from micro-organisms is inconclusive, whereas the evidence from *Acetabularia* is not. A brief summary of the main observations that have been made on *Acetabularia* will, I think, at once establish their outstanding importance:

(1) The cap formed by a particular species of *Acetabularia* has a morphology that is characteristic of that species. The morphological features of the cap are determined by genes present in the cell nucleus: when the nucleus of one species of *Acetabularia* is transplanted into the cytoplasm of another, the transplanted nucleus eventually determines the formation of a cap that has the morphology characteristic of the species from which the nucleus was derived.[6-8]

(2) Formation of the cap is a complex morphogenetic event involving net synthesis of protein,[9] the synthesis of specific enzymes,[10-13] and the synthesis of specific polysaccharides.[14] The polysaccharide composition of the wall of the cap differs from that found in the cell wall elsewhere;[14,15] and when the cap is formed not only are the characteristic cap polysaccharides synthesized, but also the enzymes necessary for their synthesis.[12,13] Cap formation involves changes in the rates of synthesis of certain other enzymes as well,[10,11] although the roles that these other enzymes play in the morphogenetic process is not clear. The formation of the cap is thus a typical example of cellular differentiation, involving a precise regulation of the synthesis of specific proteins.

(3) A perfectly normal species-specific cap can be formed *de novo* many weeks after the nucleus has been removed from the cell.[2,4] The regulated synthesis of specific enzymes that accompanies cap formation in the presence of the nucleus also takes place in its absence[10-13] (Figs. 1 and 2). Moreover, in the case of the enzymes involved in the synthesis of the cap polysaccharides, there is strong evidence that they are specified by the DNA in the cell nucleus.[13,16]

(4) All the information necessary for the production of the cap passes from the nucleus to the cytoplasm long before the cap is normally formed. In *Acetabularia cliftonii* removal of the nucleus in a very young plant often provokes a very premature formation of the

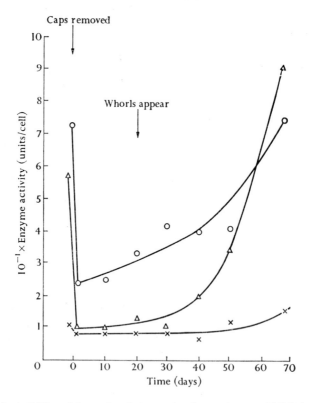

FIG. 1. Activities of three phosphatases, showing optima at pH 5 (○), pH 8·5 (×),and pH 12 (△), in regenerating nucleate cells. Caps were removed from the cells and enzyme activities were measured during regeneration. Whorls are formed a little before the onset of cap formation, which is complete in 6–8 weeks. (From Spencer and Harris.[10])

cap.[17] Premature caps may be produced by enucleation in this species at least 70 days before they are normally formed in the intact plant.[18] Premature caps may also be produced in other *Acetabularia* species by exposing the cells to appropriate concentrations of certain plant hormones.[19] Both the formation of the cap and the synthesis of enzymes normally associated with cap formation can be induced prematurely by these hormones in enucleate cells.[19,20] It is clear that the information for the production of the cap is delivered to the cytoplasm many days before it is used.

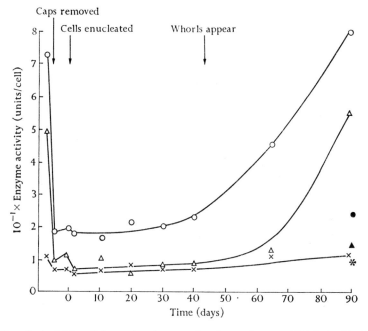

FIG. 2. Activities of three phosphatases, showing optima at pH 5 (○), pH 8·5 (×), and pH 12 (△), in regenerating *enucleate* cells. Caps were removed and the cells enucleated 8 days later. The activity of these three enzymes is also shown in cells that failed to regenerate: pH 5 (●), pH 8·5 (▲), pH 12 (∗). (From Spencer and Harris.[10])

(5) Information for the production of the cap may be present in the cytoplasm of the cell without being expressed. Formation of the cap in *Acetabularia crenulata* may be suppressed if the cells are grown under conditions of restricted illumination. The cells continue growing under these conditions, and produce grossly elongated stalks

without caps. If the nuclei are removed from these elongated stalks and the illumination is then increased, normal caps are formed on these enucleate stalks. The information for production of the cap is therefore present in the cytoplasm, but the expression of this information does not take place under conditions of inadequate illumination.[4]

(6) In the absence of the cell nucleus the information for the production of the cap is extremely stable. Enucleate stalks may be maintained for many weeks under conditions in which cap formation is inhibited, but even after this period of time the enucleate stalks will form caps when they are transferred to appropriate cultural conditions.[4]

While none of these observations deals directly with the metabolism of RNA in the cell, they none the less provide some very precise information about the behaviour in *Acetabularia* of that family of RNA molecules that is involved in the transfer of genetic information to the cytoplasm. The outstanding metabolic characteristic of the RNA molecules that carry the information for production of the cap is their persistence in the cytoplasm for long periods after removal of the nucleus. Although the original source of supply of these molecules has been eliminated by the removal of the nucleus, enough RNA to provide all the information necessary to produce a normal cap persists for many weeks, even under limiting cultural conditions. The cytoplasm of *Acetabularia*, like that of other organisms, contains active ribonucleases,[21] so that one obvious conclusion that can be drawn from these experiments is that the RNA that carries this genetic information is either present in the cytoplasm in a form that is very resistant to intracellular ribonucleases, or that this RNA is removed from the action of these enzymes in some way, perhaps by sequestration of the RNA or of the enzymes within specific cytoplasmic structures.

Two formal objections can be raised to this conclusion. The first is that the cytoplasm of *Acetabularia* contains DNA,[22] and that the RNA carrying the information for cap morphogenesis may be continually produced, or produced when required, from cytoplasmic DNA.[23] As far as the two well established forms of cytoplasmic DNA are concerned (the DNA of chloroplasts and mitochondria), this possibility can be dismissed. We know, from the nuclear transplantation experiments, that the specific morphological features of the cap are determined by the cell nucleus, not by the chloroplasts or the mitochondria; transplantation of chloroplasts or of crude cytoplasm has no effect on cap morphology.[5] If the templates that determine morphogenesis of the cap are produced from cytoplasmic DNA, we must envisage a cytoplasmic DNA that is a copy of the nuclear DNA. This idea implies that the transfer of information from nucleus to cytoplasm is, in some cases, effected by DNA not RNA, and that the specifications for at least some proteins are represented in both nuclear and cytoplasmic DNA. This model is unattractive for a variety of reasons. For example, there is no obvious reason why just those templates that determine cap morphogenesis should have dual representation in both nuclear and cytoplasmic DNA; and, if the phenomenon is more general, one is forced to consider the possibility of a widespread duplication of the genes in both nucleus and cytoplasm, a state of affairs that makes nonsense of most forms of genetic analysis, and for which there is no chemical evidence. Moreover, where there is good evidence that the specifications for a particular characteristic are encoded in cytoplasmic DNA, as, for example, in the case of the chloroplast, genetic analysis reveals a non-mendelian or cytoplasmic form of inheritance;[24] whereas nuclear transplantation experiments in *Acetabularia* indicate a simple and direct determination of the cap characteristics by the nucleus. Indeed, for the chloroplasts of *Acetabularia*, there is evidence that they do not contain nearly enough DNA to specify all the proteins necessary for chloroplast function,[5] to say nothing of all those necessary for the growth and morphogenesis of the cap; and it has even been shown that some of the structural proteins of the chloroplasts themselves are coded by nuclear DNA.[25,26]

The other possibility that could account for the persistence of this information in the enucleate cell is that the relevant RNA might be replicated in the cytoplasm. If the RNA templates could be copied in the cytoplasm, the information could persist without necessarily having a long life. The idea that normal cellular RNA templates might be replicated in the cytoplasm of the cell has a long history, but in recent years it has met with strong resistance. There is no doubt that net synthesis of RNA can take place in the cytoplasm of *Acetabularia* after removal of the nucleus.[27] Indeed, the great bulk of the RNA in *Acetabularia* is synthesized in the cell cytoplasm.[28] Most of this cytoplasmic RNA synthesis takes place in chloroplasts and mitochondria and is accounted for by the production of transfer

RNA and the ribosomal RNA components characteristic of these organelles; some less well defined classes of RNA also appear to be synthesized on the DNA of the chloroplasts and mitochondria.[28-32] However, the recent discovery in normal cells of enzymes that transcribe RNA into DNA (reverse transcriptases)[33-35] and of enzymes that copy RNA[36,37] must re-open the possibility that cytoplasmic RNA templates might, under certain circumstances, be replicated, either directly or through DNA intermediates. In any case, whether the persistence of the information in *Acetabularia* is due to the cytoplasmic replication of RNA templates, or simply to their long life, it is clear that this information does not have to be continually replenished by the synthetic activity of the cell nucleus.

The second important conclusion that can be drawn from the *Acetabularia* experiments is that the actual expression of the information, that is, the synthesis of the specific protein, the synthesis of the specific polysaccharide, the morphogenetic event itself, is determined by events that take place in the cytoplasm, not in the nucleus. There is clearly no inevitable relationship between the time at which the genetic information is transferred from the nucleus to the cytoplasm and the time at which it is expressed. The RNA templates for the cap-forming enzymes may be delivered to the cytoplasm weeks before the enzymes are synthesized in appreciable amounts, and, in the enucleate cell, the formation of the cap with all its concomitant regulation of enzyme synthesis may be induced prematurely or greatly delayed by simple manipulations of the environment. The conclusion seems inescapable that the expression of the genetic information is effected by means of cytoplasmic regulatory mechanisms that initiate, regulate, and suppress the synthesis of proteins on pre-existing templates.

The experiments on *Acetabularia* also throw some light on two related questions: whether there is great variation in the lifetimes of different RNA templates, and whether this variation, if it exists, is closely related to the regulation of protein synthesis. Although the behaviour of only a dozen or so specific enzymes has been studied in enucleate *Acetabularia* cells,[5] it must be borne in mind that the enucleate cell is capable of growth and regeneration as well as morphogenesis. A section of stalk containing the growing tip but no nucleus will, under appropriate conditions, regenerate both a new stalk and a cap.[2] These regenerative processes finally produce an essentially normal *Acetabularia* cell, although, of course, without a nucleus.

Enucleate growth under these conditions cannot be an unregulated process, since the end result is a cell which, from both the morphological and physiological point of view, is essentially normal: all the normal cytoplasmic structures are present and all the normal cytoplasmic functions are carried out. We cannot, of course, exclude the possibility that some RNA templates, whose products we are not examining, are short lived; but it is clear that all the information required for the development of an essentially normal *Acetabularia* cell persists for many weeks after enucleation. Nor is it likely that the cessation of certain syntheses at particular stages of development, for example, the cessation of stalk growth when the cap is formed, is determined by the exhaustion of the templates that support these syntheses: under appropriate cultural conditions the stalk may be induced to continue growing long after it would normally have stopped. It therefore seems improbable that the genetic information in the cytoplasm of *Acetabularia* has a wide spectrum of stability. Under clement cultural conditions the lifetime of most of this information must be measured in weeks at least. It is, of course, to be expected that on this time scale some variation in the life span of different RNA templates would occur, but it is hard to imagine that this variation could play any important role in regulating the synthesis of the great majority of the cytoplasmic proteins formed during the course of development. Information for the synthesis of specific proteins can certainly be present in the cytoplasm of the cell without being expressed; and this implies the existence of cytoplasmic regulatory mechanisms that suppress the synthesis of proteins without destroying their templates.

While all these experiments leave no doubt that the cytoplasm enjoys a high degree of regional autonomy, some recent observations indicate that the genetic information in the cytoplasm may none the less turn over more rapidly when the nucleus is present than when it is absent. The enzymes malate dehydrogenase and lactate dehydrogenase exhibit electrophoretic isoenzyme patterns that differ from one species of *Acetabularia* to another. Both of these enzymes continue to be synthesized after removal of the cell nucleus and the species-specific isoenzyme patterns are maintained in the enucleate cytoplasm until the last stages of cap formation (a period of three months or more depending on experimental conditions). If, however, a nucleus from a different species of *Acetabularia* is introduced into the enucleate cytoplasm, the pre-existing cytoplasmic isoenzyme pattern is abolished within three to five weeks and is replaced by the isoenzyme pattern characteristic of the species from which the nucleus was taken.[38,39] It has, moreover, been shown that the new isoenzyme pattern is formed by *de novo* synthesis of the enzyme proteins.[25] This finding indicates not only that the new nucleus is able to determine the synthesis of a new family of enzymes in the foreign cytoplasm, but also that it is able to suppress the synthesis of the enzymes specified by the previous nucleus. We do not know whether this suppression is achieved by the destruction of the pre-existing cytoplasmic RNA templates or by some other mechanism; nor do we know whether a nucleus operating normally within its own homologous cytoplasm produces a similar effect. But the possibility must be envisaged that the nucleus might determine a slow turnover of cytoplasmic RNA templates and that this turnover might stop when the nucleus is removed. Although such considerations make it difficult to estimate the precise lifetime of RNA templates in normal *Acetabularia* cells, they do not obscure the general principles governing the regulation of growth and morphogenesis in this organism. The study of *Acetabularia* leaves no doubt that growth and morphogenesis are regulated not by mechanisms that govern the detailed transcription of the genes, but by mechanisms that operate in the cytoplasm of the cell.

3. Other enucleate cells

We have now to consider how far *Acetabularia* can be regarded as representative of higher animal and plant cells as a whole. It is at once obvious that *Acetabularia* is exceptional in some respects. It is, to begin with, of immense size for a single mononucleate cell and, as far as I am aware, no other cell that has so far been studied survives enucleation for so long, or with so little impairment of physiological function. But a closer examination of the peculiarities of *Acetabularia* suggests that these differences do not represent fundamental differences in cellular organization. *Acetabularia* remains mononucleate throughout most of its life cycle, despite its huge size, because nuclear division in this cell is delayed until a very late stage in its development. The nucleus increases in size throughout the many weeks of cell growth and reaches enormous proportions; but it remains a single nucleus until a mature cap has been formed. Only then does the giant nucleus give rise to the secondary nuclei from which, by repeated mitosis, the nuclei of the 7000–15 000 gametes are eventually produced.[4] It is thus merely the phenomenon of nuclear growth without nuclear division that distinguishes *Acetabularia* from many coenocytic organisms, which may also be single giant cells, but which contain many nuclei that divide as the cell grows. In other respects *Acetabularia* is a typical photosynthetic marine alga, and it would, *a priori*, be very surprising if its physiological processes proved to be regulated by mechanisms that differed in principle from those operating in other marine algae.

How far do enucleation studies in other cells support or contradict the conclusions drawn from *Acetabularia*? The number of cases that can be discussed is limited, for in most other cells enucleation presents more formidable technical problems than it does in *Acetabularia*; and it must be admitted at the outset that no other enucleate cell that has so far been examined can accomplish the complete regeneration and morphogenesis of which *Acetabularia* is capable. However, an examination of the behaviour of those cells in which the effects of enucleation have been studied indicates clearly that the differences between them and *Acetabularia* are matters of degree and do not reflect fundamentally different modes of biological organization. The cells of *Spyrogyra* survive enucleation for more than 2 months. They grow in the absence of the nucleus, form new cytoplasm containing specific cytoplasmic organelles, synthesize proteins, and carry out all their normal physiological functions.[40] No formal investigation has been made of the ability of the enucleate cytoplasm in *Spyrogyra* to regulate the synthesis of specific enzymes, but it is difficult to imagine that the enucleate cell does not possess this ability since, like *Acetabularia*, it is capable of ordered growth and ordered physiological function. The enucleated egg of the sea urchin *Arbacia* is capable of repeated cell division after parthenogenetic stimulation and, under suitable conditions, will form a blastula that may develop functional cilia.[41] In this case it has been shown that appropriate stimulation of the enucleate egg initiates a wave of protein synthesis in the quiescent cytoplasm comparable to that produced by fertilization in the normal egg.[42] This again shows that the information for the synthesis of these proteins is present in the egg some time before it is expressed, and that the cytoplasm itself contains the regulatory mechanisms necessary to determine the onset of this synthesis. It has been formally demonstrated that a rapid increase in the rate of synthesis of microtubule proteins takes place under these conditions.[43] Protein synthesis may be induced in frog oocytes by the administration of pituitary hormones. This induced protein synthesis is not abolished by enucleation of the oocyte. Indeed, for many hours, the rates of synthesis in nucleate and enucleate cells are indistinguishable.[44] Enucleated frog eggs,[45] the anucleate polar lobes of eggs of the mud snail *Ilyanassa obsoleta*,[46] and anucleate halves of eggs of the sea snail *Triton*[47] are all capable of unimpaired protein synthesis for long periods. Enucleate cells of *Stentor* survive for almost a week. They can differentiate to produce partially formed mouth parts, they form vacuoles and they engage in completely normal physiological activity for two days or more.[48] *Stentor* cells enucleated just before cell division can complete the division and form new daughter cells. The protozoon *Peranema trichophorum* can regenerate flagella in the absence of the nucleus.[49] Enucleate fragments of human tissue culture cells survive *in vitro* for up to 4 days.[50] These fragments move about, exhibit pinocytosis, and incorporate amino acids into protein.[51] Enucleate fragments of prospective pigment cells (melanoblasts) from the developing neural crest of urodele embryos also survive for long periods *in vitro*, and may undergo morphological differentiation to assume the dendritic character that is typical of the mature pigmented cell.[52] These fragments also synthesize pigment granules. Amoebas do not feed after enucleation and the synthetic abilities of the enucleate cytoplasm progressively diminish. None the less, synthesis of protein as measured by the incorporation of radioactive amino acids continues in the enucleate cytoplasm for many hours.[53] And finally, the mammalian reticulocyte continues to synthesize haemoglobin for some days after elimination of the cell nucleus, and the synthesis of the globin moiety can be regulated by the availability of haem. [54–56]

The studies on enucleate cells other than *Acetabularia* are obviously fragmentary, but they none the less provide consistent evidence in support of the view that the templates for the synthesis of specific proteins persist in the cytoplasm of the cell for long periods after removal of the nucleus, and that the synthesis of the proteins on these templates is regulated by control mechanisms that operate in the cytoplasm itself.

4. Actinomycin D

A major extension of the range of this sort of investigation became possible with the introduction of the antibiotic actinomycin D. This compound, when used at a high enough concentration, combines with the DNA of the cell and inhibits its transcription into RNA. Actinomycin D has therefore been used to produce a form of 'physiological enucleation', a term that grossly over-simplifies the effects of the antibiotic. It cannot be over-emphasized that actinomycin D is an extremely toxic compound, and that, at concentrations that completely inhibit the transcription of DNA, it causes the rapid dissolution of most cells. When one finds, after administering a high dose of actinomycin D, that a particular physiological function or synthetic process is impaired, one cannot therefore conclude that this function or synthetic process is immediately or closely dependent upon the transcription of DNA. It has been shown that actinomycin D may produce drastic secondary effects; and where a cell is in the process of being killed by the antibiotic many processes may run down for reasons that are only remotely connected with the transcription of DNA. For the same reasons one cannot make any deductions about the rate of decay of the templates for protein synthesis from the changes produced by actinomycin D in the rate of this synthesis. The synthesis of proteins may become progressively impaired by the antibiotic for reasons that have nothing to do with the decay of the templates. Moreover, it is now clear that high concentrations of actinomycin D may induce extensive degradation of all families of RNA in the cell,[57] so that deductions about the normal life span of RNA templates made from observations on actinomycin D-poisoned cells are hazardous in the extreme.

On the other hand, if a particular physiological function persists for long periods in the presence of high concentrations of actinomycin D, this is presumptive evidence that the function in question is not immediately dependent on the transcription of DNA. If the synthesis of a particular protein continues after all RNA synthesis has been suppressed, one can conclude that the templates for the synthesis of this protein are stable in the sense that they do not have to be continually replaced by fresh synthesis; and if the synthesis of a particular protein can be regulated under such conditions, one can conclude that the regulatory mechanisms are cytoplasmic in the sense that they do not operate via transcription of the DNA. Thus, with actinomycin D, only the positive result, the persistence of function in the absence of RNA synthesis, has probative value; the negative result, the impairment of function, is, without other evidence, uninterpretable.

So much work has been done with actinomycin D since its introduction some years ago, that it would be difficult to give a complete catalogue of cases in which synthesis of a protein has been initiated in the presence of high concentrations of actinomycin D, or in which synthesis of a protein persists and continues to be regulated in the presence of the antibiotic. The following list is a selection of the more convincing examples that have come to my notice: synthesis of proteins during early development of sea urchin[58-62] and starfish[63] embryos; synthesis of a number of polysaccharide-forming enzymes during the development of the slime mould *Dictyostelium*;[64] induced synthesis of a number of enzymes and other proteins in mammalian liver and in cultures of hepatoma cells;[65-71] synthesis of protein in rat heart cells in culture;[72] synthesis of a specific plasma phosphoprotein induced in male chickens by the administration of diethylstilboestrol;[73] synthesis of glutamine synthetase in developing embryonic chick neural retina;[74,75] synthesis of specific lens proteins in the eye;[76-78] stimulation of protein synthesis in isolated rat diaphragm by growth hormone,[79] and in rat diaphragm[80] and heart muscle[81] by insulin; stimulation of protein synthesis in the pituitary gland by cyclic adenosine monophosphate,[82] of amylase synthesis in the parotid gland by epinephrine,[83] and of ovalbumin synthesis in the chick oviduct by steroid hormones;[84] synthesis of thyroglobulin in the thyroid gland;[85] synthesis of proteins during the germination of plant seeds and spores;[86-89] differentiation[90] and production of amylase[91] in developing pancreatic cells of the mouse embryo; synthesis of the enzyme, 'cocoonase', in specialized glands of the silk moth;[92] initiation of haemoglobin synthesis in chick embryo explants;[93] and the anamnestic formation of antibodies.[94,95]

Although in some of the experiments listed above RNA synthesis was reduced to less than 5 per cent of the normal level, complete inhibition of the transcription of DNA cannot be achieved with actinomycin D. The results obtained by the use of this compound are therefore less free from objection than those obtained by enucleation: it can always be argued that the template for the particular protein being studied continues to be produced in the small amount of RNA that is synthesized in the presence of the antibiotic. This argument can hardly apply to those cases where protein synthesis as a whole has been measured, but it could apply to those in which the synthesis of a single specific protein has been examined. Moreover, the possibility must always be considered that accumulation of a protein may result, not only from an increase in the rate of its synthesis, but also from a decrease in the rate of its degradation.[96,97] The wide range of biological material and the large number of different proteins that have been studied make it difficult to believe that they are all specified by that small group of genes whose transcription is relatively resistant to the action of actinomycin D; and in some cases there is no possibility that the observations could be accounted for by a reduction in the rate of protein degradation.

It therefore seems reasonable to conclude that in the higher cells of plants and animals, in both protozoa and metazoa, the principles that have been shown to operate in *Acetabularia* are, in general, applicable. The time at which a particular gene is transcribed into RNA has no immediate connection with the time at which this RNA is translated into protein. The templates for protein synthesis pass to the cytoplasm in a form that is, on the whole, resistant to intracellular degradation; these templates persist in the cytoplasm for long periods after removal of the nucleus. Initiation, regulation, and suppression of protein synthesis on these essentially stable templates is effected by cytoplasmic mechanisms that can operate perfectly well in the absence of the nucleus.

We must now examine to what extent these general principles are applicable to micro-organisms.

REFERENCES

1. BERLIN, I. (1953). *The hedgehog and the fox*. Weidenfeld & Nicolson, London.
2. HÄMMERLING, J. (1934) Regenerationsversuche an kernhaltigen und kernlosen Zellteilen von *Acetabularia Wettsteinii*. *Biol. Zbl.* **54**, 650.
3. HÄMMERLING, J. (1934). Über formbildende Substanzen bei *Acetabularia mediterranea*, ihre räumliche und zeitliche Verteilung und ihre Herkunft. *Wilhelm Roux Arch. EntwMech. Org.* **131**, 1.
4. HÄMMERLING, J. (1963). Nucleo-cytoplasmic interactions in *Acetabularia* and other cells. *A. Rev. Pl. Physiol.* **14**, 65.
5. SCHWEIGER, H.-G. (1969). Cell Biology of *Acetabularia*. *Curr. Top. Microbiol. Immunol.* **50**, 1.
6. HÄMMERLING, J. (1953). Nucleo-cytoplasmic relationship in the development of *Acetabularia*. *Int Rev. Cytol*, **2**, 475.
7. WERZ, G. (1961). Zur Frage der Herkunft und Verteilung cytoplasmatischer Ribonucleinsäure und ihrer Beziehungen zu "morphogenetischen Substanzen" bei *Acetabularia mediterranea*. *Z. Naturf.* **16b**, 126.
8. ZETSCHE, K. (1962). Die Aktivität implantierter Zellkerne von *Acetabularia* bei aufgehobener Photosynthese. *Naturwissenschaften* **17**, 404.
9. HÄMMERLING, J., CLAUSS, H., KECK, K., RICHTER, G., and WERZ, G. (1958). Growth and protein synthesis in nucleated and enucleated cells. *Expl Cell Res.* Suppl. **6**, 210.

10. SPENCER, T. and HARRIS, H. (1964). Regulation of enzyme synthesis in an enucleate cell. *Biochem. J.* **91**, 282.
11. TRIPLETT, E. L., STEENS-LIEVENS, A., and BALTUS, E. (1965). Rates of synthesis of acid phosphatases in nucleate and enucleate *Acetabularia* fragments. *Expl Cell Res.* **38**, 366.
12. ZETSCHE, K. (1966). Regulation der UDP-Glucose 4-Epimerase Synthese in kernhaltigen und kerlosen Acetabularien. *Biochim. biophys. Acta* **124**, 332.
13. ZETSCHE, K. (1968). Regulation der UDPG-Pyrophosphorylaseaktivität in *Acetabularia.* I. Morphogenese und UDPG-Pyrophosphorylasesynthese in kernhaltigen und kernlosen Zellen. *Z. Naturf.* **23b**, 369.
14. WERZ, G. (1963). Vergleichende Zellmembrananalysen bei verschiedenen Dasycladaceen. *Planta* **60**, 322.
15. ZETSCHE, K. Unterschiedliche Zusammensetzung von Stiel- und Hutzellwand bei *Acetabularia mediterranea. Planta* **76**, 326.
16. GRIENINGER, G. E. and ZETSCHE, K. (1972). Die Aktivität von phosphoglucose-isomerase und phosphoglucomutase während der Morphogenese kernhaltiger und kernloser Acetabularien. *Planta (Berl.)* **104**, 329.
17. WERZ, G. (1965). Determination and realization of morphogenesis in *Acetabularia. Brookhaven Symp. Biol.* No. 18, 185.
18. HÄMMERLING, J. and ZETSCHE, K. (1966). Zeitliche Steuerung der Formbildung von *Acetabularia. Umschau* **15**, 489.
19. ZETSCHE, K. (1963). Der Einfluss von Kinetin und Gibberellin auf die Morphogenese kernhaltiger und kernloser *Acetabularien. Planta* **59**, 624.
20. SPENCER, T. (1968). Effect of kinetin on the phosphatase enzymes of *Acetabularia. Nature, Lond.* **217**, 62.
21. SCHWEIGER, H.-G. (1966). Ribonuclease-Aktivität in *Acetabularia. Planta* **68**, 247.
22. GIBOR, A. and IZAWA, M. (1963). The DNA content of the chloroplasts of *Acetabularia. Proc. natn. Acad. Sci. U.S.A.* **50**, 1164.
23. SCHWEIGER, H.-G. and BERGER, S. (1964). DNA-dependent RNA synthesis in chloroplasts of *Acetabularia. Biochim. biophys. Acta* **87**, 533.
24. SAGER, R. (1965). On the evolution of genetic systems. *Evolving genes and proteins* (Eds. V. BRYSON and H. J. VOGEL), p. 591. Academic Press, New York.
25. SCHWEIGER, H.-G., APEL, K., and KLOPPSTECH, K. (1972). Source of genetic information of chloroplast proteins in *Acetabularia. Advances in the Biosciences* **8**, 249. Pergamon Press–Vieweg, Oxford.
26. APEL, K. and SCHWEIGER, H.-G. (1972). Nuclear dependency of chloroplast proteins in *Acetabularia. Eur. J. Biochem.* **25**, 229.
27. SCHWEIGER, H.-G. and BREMER, H. J. (1961). Cytoplasmatische RNS-synthese in kernlosen Acetabularien. *Biochim. biophys. Acta* **51**, 50.
28. SCHWEIGER, H.-G., DILLARD, W. L., GIBOR, A., and BERGER, S. (1967). RNA-Synthesis in *Acetabularia. Protoplasma* **64**, 1.
29. BERGER, S. (1967). RNA-synthesis in *Acetabularia. Protoplasma* **64**, 13.
30. DILLARD, W. L. and SCHWEIGER, H.-G. (1969). RNA synthesis in *Acetabularia. Protoplasma* **67**, 87.
31. FARBER, F. E. (1969). Studies on RNA metabolism in *Acetabularia mediterranea. Biochim. biophys. Acta* **174**, 1.
32. FARBER, F. E. (1969). Studies on RNA metabolism in *Acetabularia mediterranea. Biochim. biophys. Acta* **174**, 12.
33. FRIDLENDER, B., FRY, M., BOLDEN, A., and WEISSBACH, A. (1972). A new synthetic RNA-dependent DNA polymerase from human tissue culture cells. *Proc. natn. Acad. Sci. U.S.A.* **69**, 452.

34. WARD, D. C., HUMPHRYES, K. C., and WEINSTEIN, I. B. (1972). Synthetic RNA-dependent DNA polymerase activity in normal rat liver and hepatomas. *Nature, Lond.* **237**, 499.

35. BOBROW, S. N., GRAHAM SMITH, R., REITZ, M. S., and GALLO, R. C. (1972). Stimulated normal lymphocytes contain a ribonuclease-sensitive DNA polymerase distinct from viral RNA-directed DNA polymerase. *Proc. natn. Acad. Sci. U.S.A.* **69**, 3228.

36. LOUIS, B. G. and FITT, P. S. (1971). Nucleic acid enzymology of extremely halophilic bacteria. *Biochem. J.* **121**, 629.

37. LOUIS, B. G., PETERKIN, P. I., and FITT, P. S. (1971). Nucleic acid enzymology of extremely halophilic bacteria. *Biochem. J.* **121**, 635.

38. SCHWEIGER, H.-G., MASTER, R. W. P., and WERZ, G. (1967). Nuclear control of a cytoplasmic enzyme in *Acetabularia*. *Nature, Lond.* **216**, 554.

39. REUTER, W. and SCHWEIGER, H.-G. (1969). Kernkontrollierte lactatdehydrogenase in *Acetabularia*. *Protoplasma* **68**, 357.

40. HÄMMERLING, J. (1959). Spirogyra und Acetabularia (Ein Vergleich ihrer Fähigkeiten nach Entfernung des Kernes). *Biol. Zbl.* **78**, 703.

41. HARVEY, E. B. (1940). A comparison of the development of nucleate and non-nucleate eggs of *Arbacia punctulata*. *Biol. Bull. mar. biol. Lab., Woods Hole* **79**, 166.

42. BRACHET, J., FICQ., A., and TENCER, R. (1963). Amino acid incorporation into proteins of nucleate and anucleate fragments of sea urchin eggs: effect of parthenogenetic activation. *Expl Cell Res.* **32**, 168.

43. RAFF, R. A., COLOT, H. V., SELVIG, S. E., and GROSS, P. R. (1972). Oogenetic origin of messenger RNA for embryonic synthesis of microtubule proteins. *Nature, Lond.* **235**, 211.

44. ECKER, R. E., SMITH, L. D., and SUBTELNY, S. (1968). Kinetics of protein synthesis in enucleate frog oocytes. *Science N.Y.* **160**, 1115.

45. SMITH, L. D. and ECKER, R. E. (1965). Protein synthesis in enucleated eggs of *Rana pipiens*. *Science, N.Y.* **150**, 777.

46. CLEMENT, A. C. and TYLER, A. (1967). Protein-synthesizing activity of the anucleate polar lobe of the mud snail *Ilyanassa obsoleta*. *Science, N.Y.* **158**, 1457.

47. TIEDEMANN, H. and TIEDEMANN, H. (1954). Einbau von $^{14}CO_2$ in gefurchte und ungefurchte Eihälften und in verschiedene Entwicklungsstadien von *Triton*. *Naturwissenschaften* **41**, 535.

48. TARTAR, V. (1961). *The biology of* Stentor, p. 297. Pergamon Press, Oxford.

49. TAMM, S. L. (1969). The effect of enucleation on flagellar regeneration in the protozoon *Peranema trichophorum*. *J. Cell Sci.* **4**, 171.

50. GOLDSTEIN, L., CAILLEAU, R., and CROCKER, T. T. (1960). Nuclear-cytoplasmic relationships in human cells in tissue culture. *Expl Cell Res.* **19**, 332.

51. GOLDSTEIN, L., MICOU, J., and CROCKER, T. T. (1960). Nuclear-cytoplasmic relationships in human cells in tissue culture. *Biochim. biophys. Acta* **45**, 82.

52. WILDE, C. E. (1961). The differentiation of vertebrate pigment cells. *Adv. Morphogenesis* **1**, 287.

53. MAZIA, D. and PRESCOTT, D. M. (1955). The role of the nucleus in protein synthesis in *Amoeba*. *Biochim. biophys. Acta* **17**, 23.

54. BRUNS, G. P. and LONDON, I. M. (1965). The effect of hemin on the synthesis of globin. *Biochem. biophys. Res. Commun.* **18**, 236.

55. GROSS, M. and RABINOWITZ, M. (1972). Control of globin synthesis in cell-free preparations of reticulocytes by formation of a translational repressor that is activated by hemin. *Proc. natn. Acad. Sci. U.S.A.* **69**, 1565.

56. HUNT, T., VANDERHOFF, G., and LONDON, I. M. (1972). Control of globin synthesis: the role of heme. *J. molec. Biol.* **66**, 471.
57. WIESNER, R., ACS, G., REICH, E., and SHAFIQ, A. (1965). Degradation of ribonucleic acid in mouse fibroblasts treated with actinomycin. *J. Cell Biol.* **27**, 47.
58. GROSS, P. R. and COUSINEAU, G. H. (1963). Effects of actinomycin D on macromolecule synthesis and early development in sea urchin eggs. *Biochem. biophys. Res. Commun.* **10**, 321.
59. GROSS, P. R., MALKIN, L. I., and MOYER, W. A. (1964). Templates for the first proteins of embryonic development. *Proc. natn. Acad. Sci. U.S.A.* **51**. 407.
60. GREENHOUSE, G. A., HYNES, R. O., and GROSS, P. R. (1971). Sea urchin embryos are permeable to actinomycin. *Science, N.Y.* **171**, 686.
61. TERMAN, S. A. (1970). Relative effect of transcription-level and translation-level control of protein synthesis during early development of the sea urchin, *Proc. natn. Acad. Sci. U.S.A.* **65**, 985.
62. TERMAN, S. A. (1972). Extent of post-transcriptional level control of protein synthesis in the absence of cell division. *Expl Cell Res.* **72**, 576.
63. BARROS, C., HAND, G. S., and MONROY, A. (1966). Control of gastrulation in the starfish *Asterias forbesii*. *Expl Cell Res.* **43**, 167.
64. NEWELL, P. C. (1971). The development of the cellular slime mould *Dictyostelium discoideum*: a model system for the study of cellular differentiation. *Essays in Biochemistry* **7**, 87. Academic Press, London, N.Y.
65. JOST, J.-P., KHAIRALLAH, E. A., and PITOT, H. C. (1968). Studies on the induction and repression of enzymes in rat liver. V. Regulation of the rate of synthesis and degradation of serine dehydratase by dietary amino acids and glucose. *J. biol. Chem.* **243**, 3057.
66. DRYSDALE, J. W. and MUNRO, H. N. (1965). Failure of actinomycin D to prevent induction of liver apoferritin after iron administration. *Biochim. biophys. Acta* **103**, 185.
67. GREENGARD, O. and DEWEY, H. K. (1971). The prematurely evoked synthesis of liver tryptophan oxygenase. *Proc. natn. Acad. Sci. U.S.A.* **68**, 1698.
68. THOMPSON, E. B., GRANNER, D. K., and TOMKINS, G. M. (1970). Superinduction of tyrosine aminotransferase by actinomycin D in rat hepatoma (HTC) cells. *J. molec. Biol.* **54**, 159.
69. TOMKINS, G. M., LEVINSON, B. B., BAXTER, J. D., and DETHLEFSEN, L. (1972). Further evidence for posttranscriptional control of inducible tyrosine aminotransferase synthesis in cultured hepatoma cells. *Nature, Lond. New Biol.* **239**, 9.
70. BUTCHER, F. R., BECKER, J. E., and POTTER, V. R. (1971). Induction of tyrosine aminotransferase by dibutyryl cyclic-AMP employing hepatoma cells in tissue culture. *Expl Cell Res.* **66**, 321.
71. WILKS, W. D. and McKIBBIN, J. B. (1972). Evidence for translational regulation of specific enzyme synthesis by N^6, $O^{2'}$-dibutyryl cyclic AMP in hepatoma cell cultures. *Biochem. biophys. Res. Commun.* **48**, 205.
72. McCARL, R. L. and SHALER, R. C. (1969). The effects of actinomycin D on protein synthesis and beating in cultured rat heart cells. *J. Cell Biol.* **40**, 850.
73. GREENGARD, O., GORDON, M., SMITH, M. A. and ACS, G. (1964). Studies on the mechanism of diethylstilbestrol-induced formation of phosphoprotein in male chickens. *J. biol. Chem.* **239**, 2079.

74. KIRK, D. L. (1965). The role of RNA synthesis in the production of glutamine synthetase by developing chick neural retina. *Proc. natn. Acad. Sci. U.S.A.* **54,** 1345.

75. REIF-LEHRER, L. (1971). Actinomycin-D enhancement of glutamine synthetase activity in chick embryo retinas cultured in the presence of cortisol. *J. Cell Biol.* **51,** 303.

76. PAPACONSTANTINOU, J., STEWART, J. A., and KOEHN, P. V. (1966). A localized stimulation of lens protein synthesis by actinomycin D. *Biochim. biophys. Acta,* **114,** 428.

77. SPECTOR, A. and KINOSHITA, J. H. (1965). The effect of actinomycin D and puromycin upon RNA and protein metabolism in calf lens. *Biochim. biophys. Acta,* **95,** 561.

78. YOSHIDA, K. and KATOH, A. (1972). Crystallin synthesis by chicken lens. *Expl Cell Res.* **71,** 361.

79. MARTIN, T. E. and YOUNG, F. G. (1965). An *in vitro* action of human growth hormone in the presence of actinomycin D. *Nature, Lond.* **208,** 684.

80. WOOL, I. G. and MOYER, A. N. (1964). Effect of actinomycin and insulin on the metabolism of isolated rat diaphragm. *Biochim. Biophys. Acta* **91,** 248.

81. WOOL, I. G. and CAVICCHI, P. (1966). Insulin regulation of protein synthesis by muscle ribosomes: effect of the hormone on translation of messenger RNA for a regulatory protein. *Proc. natn. Acad. Sci. U.S.A.* **56,** 991.

82. LABRIE, F., BÉRAUD, G., GAUTHIER, M., and LEMAY, A. (1971). Actinomycin-insensitive stimulation of protein synthesis in rat anterior pituitary *in vitro* by dibutyryl adenosine 3′,5′-monophosphate. *J. biol. Chem.* **246,** 1902.

83. GRAND, R. J. and GROSS, P. R. (1970). Translation level control of amylase and protein synthesis by epinephrine. *Proc. natn. Acad. Sci. U.S.A.* **65,** 1081.

84. PALMITER, R. D., OKA, T., and SCHIMKE, R. T. (1971). Modulation of ovalbumin synthesis by estradiol-17β and actinomycin D as studied in explants of chick oviduct in culture. *J. biol. Chem.* **246,** 724.

85. SEED, R. W. and GOLDBERG, I. H. (1965). Biosynthesis of thyroglobulin. *J. biol. Chem.* **240,** 764.

86. RAGHAVAN, V. (1970). Germination of bracken fern spores. *Expl Cell Res.* **63,** 341.

87. DE MAGGIO, A. E. and RAGHAVAN, V. (1972). Germination of bracken fern spore. *Expl Cell Res.* **73,** 182.

88. IHLE, J. N. and DURE, L. S. (1972). The developmental biochemistry of cottonseed embryogenesis and germination. *J. biol. Chem.* **247,** 5048.

89. CHET, I. and RUSCH, H. P. (1970). RNA and protein synthesis during germination of spherules of *Physarum polycephalum. Biochim. biophys. Acta* **224,** 620.

90. WESSELLS, N. K. and WILT, F. H. (1965). Action of actinomycin D on exocrine pancreas cell differentiation. *J. molec. Biol.* **13,** 767.

91. RUTTER, W. J., WESSELLS, N. K., and GROBSTEIN, C. (1964). Control of specific synthesis in the developing pancreas. *J. natn. Cancer Inst. Monograph* **13,** p. 51.

92. KAFATOS, F. C. and REICH, J. (1968). Stability of differentiation-specific and nonspecific messenger RNA in insect cells. *Proc. natn. Acad. Sci. U.S.A.* **60,** 1458.

93. WILT, F. H. (1965). Regulation of the initiation of chick embryo hemoglobin synthesis. *J. molec. Biol.* **12,** 331.

94. SMILEY, J. D., HEARD, J. G., and ZIFF, M. (1964). Effect of actinomycin on RNA synthesis and antibody formation in the anamnestic response *in vitro J. exp. Med.* **119,** 881.

95. GELLER, B. D. and SPIERS, R. S. (1964). Failure of actinomycin D to inhibit antitoxin production to a challenging injection of antigen. *Proc. Soc. exp. Biol. Med.* **117**, 782.
96. SCHIMKE, R. T. (1964). The importance of both synthesis and degradation in the control of arginase levels in rat liver. *J. biol. Chem.* **239**, 3808.
97. SCHIMKE, R. T., SWEENEY, E. W., and BERLIN, C. M. (1964). An analysis of the kinetics of rat liver tryptophan pyrrolase induction: the significance of both enzyme synthesis and degradation. *Biochem. biophys. Res. Commun.* **15**, 214.

2
The genetic operator model

1. The theory of Jacob and Monod

IN 1961 there appeared in the *Journal of Molecular Biology* a paper by François Jacob and Jacques Monod entitled 'Genetic regulatory mechanisms in the synthesis of proteins'.[1] In this paper a model for the regulation of protein synthesis is described that is diametrically opposed to the principal conclusions reached in Chapter 1. In its simplest form this model envisages that the mechanisms that regulate the synthesis of protein do not operate in the cytoplasm of the cell where the protein is synthesized (the 'cytoplasmic operator' model), but act directly on the genes by governing the transcription of the DNA into RNA (the 'genetic operator' model). The evidence on which Jacob and Monod based their theory was limited to experiments on bacteria and very largely to their own experiments on the regulation of the synthesis of the inducible enzyme β-galactosidase in *Escherichia coli*. A consideration of their famous paper cannot be avoided in any discussion on the mechanism of gene action, not only because it is, in itself, an exposé of great intellectual brilliance, but also because it advances a point of view that is clearly at variance with an apparently well-established body of evidence in higher cells. If the 'genetic operator' model proposed by Jacob and Monod is true for bacteria, and the 'cytoplasmic operator' model is true for higher cells, as the evidence reviewed in Chapter 1 appears to indicate, then one must conclude that the mechanisms responsible for governing the regulation of protein synthesis in higher cells are different *in principle* from those that regulate protein synthesis in bacteria; and this would be a biological generalization of the greatest importance.

Jacob and Monod allowed that the genetical experiments that formed the main part of their paper were compatible with either the 'genetic' or the 'cytoplasmic' operator model; but they considered that, on the whole, the evidence in bacteria, and especially the bio-chemical evidence, strongly favoured the 'genetic' model. Four lines of argument were advanced in support of this view.

(1) The expression of clusters of related genes in certain Gram negative bacteria occurs co-ordinately; that is to say, the synthesis of all the enzymes in a particular metabolic sequence, which may be represented on the bacterial chromosome by a group of adjacent, or closely apposed, genes, may be initiated or suppressed at one step. This fact was thought to be difficult to reconcile with the cytoplasmic operator model if only because of the size that the relevant cyto-plasmic template would have to attain. Making certain assumptions, Jacob and Monod calculated that co-ordinate regulation of a group of three enzymes each having a molecular weight of 60 000 would require a template of molecular weight $1\cdot8 \times 10^6$; and since co-ordinate regulation of groups of up to eight enzymes was known to occur, it was argued that the size of some templates would have to be substantially larger. This was thought to be unlikely, since, at the time, the RNA of *E. coli* was not thought to contain polyribonucleo-tides of a molecular weight exceeding 10^6.

(2) The induction of the enzyme β-galactosidase by an appro-priate inducer takes place in *E. coli* within 3 min;[2] and the enzyme is then synthesized at a maximal rate.[3] When the inducer is removed, synthesis of the enzyme promptly ceases (Fig. 3). If regulation of this enzyme were effected by mechanisms operating at the genetic level, one might expect that the kinetics of induction would be mimicked by the introduction of the β-galactosidase gene into a cell which lacked it, and that the kinetics of the cessation of synthesis would be mimicked by removal of the gene from the cell. When the structural gene for β-galactosidase was transferred by sexual conjugation from a cell that possessed the gene into one that lacked it, it was indeed found that synthesis of the enzyme in the recipient cell began within a couple of minutes, and that the enzyme was synthesized at the maximal rate.[4] Direct removal of the gene from the cell is hardly possible in bacteria; but it was thought that indirect removal of the gene might be achieved if a large dose of radioactive phosphorus was introduced into the chromosome bearing the β-galactosidase gene before this chromosome was transferred to a recipient cell that lacked it. It was assumed that the decay of the radioactive phos-phorus would destroy the gene *in situ*. When this experiment was

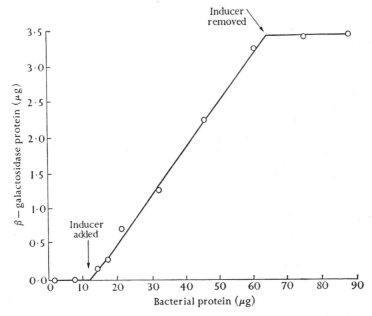

FIG. 3. Kinetics of induced synthesis of β-galactosidase in *Escherichia coli*. A differential plot expressing the accumulation of β-galactosidase as a function of the increase in the mass of cells in a growing culture. (Redrawn from Cohn.[3])

performed it was found that the ability of the recipient cell to synthesize β-galactosidase diminished as decay of the radioactive phosphorus caused progressive disintegration of the chromosome.[4] This result was interpreted to mean that integrity of the chromosome was essential for synthesis of β-galactosidase to occur.

(3) Infection of *E. coli* with certain virulent bacteriophages φ11, T2 and T4, results in rapid cessation of the synthesis of virtually all bacterial proteins, including β-galactosidase.[5–7] These phages induce depolymerization of the bacterial DNA.[8] Infection of *E. coli* with phage λ, however, allows β-galactosidase synthesis to continue almost until the time of lysis: this phage does not depolymerize the bacterial DNA.[9] These findings were thought to lend further support to the idea that integrity of the bacterial chromosome was essential for protein synthesis.

(4) In *E. coli* the pyrimidine analogue 5-fluorouracil is rapidly incorporated into RNA. When the alkaline phosphatase made by the bacterium in the presence of 5-fluorouracil was examined,

it was found to be abnormally sensitive to inactivation by heat.[10] In a strain of *E. coli* that synthesized β-galactosidase constitutively (that is, even in the absence of an appropriate inducer) the rate of synthesis of active enzyme was rapidly reduced by 5-fluorouracil, but a protein that cross-reacted with anti-β-galactosidase antiserum continued to be produced.[11] This protein was thought to be a structurally modified, inactive form of β-galactosidase. In its effects on protein synthesis 5-fluorouracil was said to be remarkable in two respects. It changed the properties of the proteins synthesized in its presence almost immediately (abnormal enzymes were thought to be synthesized virtually from the time of addition of the analogue); and the degree of abnormality of these proteins remained constant with time. These characteristics were thought to indicate that *all* the alkaline phosphatase or β-galactosidase molecules made after the addition of 5-fluorouracil were abnormal; and it was therefore deduced that these molecules could not have been made on templates present in the cell before the analogue was added. If true, this conclusion obviously implied that the act of transcription of a particular gene directly and immediately influenced the synthesis of the corresponding protein.

How convincing are these four lines of argument?

2. Examination of the evidence

(1) As Jacob and Monod themselves admit, the argument based on the assumption that *E. coli* does not contain any RNA molecules big enough to form a template for the co-ordinate regulation of a metabolically related group of enzymes is a very weak one. Measurements of the molecular weight of RNA are fraught with difficulties, and no confident statement can be made, even today, about the true dimensions of some families of RNA molecules, especially when they have a low order of secondary structure.[12, 13] I shall have occasion at a later stage to discuss in some detail the errors inherent in attempts to deduce the size of RNA molecules from their sedimentation behaviour; but at this stage it is enough to say that the idea that a template may be 'polycistronic', that is, that it can specify the amino acid sequences of a group of related proteins, is now generally accepted.

(2) The observations on cells that have received the β-galactosidase gene by conjugation, and from which the gene has supposedly

been removed by decay of radioactive phosphorus in the chromosome, constitute a more impressive argument in support of the genetic operator model. Of the two groups of experiments, those involving removal of the gene are obviously the more telling. The fact that β-galactosidase synthesis in the recipient cell begins within 2 or 3 min of receipt of the gene is compatible with almost any model for the regulatory process, provided that the gene is transcribed very soon after it enters the recipient cell. Two or three minutes may represent as much as one tenth of the generation time of an *E. coli* cell, so that there is ample opportunity during the lag phase that precedes synthesis of the enzyme for virtually any form of regulation to occur. The observation that synthesis of β-galactosidase in the recipient cell begins, and continues for some time, at the maximal rate also provides no evidence about the site of regulation. Jacob and Monod reason that this finding indicates either that the gene produces templates that act as short-lived intermediates, or that the gene produces a limited number of templates and then stops functioning. But this reasoning applies only if there is a fixed relationship between the number of templates produced and the amount of enzyme formed; and this we cannot assume. In animal and plant cells it is clear that templates may be present in the cytoplasm of the cell without being expressed; and when synthesis of a particular protein takes place we do not know whether all the cytoplasmic templates for that protein are translated, or only some of them. And we certainly do not know that the maximum rate of synthesis of a particular protein in the whole cell is determined only and simply by the number of templates for that protein that it contains.

The experiments in which the bacterial chromosome bearing the β-galactosidase gene is destroyed by decay of radioactive phosphorus are, in principle, analogous to the enucleation experiments that have been carried out on higher cells. In the latter, as I described in Chapter 1, it is in general the case that synthesis of specific proteins continues after removal of the nucleus; and in many instances it has been shown that this synthesis can be regulated by the enucleate cytoplasm. At first glance the results of the radioactive phosphorus decay experiments appear to indicate that this is not the case for bacteria, at least for the enzyme β-galactosidase in *E. coli*. In the experiments described by Jacob and Monod[4] the zygote that has received the radioactive chromosome bearing the β-galactosidase gene rapidly loses its ability to synthesize the enzyme as decay of the radioactive phosphorus takes place. However, these experiments have been re-examined by McFall,[14] who showed that the results were open to a quite different interpretation. In order to study the effect of the radioactive decay, the cells are maintained for the required period in a frozen state, and then thawed to permit assay of the enzyme. Glycerol is normally added to the medium to prevent extensive disruption of the cell by the process of freezing and thawing; and this was done in the experiments described by Jacob and Monod.[4] However, glycerol is a metabolizable source of carbon for *E. coli*, and, like other sources of carbon, it suppresses the induced formation of β-galactosidase, a phenomenon originally called the 'glucose' effect[15] and now usually described as an example of "catabolite repression'. McFall showed that if glycol, which is not a metabolizable source of carbon, is used instead of glycerol, then the ability of the radioactive zygotes to synthesize β-galactosidase is relatively resistant to decay of the isotope in the bacterial chromosome. Even when this decay has reduced the viability of the organism to 0·1 per cent, β-galactosidase synthesis can occur at about 25 per cent of the normal rate. An essentially similar result was obtained with the enzyme phosphatase.[15] Thus, these experiments involving the transfer of a radioactive chromosome, far from demonstrating the dependence of enzyme synthesis on the integrity of the chromosome, actually show that substantial synthesis of enzyme can continue after the radioactive decay of the chromosome has taken place; and they also show that this continued synthesis of enzyme is still susceptible to regulation by catabolite repression. It would be tempting to draw an analogy between these findings and the results obtained with enucleated eukaryotic cells in which protein synthesis also persists and continues to be regulated after removal of the nucleus; but recent experiments with a radiation-sensitive strain of *E. coli* indicate that radioactive phosphorus decay in the chromosome has little effect on transcription of the DNA or on enzyme synthesis,[16] so that all this work involving the transfer of radioactive chromosomes is essentially uninterpretable.

(3) The argument based on the different effects produced in bacteria by the T-even phages on the one hand and λ phage on the other can also be dismissed. It has been shown that depolymerization of the bacterial DNA is a relatively late and secondary effect produced by infection with the T-even phages.[17] The synthetic processes of the bacterium can be inhibited by the T-even phages even when the

bacterial DNA can be shown to be unimpaired. Moreover, non-infective 'ghosts' of phage T2 (shells of the phage not containing nucleic acid) are capable of inhibiting the synthesis of protein in the bacterium. The inhibition produced by phage ghosts involves no degradation of the bacterial DNA and is reversible.[18] Indeed, recent experiments with phage T4 indicate that the phage acts not by suppressing the transcription of the bacterial genes, but by preventing the RNA made on these genes from being translated into protein.[19-21] It is, in any case, clear that the differences between phages that do grossly inhibit bacterial protein synthesis and those that do not, cannot be used to support the idea that integrity of the bacterial chromosome is essential for bacterial protein synthesis.

(4) We come finally to the very complex problem of the effects produced by 5-fluorouracil. Jacob and Monod state that the effects of 5-fluorouracil are virtually immediate and involve the production of homogeneously abnormal proteins. However, the experiment on alkaline phosphatase to which they refer[10] shows that, even under normal conditions, the induced synthesis of this enzyme is preceded by a prolonged lag period; and, in the presence of the analogue, this lag approaches 30 min which is close to one complete generation time for *E. coli*. In the case of β-galactosidase, induced synthesis of the enzyme did not occur at all in the presence of the analogue;[11] and all observations were therefore limited to a constitutive strain of *E. coli* in which synthesis of the enzyme was not completely abolished by 5-fluorouracil. In the presence of the analogue synthesis of β-galactosidase in this constitutive strain continued at about 20 per cent of the normal rate, but the cells produced in much larger amounts a protein (or proteins) that were enzymatically inactive but cross-reacted with antiserum against β-galactosidase. The assumption was made that the cross-reacting protein was an altered, enzymatically inactive, form of β-galactosidase induced by the action of the fluorouracil. However, other interpretations are possible. It is known, for example, that even under normal conditions (that is, in the absence of 5-fluorouracil) large amounts of protein are formed in *E. coli* that are enzymatically inactive and cross-react with anti-β-galactosidase antiserum (the PZ proteins).[3] In the absence of more detailed characterization of the cross-reacting protein formed in the presence of 5-fluorouracil it is therefore impossible to say whether it is indeed an abortive form of the enzyme or whether it is something else altogether. A recent study of the effects of 5-fluorouracil

on induced synthesis of β-galactosidase in *E. coli* has, in fact, shown that the inhibition of β-galactosidase synthesis is due, not to the formation of a false template, but to catabolite repression resulting from abnormal accumulation of the intermediates of carbohydrate metabolism. Synthesis of perfectly normal enzyme occurs in the presence of 5-fluorouracil under conditions where this catabolite repression is relieved, even though the analogue is incorporated into RNA.[22] Other studies show that more than half the uracil in the RNA of growing bacteria can be replaced by 5-fluorouracil with very little metabolic disturbance: the cells divide more slowly, but the overall rate of protein synthesis remains proportional to the growth rate.[23, 24] It is, in any case, very difficult to draw firm conclusions about the mechanisms by which substances like 5-fluorouracil exert their effects. Whether changes in the behaviour of a particular enzyme are due directly to the incorporation of the analogue into its template, or whether they are indirect effects, cannot easily be decided. Both β-galactosidase[25] and alkaline phosphatase[26] are polymeric enzymes that may exist in the cytoplasm of the cell in multiple molecular forms. Alterations in the temperature sensitivity or in other properties of these enzymes might be produced by essentially secondary changes in their physical state. A rich literature testifies to the complexity of the effects produced in cells by nucleic acid analogues.

3. Negative control and repressors

At the time that Jacob and Monod put forward their genetic operator model, the map of the genetic region concerned with the synthesis of β-galactosidase was thought to contain five components: three of these were apparently structural genes specifying β-galactosidase (*z*), galactoside permease (*y*), and galactoside transacetylase (*a*); and two, *i* and *o*, were elements concerned with regulation of the activity of the structural genes. Mutations at the *i* locus affected the inducibility of β-galactosidase synthesis by exogenous inducers; mutations at the *o* ('operator') locus affected the expression of the whole group of structural genes. Genetic mapping indicated that the order of the genes in this region was *i o z y a*. An additional genetic locus was later discovered that also appeared to regulate or facilitate transcription of the structural genes. This was named the *p* ('promoter') locus and appeared to map between *o* and *z*. The complete genetic map for this region was thus thought to be *i o p z y a* in that order. This cluster of genes, all concerned with the synthesis of β-galactosidase, was called an 'operon' (the *lac* operon), a term that was soon widely used to describe any closely linked sequence of metabolically related genes that could be regulated co-ordinately as a single unit.

The idea that the expression of bacterial genes was controlled by the action of specific repressors arose initially from experiments involving sexual conjugation between strains of *E. coli* bearing mutations at the *i* locus. Wild type strains of *E. coli* normally synthesize β-galactosidase only when exposed to galactosides or certain other structurally related compounds. Such strains are said to be 'inducible' for β-galactosidase and are referred to as i^+. There are, however, mutations at the *i* locus that confer on the organism the ability to synthesize large amounts of β-galactosidase in the absence of exogenous inducers. These mutant strains are termed 'constitutive' and are referred to as i^-. When i^+ and i^- organisms were mated, it was found that the heterogenotes were i^+, that is, they did not synthesize β-galactosidase in the absence of an inducer.[27] Non-synthesis (inducibility) of the enzyme was thus found to be dominant over synthesis (constitutivity). Enzymes that show dominance of non-synthesis in this situation are commonly said to be under 'negative control'. In order to explain negative control, Jacob and Monod postulated that the product of the *i* gene was a specific repressor that inhibited the expression of the whole *lac* operon. Initially, the precise nature of this repressor was not specified; but, in due course, a more precise model was advanced in which it was proposed that the repressor was a protein that acted by virtue of its specific ability to bind to the *o* region of the operon and thus inhibit the transcription of the whole group of genes concerned with the synthesis of β-galactosidase.

Science does not proceed simply by the exercise of inexorable logic; and it often happens that an intuitive notion based on inadequate evidence may none the less prove to contain an important element of truth. Although none of the experiments adduced by Jacob and Monod in support of the genetic operator model, as opposed to the cytoplasmic operator model, were at all decisive, and although crosses between i^+ organisms and different kinds of i^- mutants can yield almost any pattern of dominance or recessivity for the synthesis of β-galactosidase,[28] it is remarkable that later workers did eventually succeed in isolating a repressor which was a protein and which did bind specifically to the *o* region of the DNA of the *lac* operon. In 1966 Gilbert and Müller-Hill,[29] using the technique of equilibrium dialysis, identified in extracts of *i*$^+$ *E. coli* small amounts of a protein that bound isopropyl-thiogalactoside, an inducer of β-galactosidase, with great affinity. This protein was partially purified and was found to attach, again with great affinity, to preparations of DNA from bacteriophages carrying the *E. coli lac* genes, but not to preparations of DNA from bacteriophages that did not carry these genes.[30] The affinity of this protein for the DNA of the *lac* region was strongly modified by mutations that mapped in the *o* region. These experiments thus demonstrated the existence of a protein, apparently specified by the *i* gene, that interacted both with exogenous inducer and with the *o* region of the *lac* operon. Gilbert and Müller-Hill concluded that this protein was the repressor predicted by Jacob and Monod, and that it acted, precisely as Jacob and Monod had proposed, by attaching specifically to the operator region of the *lac* DNA.

Further work has reinforced this conclusion. The *lac* repressor has been isolated and shown to be a tetramer of four identical subunits each with a molecular weight of about 4000.[31] Extensive studies have been done on the binding of the repressor to normal, mutant, and artificially modified *o* regions in the *lac* DNA and to synthetic DNA polymers.[32-38] It has, moreover, been demonstrated that the repressor can, by attaching to the *o* region, inhibit the transcription of the *lac* operon *in vitro*.[39-41] Repressor proteins acting in a similar way have also been characterized for the *gal* operon in *E. coli*[42] (the group of genes concerned with the metabolism of galactose) and for the bacteriophages λ and 434.[43-46] There is thus every reason to accept that the expression of some genes in bacteria does involve a control element that acts by binding to specific regions of the DNA and inhibiting transcription at these loci.

4. Positive control and activators

More refined mapping of the *lac* region revealed, however, that the regulatory mechanisms were not as simple as the preceding section might indicate. The *p* region was eventually found to lie not between *o* and *z*, but between *i* and *o*, so that the correct gene order was *i p o z y a*.[47] Transcription was therefore initiated at or near *p*, not at *o*, and mutations at *p* affected the expression of the whole *lac* operon. Even more important, it was shown that catabolite repression, that is the suppression of the synthesis of β-galactosidase by alternative sources of carbohydrate, could take place even in mutants of *E. coli* in which the whole of the *i* and *o* regions of the *lac* operon had been completely deleted.[48] It was therefore clear that some regulatory system other than the binding of repressor to operator was involved in the control of the synthesis of this enzyme. Further clarification of this regulatory system came from an unexpected source: the growing interest in the remarkable biological properties of adenosine 3',5'-monophosphate (cyclic AMP).[49] When the effect of cyclic AMP on enzyme synthesis in *E. coli* was examined, it was found that this compound could completely abolish catabolite repression of β-galactosidase synthesis.[50, 51] In due course a protein was isolated by virtue of its ability to bind cyclic AMP,[52, 53] and this protein, when coupled to the nucleotide, was found to attach specifically to the *p* locus and to stimulate transcription of the whole *lac* operon.[54, 55] The cyclic AMP-receptor protein complex thus functioned not negatively as a repressor of transcription, but positively as an activator. Finally, the complete transcriptional regulatory system for the *lac* operon was reconstituted *in vitro*, and it was then shown not only that transcription required cyclic AMP and its receptor protein, but also that transcription was blocked by attachment of the *lac* repressor to the *o* locus.[39–41] The transcriptional regulation of β-galactosidase was thus shown to be mediated by a balanced system of interacting positive and negative elements, proteins operating both by stimulating transcription and by inhibiting it.

Similar dual control systems appear to exist for other genetic loci, and there is evidence that cyclic AMP is involved in many of them. Cyclic AMP can reverse catabolite repression of many enzymes, for example, the enzymes of the *lac* and *gal* operons, glycerokinase, glycerophosphate permease, enzyme II of the fructose pathway, the enzymes involved in the utilization of arabinose, tryptophanase, serine deaminase and thymidine phosphorylase.[56, 57] Indeed, it is possible that any enzyme subject to catabolite repression by glucose may be regulated by mechanisms involving cyclic AMP. In the case of the *gal* operon, cyclic AMP and its receptor protein have been shown to be essential for transcription of the genes in a reconstituted cell-free system *in vitro*.[58, 59] The mechanism of control appears to be very similar to that described for the *lac* operon. The induction of guanosine monophosphate reductase in *E. coli* also requires cyclic AMP, although in this case the enzyme is not subject to catabolite repression.[60] Cyclic AMP and its receptor protein thus appear to provide a mechanism for stimulating the transcription of a large number of different genetic loci in *E. coli* and in other microorganisms,[56] although it is clear that there are genes that do not respond to this mechanism.[61, 62]

It has been mentioned that crosses between strains of *E. coli* inducible (i^+) or constitutive (i^-) for β-galactosidase may be either i^+ or i^- in phenotype, that is, the synthesis of the enzyme in the absence of inducer may be either dominant or recessive.[28] At several other genetic loci that have been studied in *E. coli*, for example, the arabinose,[63, 64] rhamnose[65], and maltose[66] operons, and the group of genes governing sulphate reduction,[67] constitutivity is commonly found to be dominant over inducibility in the heterogenote; and control systems have therefore been sought that act positively rather than negatively. A most detailed analysis has been made of the arabinose system, where again, a specific protein has been isolated that appears to act by stimulating the transcription of the relevant genes.[68-70] Positive regulators have also been revealed in the system of controls governing the development of λ phage.[71]

5. The control of translation in bacteria

Can we then assume that there are no important translational controls in bacteria and that the rate of synthesis of a particular protein is determined simply by the amount of RNA transcribed from the relevant gene? (The genetic operator model, *tout court*). The short answer to this question is no. Purification and measurement of the proteins specified by the *lac* genes in *E. coli* suggested that even at this *locus classicus* of transcriptional control, some factors in addition to transcription of the relevant genes determined the actual amounts of the different proteins that were synthesized. It was found that when the *lac* operon was induced, β-galactosidase, the product of the *z* gene, and thiogalactoside transacetylase, the product of the *a* gene, were made in different molar amounts; and the ratio of the molar concentrations of the two proteins in the cell can be altered by altering the temperature at which the bacteria are grown.[72, 73] The enzymes specified by the histidine operon are also made in different molar amounts.[74] If, as is now generally thought, the sequence of genes in an operon is transcribed into a single unit of polycistronic RNA, synthesis of different molar amounts of enzyme on different parts of this polycistronic RNA, and modulation of these differences by cultural conditions, must involve regulatory mechanisms that operate in some way other than by initiating or repressing the transcription of the whole operon.†

In the case of RNA phages there is no doubt that specific regulatory mechanisms operate at the level of translation. Experiments with the f2 group of RNA phages (f2, MS2, R17, fr) make it clear that different regions of the RNA are not only translated at different rates, but also at different times;[76–80] and the independent translation of the genes seen *in vivo* can be reproduced in cell-free systems *in vitro*.[81] In the MS2 phage, a translational control system rather similar in its mode of action to the *lac* repressor has been delineated. One of the genes in this phage codes for the synthesis of a 'coat' protein for the phage; and it has been shown that this coat protein acts as a specific translational repressor of an adjacent gene coding for the phage-specific RNA polymerase. The coat protein has been shown to bind specifically to a region of the RNA between the coat protein gene and the polymerase gene and to inhibit the translation of the latter in a cell-free system.[82, 83] The evidence for translational control in this case is thus very similar in kind to the evidence for transcriptional control in the *lac* system. In the *lac* system, however, it is the product of a separate gene, *i*, that regulates the transcription of the *lac* structural genes, *z*, *y* and *a*; whereas in the RNA bacteriophage, it is the product of one of the structural genes within the polycistronic RNA sequence, that regulates the translation of the other structural genes. This form of 'autoregulation' may well be widespread in bacteria, for there is a good deal of evidence that the product of the first structural gene in a metabolically related sequence of genes may itself play a crucial role in the expression of the other genes in the operon.[84] For example, it has been shown that in the histidine operon, which is normally repressible by histidine, the first enzyme in the metabolic sequence, phosphoribosyl transferase, is itself involved in the mechanism of repression:[85, 86] mutations affecting the structure of this enzyme alone may render the whole operon insensitive to repression by histidine.[87] At the arabinose locus mutations in structural genes may result in hyperinducibility of the operon.[57, 88]

† The transcription product of a bacterial operon might not always be polycistronic; it has recently been suggested that transcription might under certain conditions be terminated prematurely within the operon so that more RNA copies might be produced from proximal genes than from distal ones.[75]

Specific translational repression may also be exercised by the products of genes that are not part of the RNA sequence being repressed. There is a class of virulent DNA bacteriophages (T7, ϕ11, W31, T3 and ϕ1) that are able to grow only in female cells and not in male cells possessing the episomic F sex factor. When male *E. coli* cells are infected with phage T7 or ϕ11, synthesis of all but the earliest phage proteins is inhibited even though all the phage genes that are normally transcribed in permissive female cells are also transcribed in non-permissive male cells.[89, 90] F factor mutants have been isolated that permit synthesis of the proteins normally suppressed in the male cell, and in such mutants lytic development of the phage occurs.[89] Some product specified by the F factor episome, and subject to mutation, acts in this system as a specific repressor of the translation of some, but not all, of the RNA sequences transcribed from the phage genes.

These translational controls in bacteriophages are clearly homologous to the transcriptional controls that have been delineated for the *lac* region in *E. coli* and for other bacterial operons; but the question remains whether genetic regions that are regulated by transcriptional controls are also subject to further regulation at the level of translation. Present evidence indicates that they are. The best studied system is the group of genes in *E. coli* that specifies the enzymes responsible for the biosynthesis of tryptophan—the *tryp* operon.[91] This operon is repressible by tryptophan, and it has been shown that when tryptophan is given, the intracellular content of the RNA sequences transcribed specifically from the *tryp* genes immediately falls to a much lower level than that found in unrepressed cultures. So long as tryptophan is present in the medium, this lower level is maintained. If, however, the rate of synthesis of specific *tryp* enzymes is examined (phosphoribosyl anthranilate transferase and tryptophan synthetase), one finds that although the amount of RNA coding for these enzymes remains constant in the presence of tryptophan, the rate of enzyme synthesis changes. Initially, this rate may fall to almost zero, but over a period corresponding to about two cell generations, it increases progressively until a rate characteristic for steady-state repressed cultures is reached. It thus appears that even when an operon is subject to transcriptional control, regulation at the level of translation none the less persists, and this translational regulation governs the rate of synthesis of the specific proteins even when the level of the RNA sequences specifying these proteins remains constant. The molecule or molecules responsible for this translational regulation must obviously be able to recognise tryptophan; and the suggestion has therefore again been made that the enzyme anthranilate synthetase, which is the first of the sequence of enzymes specified by the *tryp* operon and which does have a tryptophan recognition site, might itself be the regulatory agent. If this were so, the progressive change in the rate of translation of the *tryp* RNA sequences over two cell generations might be explained by progressive dilution by growth of the essentially stable anthranilate synthetase enzyme protein. A similar form of translational control has been revealed for the *arg* operon in *E. coli*, the group of genes specifying the enzymes responsible for arginine biosynthesis.[92]

6. Experiments with actinomycin D and other inhibitors of transcription

I have already discussed the reservations that must be made in the interpretation of experiments done with actinomycin. They apply to bacteria no less than to higher cells, and they apply to other inhibitors of transcription such as the now popular rifampicin. Actinomycin, at concentrations that effectively inhibit transcription, may produce severe secondary effects in bacteria; in some species these may be so severe that the cells undergo lysis.[93] Rifampicin appears to be even more destructive: it damages ribosomes in *E. coli*[94] and rapidly kills sporulating *B. subtilis* cells.[95] Once again, only positive results with these compounds have any meaning. If synthesis of a protein continues, or continues to be regulated, when transcription is effectively stopped by actinomycin or rifampicin, this suggests the operation of mechanisms other than those that govern transcription; the finding that a particular protein ceases to be synthesized is, on the other hand, uninterpretable without additional evidence.

Several cases in which the synthesis of proteins continues to be regulated in the presence of actinomycin or rifampicin are worth mentioning. The enzymes of the *arg* operon in *E. coli*, for which translational control elements have been revealed without the use of inhibitors of transcription, as described above,[92] also appear to be susceptible to some measure of regulation in the presence of these inhibitors. In appropriate auxotrophic strains, it has been shown that the synthesis of acetylornithinase and ornithine transcarbamylase is repressible by arginine even when transcription has apparently been stopped by rifampicin or miracil D (another inhibitor of transcription).[96,97] As mentioned earlier, catabolite repression of many enzymes in *E. coli* can be reversed by cyclic AMP. It seems clear for some of these enzymes that transcriptional controls operating through a specific cyclic AMP receptor protein are involved. However, in the case of tryptophanase, cyclic AMP stimulates synthesis of the enzyme even when transcription is stopped by actinomycin or proflavine or by removal of the inducer.[62] In the presence of guanosine triphosphate, cyclic AMP appears to bind specifically to the 'G translocation factor', a protein that participates in the mechanism of translation.[98,99] Even in the control of β galactosidase, cyclic AMP seems to have some effect on translation as well as transcription: catabolite repression can be relieved by cyclic AMP under conditions in which transcription has been stopped by proflavine.[100,101]

7. Comparisons between bacteria and eukaryotic cells

The term 'operon' implies that the functional significance of clustering of related genes is to be explained in terms of co-ordinate regulation of the corresponding enzymes. This is unlikely. Sequences of metabolically related enzymes may be regulated co-ordinately whether the corresponding genes show close linkage or not. This is true not only for higher cells, but also for bacteria. In higher cells genes coding for a metabolically related sequence of enzymes are not in general closely linked.[102] When homologous groups of genes are examined, it is found that genes that are clustered in *E. coli* are not linked in fungi;[103] and even in *E. coli*, genes specifying a sequence of related enzymes may be clustered, as in the *lac* region, dispersed, as in the case of the enzymes mediating proline biosynthesis,[104] or partly clustered and partly dispersed, as in the case of the enzymes mediating arginine biosynthesis.[105,106] Yet all these enzyme sequences are regulated co-ordinately without difficulty. It is thus obvious that gene clustering cannot be a prerequisite for co-ordinate regulation. An alternative possibility is that gene clustering might facilitate the assembly of related proteins where these normally function together as a multi-enzyme complex; but not all sequences of metabolically related enzymes form such structural complexes. Another possibility is that gene clustering may provide a selective advantage for organisms in which sexual conjugation is achieved by the mechanical passage of a single chromosome from one cell to another. This form of sexuality, which is limited to certain bacteria, involves a high risk that the chromosome might break during the act of conjugation. It might be an advantage to minimize the incidence of breaks that would result in the delivery of an incomplete set of metabolically related genes to the recipient cell, and clustering of such genes would obviously achieve this end. One would then expect not to find gene clustering in organisms that do not exhibit this form of sexuality; and this does appear to be the case. It is, in any case, clear that the biological significance of gene clustering is more complex than is implied by the term 'operon', and it is likely that we shall find a more satisfactory explanation for this phenomenon in evolutionary terms than in terms of metabolic regulation.

In attempting to assess how far bacteria differ from higher cells in their mechanisms for regulating protein synthesis, it would obviously be a great advantage if one could compare the same metabolic event in the two situations. This is by no means easy. By far the most detailed studies on the regulation of protein synthesis in bacteria have been carried out on abrupt changes induced in a sequence of related enzymes represented genetically by a cluster of closely linked genes. Events of this sort may be without parallel in the cells of higher animals or plants. The latter are not normally exposed to abrupt qualitative changes in their nutrient supply and cannot, in general, survive such changes. It would therefore not be surprising if they lacked mechanisms for rapid adaptation to alternative sources of carbohydrate or of amino acids, such as are found in bacteria. Even modest changes in the levels of the common metabolic enzymes require the passage of several hours, or even days, in higher animal or plant cells; and the genes specifying related sequences of such enzymes are not, in general, closely linked. It is difficult in higher cells to find an event that is closely analogous to the induction of β-galactosidase in *E. coli*. There are, however, two highly regulated processes that do take place in both bacteria and eukaryotic cells and have been extensively studied in both situations: sporulation and germination. Spores, or biologically equivalent bodies, are formed under appropriate conditions by a wide range of plants, and the over-all pattern of sporulation in these eukaryotic organisms is essentially similar to that seen in bacteria. In both cases an elaborate programme of biochemical and morphological changes results in the production of cells encased in materials that are highly resistant to inclement changes in the environment and thus ensure the survival of the cell until conditions propitious for growth are again established.

The development of the cap in *Acetabularia*, which permits the formation and release of cysts containing the gametes, is an example of
this process; the development of fruiting bodies in certain myxo-
mycetes is another. I have already discussed in some detail the experiments that have been done on *Acetabularia* cells from which the
nucleus has been removed. These experiments have established that
the whole intricate process of stalk and cap formation does not
require the concomitant presence of the cell nucleus. All the information required for the development of the cap passes to the cytoplasm
of the cell long before it is expressed; and the biochemical changes
that result in cap formation are elaborated by cytoplasmic regulatory
mechanisms that operate perfectly well in the absence of the relevant
genes. Essentially the same principles appear to hold for the formation of the fruiting body in the slime mould *Dictyostelium* (Plate 2).
In the latter case enucleation is not possible, since a large number of
cells contribute to the process but the results obtained by the use
of actinomycin D suggest that the over-all organization of the
fruiting body is achieved in the same way as the formation of the
cap in *Acetabularia*. Several proteins associated specifically with the
progressive morphological differentiation have been shown to be
synthesized many hours after RNA synthesis has been largely
inhibited by high doses of actinomycin D;[107–112] and detailed analysis
of the patterns of response to this antibiotic indicates that the information for any particular event in the fruiting process is delivered
to the cytoplasm of the cells some time before that event actually takes
place.[113] In bacteria sporulation appears to be controlled in the same
way (Plate 3). Similar experiments with actinomycin D indicate that
the synthesis of proteins associated specifically with sporulation is
initiated at the appropriate time even when transcription is inhibited.[95, 114–117] The onset of decisive morphogenetic events is far
removed in time from the transcription of the corresponding genes.[118]
The same holds true for the process of germination during which
the spore, cyst, or seed resumes vegetative growth. Germination in
wheat embryos induces a wave of protein synthesis that may continue for as long as 24 hours without appreciable RNA synthesis;[119]
and the rate of protein synthesis during this period is subject to
regulation by the plant hormones gibberellic and abscisic acid.[120]
During the early stages of the germination of cotton seeds, synthesis
of total protein and of specific enzymes is insensitive to concentrations of actinomycin D that largely inhibit transcription;[121, 122] and

this is also true for the germination of bracken spores.[123] In bacteria, similar experiments with actinomycin D indicate that decisive events in the germination of the bacterial spore are also not dependent on concomitant transcription. Observations on the germination of microcysts of the fruiting myxobacterium *Myxococcus xanthus* indicate that the information necessary for germination is delivered to the cytoplasm of the cell at least 4 or 5 hours before it is expressed.[124]

It thus appears that in two fundamental biological processes that bacteria share with higher cells, the over-all pattern of organization, not only in the higher cells, but also in the bacteria, follows the general principles that have been derived from the study of *Acetabularia*. During sporulation and germination there appears to be no close coupling, either in bacteria or in higher cells, between the time at which a gene is transcribed and the time at which the corresponding template is translated into protein. The mechanisms that actually initiate the synthesis of the proteins specific for these two forms of differentiation, and that regulate their subsequent production, do not operate simply by controlling the transcription of the relevant genes.

REFERENCES

1. JACOB, F. and MONOD, J. (1961). Genetic regulatory mechanisms in the synthesis of proteins. *J. molec. Biol.* **3**, 318.
2. PARDEE, A. B. and PRESTIDGE, L. S. (1961). The initial kinetics of enzyme induction. *Biochim. biophys. Acta* **49**, 77.
3. COHN, M. (1957). Contributions of studies on the β-galactosidase of *Escherichia coli* to our understanding of enzyme synthesis. *Bact. Rev.* **21**, 140.
4. RILEY, M., PARDEE, A. B., JACOB, F., and MONOD, J. (1960). On the expression of a structural gene. *J. molec. Biol.* **2**, 216.
5. COHEN, S. S. (1949). Growth requirements of bacterial viruses. *Bact. Rev.* **13**, 1.
6. MONOD, J. and WOLLMAN, E. (1947). L'inhibition de la croissance et de l'adaptation enzymatique chez les bactéries infectées par le bactériophage. *Annls Inst. Pasteur, Paris* **73**, 937.
7. BENZER, S. (1953). Induced synthesis of enzymes in bacteria analyzed at the cellular level. *Biochim. biophys. Acta* **11**, 383.
8. LURIA, S. E. and HUMAN, M. L. (1950). Chromatin staining of bacteria during bacteriophage infection. *J. Bact.* **59**, 551.
9. SIMINOVITCH, L. and JACOB, F. (1952). Biosynthèse induite d'un enzyme pendant le développement des bactériophages chez *Escherichia coli* K12. *Annls Inst. Pasteur, Paris* **83**, 745.
10. NAONO, S. and GROS, F. (1960). Synthèse par *E. coli* d'une phosphatase modifiée en présence d'un analogue pyrimidique. *C. r. hebd. Séanc. Acad. Sci., Paris* **250**, 3889.

11. BUSSARD, B., NAONO, S., GROS, F., and MONOD, J. (1960). Effets d'un analogue de l'uracile sur les propriétés d'une protéine enzymatique synthétisée en sa présence. *C. r. hebd. Séanc. Acad. Sci., Paris* **250**, 4049.

12. SEDAT, J., LYON, A., and SINSHEIMER, R. L. (1969). Purification of *Escherichia coli* pulse-labelled RNA by benzoylated DEAE-cellulose chromatography. *J. molec. Biol.* **44**, 415.

13. BRAMWELL, M. E. (1972). A comparison of gel electrophoresis and density gradient centrifugation of heterogeneous nuclear RNA. *Biochim. biophys. Acta* **281**, 329.

14. McFALL, E. (1961). Effects of ^{32}P decay on enzyme synthesis. *J. molec. Biol.* **3**, 219.

15. MONOD, J. (1947). The phenomenon of enzymatic adaptation. *Growth* **11**, 223.

16. DAVERN, C. I. (1968). Effect of ^{32}P decay upon RNA transcription by a radiation-sensitive strain of *Escherichia coli. J. molec. Biol.* **32**, 151.

17. NOMURA, M., MATSUBARA, K., OKAMOTO, K., and FUJIMURA, R. (1962). Inhibition of host nucleic acid and protein synthesis by bacteriophage T4: its relation to the physical and functional integrity of host chromosome. *J. molec. Biol.* **5**, 535.

18. FRENCH, R. C. and SIMINOVITCH, L. (1954). The action of T2 bacteriophage ghosts on *Escherichia coli* B. *Can. J. Microbiol.* **1**, 757.

19. DUCKWORTH, D. H. (1970). Inhibition of translation of preformed *lac* messenger ribonucleic acid by T4 bacteriophage. *J. Virol.* **5**, 653.

20. KENNELL, D. (1970). Inhibition of host protein synthesis during infection of *Escherichia coli* by bacteriophage T4. *J. Virol.* **6**, 208.

21. FABRICANT, R. and KENNELL, D. (1970). Inhibition of host protein synthesis during infection of *Escherichia coli* by bacteriophage T4. *J. Virol.* **6**, 772.

22. HOROWITZ, J. and KOHLMEIER, V. (1967). Formation of active β-galactosidase by *Escherichia coli* treated with 5-fluorouracil. *Biochim. biophys. Acta* **142**, 208.

23. SAUNDERS, P. P., BASS, R. E., and SAUNDERS, G. I. (1968). Properties of 5-fluorouracil-containing ribonucleic acid and ribosomes from *Bacillus subtilis. J. Bact.* **96**, 525.

24. SAUNDERS, P. P., SCHULTZ, G. A., and SAUNDERS, G. I. (1968). Effect of 5-fluorouracil on the growth and morphology of a polyauxotrophic strain of *Bacillus subtilis. J. Bact.* **96**, 560.

25. APPEL, S. H., ALPERS, D. H., and TOMKINS, G. M. (1965). Multiple molecular forms of β-galactosidase. *J. molec. Biol.* **11**, 12.

26. LEVINTHAL, C., SIGNER, E. R., and FETHEROLF, K. (1962). Reactivation and hybridization of reduced alkaline phosphatase. *Proc. natn. Acad. Sci. U.S.A.* **48**, 1230.

27. JACOB, F. and MONOD, J. (1961). On the regulation of gene activity. *Cold Spring Harb. Symp. quant Biol.* **26**, 193.

28. BECKWITH, J. R. (1970). *Lac*: the genetic system. In *The lactose operon* (eds. J. R. BECKWITH and D. ZIPSER), p. 11, Cold Spring Harbor Laboratory, New York.

29. GILBERT, W. and MÜLLER-HILL, B. (1966). Isolation of the *lac* repressor. *Proc. natn. Acad. Sci. U.S.A.* **56**, 1891.

30. GILBERT, W. and MÜLLER-HILL, B. (1967). The *lac* operator is DNA. *Proc. natn. Acad. Sci. U.S.A.* **58**, 2415.

31. MÜLLER-HILL, B., BEYREUTHER, K., and GILBERT, W. (1971). *lac* Repressor from *Escherichia coli. Meth. Enzym.* (eds. L. GROSSMAN and K. MOLDAVE), **21**, Part D, 483.

32. RIGGS, A. D., SUZUKI, H., and BOURGEOIS, S. (1970). *lac* Repressor-operator interaction. I Equilibrium studies. *J. molec. Biol.* **48,** 67.
33. RIGGS, A. D., NEWBY, R. F., and BOURGEOIS, S. (1970). *lac* Repressor-operator interaction. II Effects of galactosides and other ligands. *J. molec. Biol.* **51,** 303.
34. RIGGS, A. D., BOURGEOIS, S., and COHN, M. (1970). The *lac* repressor-operator interaction. III Kinetic studies. *J. molec. Biol.* **53,** 401.
35. LIN, S. and RIGGS, A. D. (1971). *lac* Repressor binding to operator analogues. *Biochem. biophys. Res. Commun.* **45,** 1542.
36. LIN, S. and RIGGS, A. D. (1972). *lac* Operator analogues: bromodeoxyuridine substitution in the *lac* operator affects the rate of dissociation of the *lac* repressor. *Proc. natn. Acad. Sci. U.S.A.* **69,** 2574.
37. RIGGS, A. D. (1972). *lac* Repressor binding to non-operator DNA. *J. molec. Biol.* **72,** 671.
38. ADLER, K., BEYREUTHER, K., FANNING, E., GEISLER, N., GRONENBORN, B., KLEMM, A., MÜLLER-HILL, B., PFAHL, M., and SCHMITZ, A. (1972). How *lac* repressor binds to DNA. *Nature, Lond.* **237,** 322.
39. DE CROMBRUGGHE, B., CHEN, B., GOTTESMAN, M., PASTAN, I., VARMUS, H. E., EMMER, M., and PERLMAN, R. L. (1971). Regulation of *lac* mRNA synthesis in a soluble cell-free system. *Nature, Lond. New Biol.* **230,** 37.
40. DE CROMBRUGGHE, B., CHEN, B., ANDERSON, W., NISSLEY, P., GOTTESMAN, M., PASTAN, I., and PERLMAN, R. (1971). *lac* DNA, RNA polymerase and cyclic AMP receptor protein, cyclic AMP, *lac* repressor and inducer are the essential elements for controlled *lac* transcription. *Nature, Lond. New Biol.*, **231,** 139.
41. CHEN, B., DE CROMBRUGGHE, B., ANDERSON, W. B., GOTTESMAN, M. E. PASTAN, I., and PERLMAN, R. L. (1971). On the mechanism of action of *lac* repressor. *Nature, Lond. New Biol.* **233,** 67.
42. PARKS, J. S., GOTTESMAN, M., SHIMADA, K., WEISBERG, R. A., PERLMAN, R. L , and PASTAN, I. (1971). Isolation of the *gal* repressor. *Proc. natn. Acad Sci. U.S.A.* **68,** 1891.
43. PTASHNE, M. (1967). Isolation of the λ phage repressor. *Proc. natn. Acad. Sci. U.S.A.* **57,** 306.
44. PTASHNE, M. (1967). Specific binding of the λ phage repressor to DNA. *Nature, Lond.* **214,** 232.
45. PIRROTTA, V. and PTASHNE, M. (1969). Isolation of the 434 phage repressor. *Nature, Lond.* **222,** 541.
46. STEINBERG, R. A. and PTASHNE, M. (1971). *In vitro* repression of RNA synthesis by purified λ phage repressor. *Nature, Lond. New Biol.* **203,** 76.
47. IPPEN, K., MILLER, J. H., SCAIFE, J., and BECKWITH, J. (1968). A new controlling element in the *lac* operon of *E. coli. Nature, Lond.* **217,** 825.
48. MONOD, J. (1970). *Control processes in multicellular organisms* (Eds. G. E. W. WOLSTENHOLME and J. KNIGHT) p. 76. Churchill, London.
49. ROBISON, G. A., BUTCHER, R. W., and SUTHERLAND, E. W. (1971). *Cyclic AMP.* Academic Press, New York and London.
50. PERLMAN, R. L. and PASTAN, I. (1968). Regulation of β-galactosidase synthesis in *Escherichia coli* by cyclic adenosine 3′,5′-monophosphate. *J. biol. Chem.* **243,** 5420.
51. PERLMAN, R. L., DE CROMBRUGGHE, B., and PASTAN, I. (1969). Cyclic AMP regulates catabolite and transient repression in *E. coli. Nature, Lond.*, **233,** 810.

52. ERON, L., ARDITTI, R., ZUBAY, G., CONNAWAY, S., and BECKWITH, J. R. (1971). An adenosine 3′,5′-cyclic monophosphate-binding protein that acts on the transcription process. *Proc. natn. Acad. Sci. U.S.A.* **68**, 215.

53. ANDERSON, W. B., SCHNEIDER, A. B., EMMER, M., PERLMAN, R. L., and PASTAN, I. (1971). Purification and properties of the cyclic 3′,5′-monophosphate receptor protein which mediates cyclic adenosine 3′,5′-monophosphate-dependent gene transcription in *Escherichia coli*. *J. biol. Chem.* **246**, 5929.

54. VARMUS, H. E., PERLMAN, R. L. and PASTAN, I. (1970). Regulation of *lac* transcription in *Escherichia coli* by cyclic adenosine 3′,5′-monophosphate. *J. biol. Chem.* **245**, 6366.

55. DE CROMBRUGGHE, B., CHEN, B., ANDERSON, W. B., GOTTESMAN, M. E., PERLMAN, R. L., and PASTAN, I. (1971). Role of cyclic adenosine 3′,5′-monophosphate and the cyclic adenosine 3′,5′-monophosphate receptor protein in the initiation of *lac* transcription. *J. biol. Chem.* **246**, 7343.

56. DE CROMBRUGGHE, B., PERLMAN, R. L., VARMUS, H. E., and PASTAN, I. (1969). Regulation of inducible enzyme synthesis in *Escherichia coli* by cyclic adenosine 3′,5′-monophosphate. *J. biol. Chem.* **244**, 5828.

57. KATZ, L. and ENGLESBERG, E. (1971). Hyperinducibility as a result of mutation in structural genes and self-catabolite repression in the *ara* operon. *J. Bact.* **107**, 34.

58. PARKS, J. S., GOTTESMAN, M., PERLMAN, R. L., and PASTAN, I. (1971). Regulation of galactokinase synthesis by cyclic adenosine 3′,5′-monophosphate in cell-free extracts of *Escherichia coli*. *J. biol. Chem.* **246**, 2419.

59. NISSLEY, S. P., ANDERSON, W. B., GOTTESMAN, M. E., PERLMAN, R. L., and PASTAN, I. (1971). *In vitro* transcription of the *gal* operon requires cyclic adenosine monophosphate and cyclic adenosine monophosphate receptor protein. *J. biol. Chem.* **246**, 4671.

60. BENSON, C. E., BREHMEYER, B. A., and GOTS, J. S. (1971). Requirement of cyclic AMP for induction of GMP reductase in *Escherichia coli*. *Biochem. biophys. Res. Commun.* **43**, 1089.

61. PERLMAN, R. and PASTAN, I. (1968). Cyclic 3′,5′-AMP: stimulation of β-galactosidase and tryptophanase induction in *E. coli*. *Biochem. biophys. Res. Commun.* **30**, 656.

62. PASTAN, I. and PERLMAN, R. (1969). Stimulation of tryptophanase synthesis in *Escherichia coli* by cyclic 3′,5′-adenosine monophosphate. *J. biol. Chem.* **244**, 2226.

63. ENGELSBERG, E., IRR, J., POWER, J., and LEE, N. (1965). Positive control of enzyme synthesis by gene *C* in the L-arabinose system. *J. Bact.* **90**, 946.

64. ENGELSBERG, E., SHEPPARD, D., SQUIRES, C., and MERONK, F. (1969). An analysis of 'revertants' of a deletion mutant in the *C* gene of the L-arabinose gene complex in *Escherichia coli* B/r: isolation of initiator constitutive mutants (I°). *J. molec. Biol.* **43**, 281.

65. POWER, J. (1967). The L-rhamnose genetic system in *Escherichia coli* K-12. *Genetics* **55**, 557.

66. HATFIELD, D., HOFNUNG, M., and SCHWARTZ, M. (1969). Genetic analysis of the maltose A region in *Escherichia coli*. *J. Bact.* **98**, 559.

67. JONES-MORTIMER, M. C. (1968). Positive control of sulphate reduction in *Escherichia coli*. *Biochem. J.* **110**, 589 and 597.

68. WILCOX, G., CLEMETSON, K. J., SANTI, D. V., and ENGLESBERG, E. (1971). Purification of the *ara* C protein. *Proc. natn. Acad. Sci. U.S.A.* **68**, 2145.

69. ZUBAY, G., GIELOW, L., and ENGLESBERG, E. (1971). Cell free studies on the regulation of the arabinoseo peron. *Nature, Lond. New Biol.* **233**, 164.

70. GREENBLATT, J. and SCHLEIF, R. (1971). Arabinose C protein: regulation of the arabinose operon *in vitro. Nature, Lond. New Biol.*, **233**, 166.

71. THOMAS, R. (1971). Control circuits. In *The bacteriophage lambda* (Ed. A. D. HERSHEY) p. 211. Cold Spring Harbor Laboratory, New York.

72. ZABIN, I. (1963). Proteins of the lactose system. *Cold Spring Harb. Symp. quant. Biol.* **28**, 431.

73. BROWN, J. L., BROWN, D. M., and ZABIN, I. (1967). Thiogalactoside transacetylase. Physical and chemical studies of subunit structure. *J. biol. Chem.* **242**, 4254.

74. WHITFIELD, H. J., GUTNICK, D. L., MARGOLIES, M. N., MARTIN, R. G., RECHLER, M. M., and VOLL, M. J. (1970). Relative translation frequencies of the cistrons of the histidine operon. *J. molec. Biol.* **49**, 245.

75. DE CROMBRUGGHE, B., ADHYA, S., GOTTESMAN, M., and PASTAN, I. (1973). Effect of Rho on transcription of bacterial operons. *Nature, Lond. New Biol.* **241**, 260.

76. OESCHGER, M. P. and NATHANS, D. (1966). Differential synthesis of bacterio-phage-specific proteins in MS2-infected *Escherichia coli* treated with actinomycin. *J. molec. Biol.* **22**, 235.

77. NATHANS, D., OESCHGER, M. P., EGGEN, K., and SHIMURA, Y. (1966). Bacteriophage-specific proteins in *E. coli* infected with an RNA bacterio-phage. *Proc. natn. Acad. Sci. U.S.A.* **56**, 1844.

78. LODISH, H. F. (1968). Bacteriophage f2 RNA: control of translation and gene order. *Nature, Lond.* **220**, 345.

79. LODISH, H. F. (1968). Independent translation of the genes of bacterio-phage f2 RNA. *J. molec. Biol.* **32**, 681.

80. EGGEN, K., OESCHGER, M. P., and Nathans, D. (1967). Cell-free protein synthesis directed by coliphage MS2 RNA: sequential synthesis of specific phage proteins. *Biochem. biophys. Res. Commun.* **28**, 587.

81. CAPECCHI, M. R. (1967). Polarity *in vitro. J. molec. Biol.* **30**, 213.

82. SUGIYAMA, T. and NAKADA, D. (1970). Translational control of bacterio-phage MS2 RNA cistrons by MS2 coat protein: affinity and specificity of the interaction of MS2 coat protein with MS2 RNA. *J. molec. Biol.* **48**, 349.

83. BERNARDI, A. and SPAHR, P.-F. (1972). Nucleotide sequence at the binding site for coat protein on RNA of bacteriophage R17. *Proc. natn. Acad. Sci. U.S.A.* **69**, 3033.

84. CLINE, A. L. and BOCK, R. M. (1966). Translational control of gene expres-sion. *Cold Spring Harb. Symp. quant. Biol.* **31**, 321.

85. KOVACH, J. S. BERBERICH, M. A., VENETIANER, P., and GOLDBERGER R. F. (1969). Repression of the histidine operon: effect of the first enzyme on the kinetics of repression. *J. Bact.* **97**, 1283.

86. KOVACH, J. S., PHANG, J. M., FERENCE, M. and GOLDBERGER, R. F. (1969). Studies on repression of the histidine operon. II The Role of the first enzyme in control of the histidine system. *Proc. natn. Acad. Sci. U.S.A.* **63**, 481.

87. ROTHMAN-DENES, L. and MARTIN, R. G. (1971). Two mutations in the first gene of the histidine operon of *Salmonella typhimurium* affecting control. *J. Bact.* **106**, 227.

88. ENGLESBERG, E. (1971). Regulation in the L-arabinose system. In *Metabolic Regulation* **5**, 257. Academic Press, New York.

89. MORRISON, T. G. and MALAMY, M. H. (1971). T_7 translational control mechanisms and their inhibition by F factors. *Nature, Lond. New Biol.* **231**, 37.

90. SUMMERS, W. C. and JAKES. K. (1971). Phage T_7 lysozyme mRNA transcription and translation. *Biochem. biophys. Res. Commun.* **45**, 315.

91. LAVALLÉ, R. and DE HAUWER, G. (1970). Tryptophan messenger translation in *Escherichia coli*. *J. molec. Biol.* **51**, 435.

92. LAVALLÉ, R. (1970). Regulation at the level of translation in the arginine pathway of *Escherichia coli* K12. *J. molec. Biol.* **51**, 449.

93. HARRIS, H. and SABATH, L. D. (1964). Induced enzyme synthesis in the absence of concomitant ribonucleic acid synthesis. *Nature, Lond.* **202**, 1078.

94. BLUNDELL, M. R. and WILD, D. G. (1971). Altered ribosomes after inhibition of *Escherichia coli* by rifampicin. *Biochem. J.* **121**, 391.

95. COOTE, J. G., WOOD, D. A., and MANDELSTAM, J. (1973). Lethal effect of rifampicin in *Bacillus subtilis* as a complicating factor in the assessment of the lifetime of messenger ribonucleic acid. *Biochem. J.* **134**, 263.

96. McLELLAN, W. L. and VOGEL, H. J. (1970). Translational repression in the arginine system of *Escherichia coli*. *Proc. natn. Acad. Sci. U.S.A.* **67**, 1703.

97. VOGEL, R. H., McLELLAN, W. L., HIRVONEN, A. P., and VOGEL, H. J. (1971). The arginine biosynthetic system and its regulation, in *Metabolic Regulation* (Ed. H. J. VOGEL) p. 463. Academic Press, New York and London.

98. CONWAY, T. W. and LIPMANN, F. (1964). Characterization of a ribosome-linked guanosine triphosphatase in *Escherichia coli* extracts. *Proc. natn. Acad. Sci. U.S.A.* **52**, 1462.

99. KUWANO, M. and SCHLESSINGER, D. (1970). Binding of adenosine $3',5'$-cyclic phosphate to G factor of *Escherichia coli*, and its effects on GTPase, RNAse V and protein synthesis. *Proc. natn. Acad. Sci. U.S.A.* **66**, 146.

100. ABOUD, M. and BURGER, M. (1970). The effect of catabolite repression and of cyclic $3',5'$-adenosine monophosphate on the translation of the lactose messenger RNA in *Escherichia coli*. *Biochem. biophys. Res. Commun.* **38**, 1023.

101. ABOUD, M. and BURGER, M. (1971). Accumulation of untranslated lactose-specific messenger ribonucleic acid during catabolite repression in *Escherichia coli*. *Biochem. J.* **122**, 219.

102. BODMER, W. F. (1970). The evolutionary significance of recombination in prokaryotes, *Symp. Soc. gen. Microbiol.* **20**, 279.

103. BODMER, W. F. and PARSONS, P. A. (1962). Linkage and recombination in evolution. *Adv. Genet.* **11**, 1.

104. CURTISS, R. (1965). Chromosomal aberrations associated with mutations to bacteriophage resistance in *Escherichia coli*. *J. Bact.* **89**, 28.

105. VOGEL, H. J. (1953). Path of ornithine synthesis in *Escherichia coli*. *Proc. natn. Acad. Sci. U.S.A.* **39**, 578.

106. VOGEL, H. J. and BACON, D. F. (1966). Gene aggregation: evidence for a coming together of functionally related, not closely linked genes. *Proc. natn. Acad. Sci. U.S.A.* **55**, 1456.

107. SUSSMAN, M. and SUSSMAN, R. R. (1965). The regulatory program for UDP galactose polysaccharide transferase activity during slime mold cyto-differentiation: requirement for specific synthesis of ribonucleic acid. *Biochim. biophys. Acta* **108**, 463.

108. ROTH, R., ASHWORTH, J. M., and SUSSMAN, M. (1968). Periods of genetic transcription required for the synthesis of three enzymes during cellular slime mold development. *Proc. natn. Acad. Sci. U.S.A.* **59**, 1235.

109. NEWELL, P. C. and SUSSMAN, M. (1969). Uridine diphosphate glucose pyrophosphorylase in *Dictyostelium discoideum*. Stability and developmental fate. *J. biol. Chem.* **244**, 2990.
110. SUSSMAN, M. and SUSSMAN R. (1969). Pattern of RNA synthesis and of enzyme accumulation and disappearance during cellular slime mold cytodifferentiation. *Symposia of the Society for General Microbiology*, XIX, p. 403.
111. LOOMIS, W. F. (1969). Developmental regulation of alkaline phosphatase in *Dictyostelium discoideum*. *J. Bact.* **100**, 417.
112. NEWELL, P. C., LONGLANDS, M., and SUSSMAN, M. (1971). Control of enzyme synthesis by cellular interaction during development of the cellular slime mold *Dictyostelium discoideum*. *J. molec. Biol.* **58**, 541.
113. NEWELL, P. C. (1971). The development of the cellular slime mould *Dictyostelium discoideum*: a model system for the study of cellular differentiation. *Essays Biochem.* **7**, 87.
114. ROSAS DEL VALLE, M. and ARONSON, A. I. (1962). Evidence for the synthesis of stable informational RNA required for bacterial spore formation. *Biochem. biophys. Res. Commun.* **9**, 421.
115. ARONSON, A. I. and ROSAS DEL VALLE, M. (1964), RNA and protein synthesis required for bacterial spore formation. *Biochim. biophys. Acta* **87**, 267.
116. MANDELSTAM, J. and STERLINI, J. M. (1969). "Commitment' to sporulation in *Bacillus subtilis*. *Spores IV*, p. 180. American Society for Microbiology.
117. MANDELSTAM, J. (1969). Regulation of bacterial spore formation. *Symp. Soc. gen. Microbiol.* **19**, 377.
118. MANDELSTAM, J. (1971). Recurring patterns during development in primitive organisms. *Symp. Soc. exp. Biol.* **25**, 1.
119. CHEN, D., SARID, S., and KATCHALSKI, E. (1968). Studies on the nature of messenger RNA in germinating wheat embryos. *Proc. natn. Acad. Sci. U.S.A.* **60**, 902.
120. CHEN, D. and OSBORNE, D. J. (1970). Hormones in the translational control of early germination in wheat embryos. *Nature, Lond.* **226**, 1157.
121. WATERS, L. C. and DURE, L. S. (1966). Ribonucleic acid synthesis in germinating cotton seeds. *J. molec. Biol.* **19**, 1.
122. IHLE, J. N. and DURE, L. S. (1969). Synthesis of a protease in germinating cotton cotyledons catalyzed by mRNA synthesized during embryogenesis. *Biochem. biophys. Res. Commun.* **36**, 705.
123. DEMAGGIO, A. E. and RAGHAVAN, V. (1972). Germination of bracken fern spore. *Expl Cell Res.* **73**, 182.
124. SCOTT RAMSEY, W. and DWORKIN, M. (1970). Stable mRNA and germination of *Myxococcus xanthus* microcysts. *J. Bact.* **101**, 531.

3
The search for the messenger

1. The background

PRIOR to the paper by Jacob and Monod[1] discussed in Chapter 2, there was no great controversy about which RNA in the cytoplasm acted as the template for protein synthesis. It was generally assumed, although no specific experiments were done to test the idea, that the specifications for the synthesis of proteins resided in the RNA of the ribosomes. These particles contain 85 per cent or more of the RNA in the cell cytoplasm, and it was therefore natural to assume that the bulk of the cytoplasmic RNA would be fulfilling the only role that at that time could be envisaged for it, namely to serve as a template for protein synthesis.

The ideas of Jacob and Monod changed all that. One of the most important conclusions entailed by their genetic operator model was that the templates for the synthesis of proteins had to be short lived. If the synthesis of proteins was to be regulated *only* by mechanisms that intervened at the level of DNA transcription, the RNA templates would have to be rapidly destroyed; if they were not, switching off the relevant gene would not switch off the synthesis of the corresponding protein. But there was ample evidence that the ribosomal RNA in the cytoplasm of the cell was not short-lived. Several studies on both bacterial and animal cells had shown that the bulk of the cellular RNA was not involved in rapid turnover;[2-4] and the experiments of Davern and Meselson,[5] in which density gradient centrifugation was used to measure changes in the density of RNA that had been labelled with heavy nitrogen, made it clear that, during exponential growth, almost all the RNA in the bacterial cell was essentially stable. Ribosomal RNA could not therefore be the template envisaged by Jacob and Monod. Two other considerations cast doubt upon the assumption that the ribosomal ribonucleic acid acted as the template for protein synthesis: the apparent homogeneity of its base composition and of its molecular weight. It was supposed that, since the RNA templates were synthesized on the DNA of the cell, their over-all base composition should resemble that of the DNA.[1] But it had been shown that, although the base composition of the DNA in bacteria differed widely, the overall base composition of the RNA was relatively constant: in almost all cases the RNA had a high cytidylic and guanylic acid content.[6] In animal and plant cells too, it was known that the ribosomal RNA showed little variation in base composition: it also had a high cytidylic and guanylic acid content, whereas the DNA in most higher cells had a high adenylic and uridylic acid content.[7,8] Moreover, in the ultracentrifuge, ribosomal RNA separated as two discrete components, whereas if it were to serve as a template for the synthesis of a whole range of cellular proteins, one might expect much greater heterogeneity in its sedimentation behaviour. And so it was that, almost immediately, the theory put forward by Jacob and Monod initiated a search for other families of RNA molecules having the characteristics that the genetic operator model predicted that the 'messenger'' should have.

2. The reported discovery of the 'messenger' and some doubts about the evidence

Even before the paper by Jacob and Monod was published (June 1961) two communications appeared together in the same issue of *Nature* (May 1961) claiming that the desired messenger had been found. One, by Brenner, Jacob, and Meselson,[9] was entitled 'An unstable intermediate carrying information from genes to ribosomes for protein synthesis'; the other, by Gros, Hiatt, Gilbert, Kurland, Risebrough, and Watson,[10] was entitled 'Unstable ribonucleic acid revealed by pulse labelling of *Escherichia coli*'. These two papers appeared to provide experimental verification of the genetic operator model, and thus did much to win widespread acceptance for it. The paper by Brenner *et al.* deals with the synthesis of RNA in *E. coli* infected with phage T4; that by Gros *et al.* extends the investigation to uninfected *E. coli* cells.

The essential findings in the paper by Gros *et al.* were as follows: (1) When *E. coli* cells were exposed for a very short time to [^{32}P]phosphate or [^{14}C]uracil (10–20 s at 25°C) the radioactivity was largely incorporated into an RNA fraction that differed in its sedimentation characteristics from the main ribosomal RNA components. In sucrose density gradients, under the particular experimental con-

ditions used, the 'pulse-labelled' RNA sedimented as a very heterogeneous peak that varied in position between 8S and a little less than
16S (S=Svedberg, a unit of sedimentation velocity); whereas the
ribosomal RNA sedimented as two relatively homogeneous components with sedimentation coefficients of 23S and 16S (Fig. 4).
(2) At higher concentrations of magnesium (up to 10^{-2}M) increasing
amounts of this RNA were found to sediment in the position normally
occupied by the 70S ribosomes. (3) When the pulse-labelled cells
were transferred to non-radioactive medium, radioactivity disappeared from the heterogeneous component and appeared in the
ribosomal RNA. From these findings the following conclusions were
drawn: (1) that the pulse-labelling revealed a special class of RNA
that was not ribosomal RNA or a precursor of ribosomal RNA;

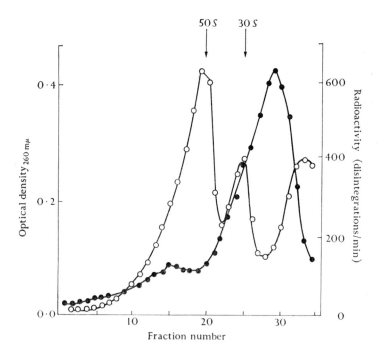

Fig. 4.   Sucrose-density-gradient sedimentation pattern of a crude extract of
Escherichia coli cells exposed to [^{14}C]uracil for 20 s. The extract was made in *tris*
buffer at pH 7·4 containing 10^{-4}M-magnesium. Centrifugation was for 2 h 45 min
at 25 000 rev/min. The optical density curve (○) shows the two families of ribosomal particles; the radioactivity curve (●) shows the distribution of the 'pulse-
labelled' RNA. (Redrawn from Gros *et al.*[10])

(2) that this RNA became attached to ribosomes at high concentrations of magnesium; and (3) that this RNA was 'metabolically unstable', that is to say, it was not only rapidly synthesized but also rapidly broken down. Were these conclusions justified?

It can be stated at the outset that no evidence was presented in this paper to support the conclusion that the pulse-labelled RNA was unstable. The passage of radioactivity from the pulse-labelled RNA to the ribosomal RNA was perfectly consistent with the idea that the pulse-labelled RNA was a precursor of the ribosomal RNA; and this interpretation of the kinetics of RNA labelling in *E. coli* had been advanced before the paper by Gros *et al.* appeared[11] and continued to be advanced by some workers after its appearance.[12] However, Gros *et al.* rejected this interpretation because of some additional experiments that they had carried out on *Staphylococcus aureus*. In this organism the pulse-labelled RNA was said to have a base composition resembling that of the DNA, and could not therefore be a precursor of the ribosomal RNA. I shall have occasion somewhat later to discuss in more detail the validity of the techniques used for measuring the base composition of pulse-labelled RNA; but I think it is fair to say that the relationship between the pulse-labelled RNA and ribosomal RNA remains incompletely resolved to the present day. There is, as far as I am aware, no convincing evidence that the base composition of the pulse-labelled RNA resembles that of the DNA, but many studies do suggest that it does have a base composition that differs from that of the ribosomal RNA. Some authors believe, from a detailed study of the distribution of radioactive phosphorus in the nucleotides released by alkali hydrolysis of the pulse-labelled RNA, that about two-thirds of it in bacteria *is* a precursor of ribosomal RNA, and that about one-third of it is something else.[13]

Analysis of the kinetics of turnover of the pulse-labelled RNA in growing bacteria has been, and continues to be, frustrated by two difficulties. The first is that when cells that have been exposed to radioactive RNA precursors are transferred to non-radioactive medium, the RNA precursor pools are only very gradually diluted with non-radioactive material, and radioactivity from these pools continues to enter RNA for some time after the cells have been transferred to the non-radioactive medium.[11] (This is an important point that will come up again when the paper by Brenner *et al.*[9] is considered.) The second is that any acute change in cultural conditions, such as is produced by transferring cells from one medium to another, induces a state of temporary shock in which the normal flow of macromolecular synthesis is disturbed. This state of shock, sometimes called 'step-down', may induce a breakdown of RNA that does not occur, or is much less marked, in cells growing in a steady state.[14] Attempts have been made to measure the turnover of pulse-labelled RNA by the use of actinomycin D,[15] which, under some, but not all, conditions,[16] suppresses residual incorporation of radioactivity from the precursor pools when the labelled cells are transferred to non-radioactive medium. But these measurements are still subject to the complication that actinomycin D induces the degradation of all families of RNA in the cell,[17] and the pulse-labelled RNA appears to be especially susceptible to this degradation.[18, 19] None the less, if the pulse-labelled RNA does indeed have a base composition that is different from the other 95 per cent or more of the RNA in the cell, it would be difficult to avoid the conclusion that at least some of the pulse-labelled RNA must be involved in rapid turnover.

We have now to consider whether the sedimentation behaviour of the pulse-labelled RNA did in fact reveal the existence of a heterogeneous family of RNA molecules which, at higher concentrations of magnesium, became attached to the ribosomes in the cell cytoplasm. A detailed study of this question has recently been made by Artman and his colleagues.[20–22] These authors found that when the pulse-labelled RNA in *E. coli* was extracted from the cells directly with phenol at low ionic strength, it did not show the sedimentation characteristics of the material produced by Gros *et al.*[10] The sedimentation of the pulse-labelled RNA extracted by phenol at low ionic strength was similar to that of the ribosomal RNA, that is to say, it sedimented mainly as two components having sedimentation coefficients of 23S and 16S. The behaviour of the pulse-labelled RNA was also indistinguishable from that of the ribosomal RNA on columns of methylated albumin. Artman *et al.* found that the pulse-labelled RNA was very susceptible to mechanical shear, and that the preparative techniques used by Gros *et al.*, which involved grinding the bacterial cells with alumina, caused fragmentation of the pulse-labelled RNA with consequent polydispersity of sedimentation. When the pulse-labelled RNA was prepared by lysis of bacterial spheroplasts (cells from which the walls had been removed by enzymatic digestion), the bulk of it was again found to sediment in the

same regions as the ribosomal RNA. Even after the ribosomal RNA
components themselves had been selectively removed by hybridization with DNA, much of the pulse-labelled RNA was still found to
sediment in the 23S and 16S regions[22] (Fig. 5). Sedat, Lyon, and
Sinsheimer[23] have examined the pulse-labelled RNA in *E. coli* after
purification by chromatography on columns of benzoylated DEAE-
cellulose. These authors found that the radioactivity that was not
associated with the ribosomal RNA components was relatively
homogeneous and had a low average molecular weight (about 72 000).
Both Artman *et al.* and Sedat *et al.* agree that the very heterogeneous
RNA described by Gros *et al.* and other authors[24-26] is an artefact
produced by aggregation of the pulse-labelled RNA with itself and
with the ribosomal RNA components. This view is strongly supported by the observation that the polydispersity of the pulse-labelled
RNA disappears when it is examined in gradients containing dimethyl
sulphoxide[23] which appears to minimize interactions between and
within polynucleotide chains.

Gros *et al.* noted that at higher concentrations of magnesium much
of the pulse-labelled RNA sedimented in the position occupied by
the 70S ribosomes, and they interpreted this behaviour as evidence

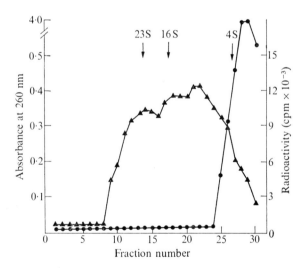

FIG. 5. Sedimentation behaviour of pulse-labelled RNA in *E. coli* after selective
removal of ribosomal RNA by hybridization with DNA. ▲, pulse-labelled RNA;
●, fragmented ribosomal RNA. (From Fry *et al.*[22])

that the pulse-labelled RNA became attached to these ribosomes. They noted, however, that this interpretation gave rise to a serious difficulty: 70S ribosomes to which the pulse-labelled RNA was attached should not sediment at 70S, but should be heavier. No satisfactory resolution of this difficulty was provided by Gros *et al.*, but it does appear to have been provided by Artman *et al.*[20] The latter authors showed that the radioactivity sedimenting at 70S at high concentrations of magnesium was not *attached to* ribosomes, but formed an integral part of the 50S and 30S ribosomal subunits, which became associated to form the 70S particle at higher concentrations of magnesium. This view was supported by the failure to release any free RNA from these particles when they were subjected to very low magnesium concentrations. Artman *et al.* conclude that the great bulk of the pulse-labelled RNA in *E. coli* forms an integral part of the newly synthesized ribosomal subunits. I do not imagine that this work will prove to be the last word on the subject; but, at the very least, the experiments of Artman *et al.* do make it clear that the effects of magnesium on the sedimentation behaviour of the pulse-labelled RNA are easily susceptible to interpretations other than the one favoured by Gros *et al.*

We come now to the paper by Brenner *et al.*[9] dealing with bacteriophage-infected *E. coli*. It was known at the time that this work was undertaken that when *E. coli* cells were infected with the T-even bacteriophages net synthesis of bacterial RNA was rapidly inhibited.[27] Brenner *et al.* examined the synthesis of RNA in cells infected with phage T4 and reached the following conclusions: (1) that no new ribosomes of any sort were made in the infected bacterial cell; (2) that the RNA made by the phage could be identified by its sedimentation behaviour, which differed from that of the bacterial ribosomal RNA; (3) that the phage messenger RNA was unstable; and (4) that the phage messenger RNA became attached to pre-existing ribosomes and acted as a template for protein synthesis while it was attached to these particles.

The crucial experiment in this paper was the one that purported to demonstrate that no new ribosomes of any sort were made in the infected cell. Clearly, if the phage does not make its own ribosomes and if the phage proteins are made on pre-existing bacterial ribosomes, then the RNA produced on the phage DNA must become involved with the bacterial ribosomes in some way. The evidence that no new ribosomes were made in the phage-infected cell was obtained in the following way. The bacteria were grown in heavy isotopes (^{15}N and ^{13}C) until all the cell constituents were uniformly labelled with these isotopes. By means of density gradient centrifugation in caesium chloride it is possible to distinguish the ribosomes extracted from these 'heavy' cells from those extracted from normal 'light' cells, since the 'heavy' ribosomes sediment to a position of higher density in the gradient. The heavy cells were then infected with the phage and transferred to medium containing 'light' isotopes (^{14}N and ^{12}C). After 7 min in this medium the cells were disrupted and the newly formed RNA, labelled from the second to the seventh minute with radioactive phosphorus, was subjected to density gradient centrifugation. The labelled RNA was found to sediment in the position occupied by the 'heavy' ribosomes, not in the position normally occupied by the 'light' ribosomes; from which the conclusion was drawn that no 'wholly new' ribosomes were formed after phage infection. However, a consideration of the behaviour of the RNA precursor pools in *E. coli* indicates that the formation of wholly 'light' ribosomes is hardly to be expected in an experiment of this sort. It is well known that when bacteria are exposed for even a few seconds to a radioactive RNA precursor and then transferred to non-radioactive medium, the radioactive RNA precursor pools are not immediately diluted with unlabelled material, but continue to feed radioactivity into RNA for many minutes afterwards.[11] After exposure for 1 min to radioactive uracil, *E. coli* cells, transferred to non-radioactive medium containing an excess of unlabelled uridine and cytidine, continue to incorporate radioactivity into RNA from the radioactive precursor pools for at least 15 min.[28] We can therefore be confident that if the cells are grown in 'heavy' isotopes until all the RNA precursor pools are uniformly 'heavy', these 'heavy' pools will continue to provide 'heavy' isotopes for RNA synthesis for many minutes after the cells have been transferred to 'light' medium. On the other hand, the amino acid pools are replaced rapidly.[29] One might therefore suppose that at least the newly synthesized ribosomal proteins would be completely 'light'. But there is evidence that the assembly of the ribosome draws on a substantial pool of preformed ribosomal protein,[30-33] so that even the protein moiety of the newly formed ribosomes would remain 'heavy' for some minutes after transfer of the 'heavy' cells to 'light' medium. It will thus be evident that the formation of *completely* 'light' ribosomes is not to be expected within the 7-min period studied by Brenner *et al.*;

whether the cells are infected with phage or not. What is to be expected is that the ribosomes synthesized immediately after transfer of the 'heavy' cells to 'light' medium would be essentially 'heavy' and that they would become progressively 'lighter' as the 'heavy' precursor pools became diluted with 'light' material. And, indeed, in the experiments of Brenner *et al.*, although the RNA synthesized after transfer of the 'heavy' cells to 'light' medium sediments with the 'heavy' ribosome band, the sedimentation pattern shows skewing to the 'light' side, which is precisely what our knowledge of the behaviour of the precursor pools predicts that it should do. The experiments of Brenner *et al.* thus do not prove that no new ribosomes are formed after phage infection; indeed, the method can hardly be sensitive enough to provide such a proof. The validity of this criticism has recently been confirmed. It is now clear that *E. coli* cells continue to synthesize many families of bacterial RNA, including ribosomal RNA, for several minutes after infection with phage T4.[34, 35]

Like Gros *et al.*, Brenner *et al.* concluded that the RNA made by the phage became attached to bacterial ribosomes at high concentrations of magnesium. The objections to this conclusion and the relevance of the recent study of Artman *et al.* on this point have already been discussed.[20] The finding that at high magnesium concentrations the newly formed RNA sediments in the *same* position as the bacterial ribosomes argues *against* the idea that this RNA is *attached to* these ribosomes. If it were, the RNA-ribosomes complex would have a higher ratio of RNA to protein than the ribosomes alone and would therefore sediment to a position of higher density in the caesium chloride gradient. The fact that the newly formed RNA sediments in the same position as the ribosomes suggests that it is an integral part of the ribosome or of some other particle having the same density. Finally, Brenner *et al.* concluded that much of the labelled phage RNA underwent intracellular degradation. There can be little objection to this conclusion, since their experiments showed a net loss of radioactivity from the RNA of the infected cell, but the biological significance of this RNA degradation is far from clear.

3. The rapidly labelled RNA in the cell nucleus

The most detailed studies on RNA metabolism that have so far been made have been carried out on animal cells, and especially on animal cells cultivated *in vitro*. I therefore propose to deal mainly with this material, but I shall draw from time to time on data derived from experiments with bacteria. The bacterial and animal cell systems appear to me to be very similar.

When animal cells are exposed for 10 to 15 min to a radioactive RNA precursor, more than 90 per cent of the radioactivity is found to be located in the cell nucleus. The fact that radioactive precursors first label the RNA in the cell nucleus was discovered by Bergstrand *et al.*[36] in 1948; and the relationship between the initial nuclear labelling and the subsequent cytoplasmic labelling has since been the subject of an extensive and complex literature.[37] The situation seems to be quite the same in bacteria. When bacteria that have a moderately well defined nuclear area, such as *E. coli*, are exposed for about a minute to a radioactive RNA precursor, most of the radioactivity is localized in the bacterial 'nucleus';[38] and more prolonged exposure to the radioactive precursor labels the bacterial cytoplasm. In animal cells this rapidly labelled nuclear RNA is not free in solution, but still appears to be attached in some way to the chromosomes.[39–41] The mode of attachment has not yet been clarified: it may be that the newly formed RNA is still bound to its DNA template by hydrogen bonds between the DNA and RNA strands, but there is some evidence that protein may be involved.[42] Whether the rapidly labelled RNA in bacteria is also attached to the bacterial chromosome is not known. In order to study this RNA in bacteria it is usually necessary to disrupt the cells and then treat the disrupted preparation with deoxyribonuclease in order to reduce its viscosity. Such treatment, of course, destroys the bacterial chromosome and thus vitiates any assessment of what might or might not be attached to it *in vivo*.

When rapidly labelled RNA is extracted from the nuclei of animal cells it shows some unusual physical properties. In sucrose density gradients its sedimentation behaviour has proved to be extraordinarily variable. The following sedimentation patterns have been described, among others: heterogeneous material sedimenting in the same areas as the 28S and 16S components;†[39] heterogeneous material sedimenting partly with the 28S and 16S components and partly less rapidly;[43] heterogeneous material sedimenting partly with the 28S and 16S components and partly more rapidly;[44–48] two broad

† 28S and 16S are the sedimentation coefficients for the two ribosomal RNA components in animal cells, calculated at infinite dilution. Higher figures, for example 30S and 18S, are sometimes given. These are not more accurate values, but are simply a reflection of what corrections one chooses to make in arriving at the sedimentation coefficient.

but relatively homogeneous components separating at 45S and 35S;[49] extremely polydisperse material having a continuous range of sedimentation coefficients from about 80S to 10S.[50] This state of affairs is not very different from that found in bacteria. Although the original papers of Brenner et al.[9] and Gros et al.[10] showed the rapidly labelled RNA in *E. coli* as a broad peak with a sedimentation coefficient somewhere between 8S and 16S, much more heterogeneous sedimentation behaviour has since been described.[24-26] The evidence in support of the view that much of this heterogeneity is due to partial degradation and aggregation of the rapidly labelled RNA has already been discussed.[20-23]

Under certain conditions of centrifugation, much of the rapidly labelled nuclear RNA has an extremely high sedimentation velocity. A correspondingly high molecular weight has therefore been attributed to it, and it has been dubbed 'giant heterogeneous nuclear RNA'.[50-52] This fraction also has a very low mobility when the pulse-labelled RNA of the cell is examined by electrophoresis in polyacrylamide gels. Recent studies indicate, however, that the unusually high sedimentation rate and low electrophoretic mobility are due to aggregation of the pulse-labelled material and do not reflect an extraordinarily high molecular weight.[53,54] When the 'giant' pulse-labelled RNA is examined under dissociating conditions, its sedimentation remains heterogeneous, but the bulk of the material sediments in much the same region as the ribosomal RNA. That this is not due to degradation of the 'giant' RNA is demonstrated first by the reversibility of the effect and second by the fact that bacteriophage RNA of known dimensions remains undegraded when subjected to the same procedures (Fig. 6A, B, C). But for charged, highly asymmetrical molecules, sedimentation coefficients, even under dissociating conditions, do not necessarily give an accurate measure of molecular weight; and two other methods have therefore been used to measure the chain length of the polynucleotides in the pulse-labelled RNA. In one, this was measured by a technique that involved digestion of the pulse-labelled RNA under controlled conditions with a purified exonuclease;[55] in the other alkali hydrolysis was used to determine the proportion of the total nucleotides released as end groups.[56] By both methods the mean polynucleotide chain length of the pulse-labelled RNA was found to be not very different from that of the ribosomal RNA. As with bacteria, it is clear that the sedimentation behaviour of the pulse-labelled RNA does not in itself delineate a functionally specific new category of RNA molecules.

Shortly after the discovery that the RNA in the cell nucleus was the first to become labelled by radioactive RNA precursors,[36] it was shown that when briefly labelled cells were transferred to non-radioactive medium, radioactivity left the nuclear RNA and appeared in the cytoplasmic RNA. This experiment, carried out by both chemical and autoradiographic methods, was confirmed in many different cells, and was generally interpreted to mean that the rapidly labelled RNA in the cell nucleus was the precursor of the more slowly labelled RNA in the cytoplasm.[57] When the sedimentation characteristics of ribosomal RNA were established, similar experiments showed that the disappearance of the radioactivity from the rapidly

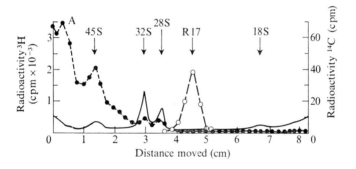

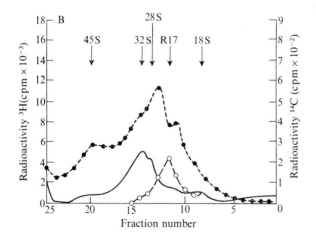

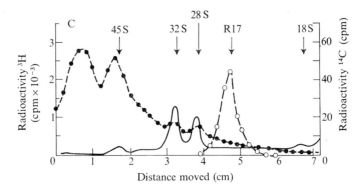

Fig. 6. Analysis of purified pulse-labelled nuclear RNA from HeLa cells. (A) Polyacrylamide gel electrophoresis of nuclear RNA after a 20 min exposure of the cells to tritiated uridine. RNA from bacteriophage R17, labelled with [14C]uridine was taken through the extraction procedure at the same time in order to check whether any degradation of RNA had taken place. The mobility of the pulse-labelled RNA in the gel suggests that it has a very high molecular weight. (B) The pulse-labelled RNA is examined by sucrose density gradient centrifugation under dissociating conditions (5mM EDTA in Tris buffer at pH 5·4). Its sedimentation behaviour now indicates that it is heterogeneous with respect to molecular weight, but that most of the material is not of higher molecular weight than the ribosomal RNA. (C) The RNA shown in (B) is precipitated from the sucrose gradient by ethanol and subjected again to electrophoresis. The pattern shown in (A) is recovered. Note that the bacteriophage R17 RNA in (C) migrates in exactly the same position as in (A). The changes shown in (B) are thus reversible, and they are not due to RNA degradation. ●, tritium-labelled nuclear RNA; ○, [14C]-labelled bacteriophage R17 RNA; ——, RNA components measured by ultraviolet absorbance. (From Bramwell.[54])

labelled RNA was associated with the appearance of radioactivity in the ribosomal RNA;[11] and it was therefore commonly believed that the rapidly labelled RNA was the precursor of the ribosomal RNA. This idea was first questioned in 1959, when it was observed that there were major discrepancies between the amount of radioactivity lost from the nuclear RNA and the amount that appeared in the cytoplasmic RNA.[58, 59] An extensive series of experiments eventually established that much of the rapidly labelled nuclear RNA was involved in a process of intracellular turnover: this RNA was not only rapidly made, but also rapidly broken down in the cell.[39, 60, 61] This conclusion, which had, in fact, been reached 2 years before the 'messenger' hypothesis was launched, and thus came 2 years too soon,[58, 59] was initially received with little enthusiasm; but it has now been confirmed in a wide range of different cells[48, 50, 62–66] and is generally accepted. However, in cells growing exponentially, ribosomal RNA appeared to be essentially stable;[4] and even in non-growing cells, it turned over at a very much slower rate than the rapidly labelled RNA.[67-69] It was therefore possible to conclude that even if some of the rapidly labelled RNA was a macromolecular precursor of ribosomal RNA, the bulk of it was not in fact converted into ribosomal RNA under the usual experimental conditions. An RNA made in the cell nucleus and then rapidly degraded was obviously an ideal candidate for the messenger RNA postulated by Jacob and Monod; but a more detailed examination of these short-lived RNA molecules revealed unexpectedly that they were not transferred to the cytoplasm before being broken down, but were rapidly degraded within the cell nucleus.[37, 39, 58-60, 70] Like the discovery of their short life, the demonstration that these RNA molecules were involved in intranuclear turnover met with resistance; but an exhaustive series of experiments now leaves little doubt that most of the short-lived nuclear RNA does not pass to the cytoplasm of the cell.[16, 50, 61, 71-84] What the function of this RNA might be remains obscure, but I shall have something to say about this question later.

Jacob and Monod proposed that the messenger RNA should have an average base composition resembling that of the DNA on which it was made; and numerous attempts have been made to identify rapidly labelled RNA fractions having a 'DNA-like' base composition. Measurement of the base composition of the rapidly labelled RNA is, however, fraught with great difficulty, and it has not so far been possible to isolate this material and determine its base composition by direct chemical analysis. An indirect method introduced by Volkin and Astrachan[85] in 1956 has been extensively used; the cells are exposed for a short period of time to radioactive phosphate and the distribution of radioactivity in the nucleotides obtained by alkali hydrolysis of the labelled RNA is taken as a measure of the base composition of the rapidly labelled fraction. This technique can obviously only be a measure of base composition if certain assumptions are made about the randomness of the distribution of the radioactive phosphorus in the polynucleotide chains. I think it is enough to say that, after extensive investigation, it is now clear that these assumptions do not hold when the cells are exposed to a radioactive RNA precursor for short periods of time, and that, consequently, the 'phosphorus pulse' method, as this technique is called, does not provide a reliable estimate of the base composition of the rapidly labelled RNA.[86–88] The extreme variability of the results obtained with this technique, the discovery of RNA fractions having a base composition resembling that of the DNA, the equally frequent failure to detect such DNA-like fractions, the dramatic changes in the composition of the rapidly labelled RNA produced by external stimuli or by changes in cultural conditions, are all reflections of the fact that the distribution of radioactivity in RNA after a short pulse of radioactive phosphorus is influenced by factors other than the base composition of the RNA synthesized during the pulse. As will be seen presently, when the role of polyadenylic acid sequences in messenger RNA is discussed, there are, in fact, no good grounds for the assumption that the mean base composition of the messenger RNA should reflect the mean base composition of the DNA from which it is transcribed.

4. Rapidly labelled RNA in the cell cytoplasm

If some of the rapidly labelled nuclear RNA consists of messengers that carry information from the genes to the cytoplasm of the cell, it should be possible to detect such molecules in the cytoplasm. An exhaustive search carried out in many laboratories, with a variety of techniques, and extending over a period of many years, has, however, failed to detect in the cytoplasm of animal cells any RNA fraction that resembles in its physical properties the rapidly labelled RNA in the cell nucleus.[39, 44, 48, 50, 65, 89–93] The first indication that the cytoplasm might not contain any RNA having the physical properties of the rapidly labelled nuclear RNA came with the observation that, under the usual conditions of sucrose gradient centrifugation, preparations of the total RNA in the cell cytoplasm, extracted by direct treatment with phenol and detergent, did not show any fraction that had either the kinetic or the sedimentation characteristics of the rapidly labelled nuclear RNA.[39, 44] When it became clear that the variable polydispersity of the rapidly labelled RNA was a reflection of its sensitivity to changes in ionic strength and cation concentration, the RNA in the cytoplasm was examined in solutions of varying ionic strength and cation concentration, but still no RNA showing the characteristics of the rapidly labelled nuclear RNA was revealed.[94] Perhaps because it has little secondary structure, the rapidly labelled RNA adheres tightly to columns of methylated albumin on kieselguhr at salt concentrations that elute all the other ribonucleic acids in the cell.[95, 96] Preparations of cytoplasmic RNA were therefore screened for the presence of molecules showing tight adherence to methylated albumin; but again, no RNA having the properties of the rapidly labelled nuclear RNA could be found.[93]

While it now appears to be generally agreed that the cytoplasm does not contain any RNA like the rapidly labelled nuclear RNA, other minor RNA components have from time to time been described in the cytoplasm and have been canvassed as the messenger molecules postulated by Jacob and Monod. When RNA is extracted directly from the cell cytoplasm with phenol and detergent, no RNA components of high molecular weight are detected, either by ultraviolet absorption or by their radioactive content, that differ greatly from the ribosomal RNA.[39,91,94] But when radioactive cells are disrupted by homogenization, and preparations of cytoplasmic ribosomes are made, minor labelled components are found that sediment apart from the ribosomes. The great majority of these minor components, whether they are found as free RNA or as RNA-protein complexes, are artefacts arising from degradation of ribosomal RNA[97,98] or from nuclear damage produced during cell fractionation.[99-101] When cells are exposed for a short period to a radioactive RNA percursor, the specific activity of the RNA in the cell nucleus may be two or three orders of magnitude higher than that of the RNA in the cytoplasm. Under such conditions the rupture of a few nuclei per thousand cells may release traces of radioactive RNA or radioactive ribonucleoprotein into what is eventually collected as the 'cytoplasmic' fraction. Probably no fractionation procedure currently available is completely free from this source of error. Indeed, it has been shown that when pulse-labelled cells are fractionated by standard homogenization procedures, the amount of pulse-labelled RNA appearing in the 'cytoplasmic' fraction increases as homogenization proceeds.[98] With the discovery that ribosomes actively engaged in protein synthesis were often gathered into clusters ('polysomes'),[102-105] attempts were made to identify messenger RNA by isolating the polysomes and extracting rapidly labelled RNA fractions from them. However, most of the rapidly labelled RNA associated with polysomes was again found to be derived from nuclei damaged during the fractionation procedure. The situation was further complicated by the demonstration that some of the RNA made in mitochondria also showed heterogeneous sedimentation behaviour.[106,107] It was clear that messenger RNA in the cell cytoplasm was not to be identified by rapidity of labelling or polydisperse sedimentation.

5. Real messengers

The inadequacy of the original experiments purporting to have identified messenger RNA and the continued failure of many laboratories to provide decisive evidence for such an RNA in the cell cytoplasm led several workers, including myself, to doubt whether a messenger RNA having the properties proposed by Jacob and Monod actually existed in higher cells and to suggest that the RNA that carried the specifications for proteins might perhaps form an integral part of the ribosomal RNA.[108, 109] But this idea had to be abandoned in the face of continuing progress in the analysis of the nucleotide sequences in ribosomal RNA. Whatever other properties messenger RNA might or might not have, it was clear that, as a class, messenger RNA molecules had to be heterogeneous with respect to nucleotide sequence, for they specified polypeptides that were heterogeneous with respect to amino-acid sequence. Sequence analysis of ribosomal RNA has, however, finally made it clear that, although minor degrees of heterogeneity do exist, both components of the ribosomal RNA are substantially homogeneous with respect to nucleotide sequence.[110–115] The information for the great bulk of the proteins in the cell had therefore to be sought elsewhere.

Physical and kinetic characteristics having proved to be such deceptive criteria, the attention of many investigators turned again to the possibility of identifying messenger RNA by its functional properties, that is, by its ability to support the synthesis of specific proteins. The first decisive success was with the haemoglobin messenger RNA. Although experiments had been done as early as 1961 suggesting that rabbit ribosomes could be programmed to synthesize sheep haemoglobin by a soluble component extracted from sheep reticulocytes, these experiments failed to win acceptance; and for almost a decade the only convincing experiments of this kind were those in which the ribosomes were programmed with artificial polyribonucleotides or with RNA extracted from bacteriophages.[117–120] Eventually, however, with further refinements of cell-free systems, unexceptional evidence was obtained that RNA from one species of animal could serve as a messenger for the synthesis of haemoglobin in cell-free preparations in which the ribosomes were derived from another species.[121–126] The haemoglobin synthesized was shown to be specific for the RNA added; and the messenger RNA was effective not only with ribosomes from cells normally involved in haemoglobin synthesis but also with ribosomes from cells of a completely different type.[125] The RNA fraction showing maximal haemoglobin messenger activity had a sedimentation coefficient of about 9S. A 9S RNA fraction isolated from rabbit reticulocytes was also shown to support the synthesis of rabbit haemoglobin when injected into frog oocytes.[127–129] Several other messenger RNA preparations have since been shown to support the synthesis of specific proteins either in heterologous cell-free systems, or in frog oocytes, or both. Here is a list of some of the more convincing examples, together with the sedimentation coefficients of the fractions showing maximal message activity: immunoglobulin light chain[130, 131] (13–14S); immunoglobulin heavy chain[132] (two bands on electrophoresis, one having an apparent molecular weight much higher than that to be expected from the chain length of the polypeptide, the other paradoxically having an apparent molecular weight lower than expected); ovalbumin[133–135] (slightly less than 18S); avidin[136] (8–9S); histone[137] (7–9S); lens α- and β-crystallins[138–140] (14S); myosin[141] (25–27S); tryptophan oxygenase[142] (no estimate of size given); α_s casein[143] (slightly less than 18S).

Although none of these translatable messengers has yet been purified to a stage that would permit complete nucleotide sequence analysis† some general properties of messenger RNA molecules appear none the less to be emerging. The first is that there is no simple relationship between the length of the polypeptide chain being specified and the apparent molecular weight of the messenger RNA specifying it. All messenger ribonucleic acids appear to be substantially longer than necessary simply to code for the corresponding polypeptide. In some cases the discrepancy is so large that the possibility must be considered that the messenger RNA either forms an integral part of a much longer sequence of concatenated messengers or that the basic messenger unit is repeated in the RNA chain as a consequence of gene duplication. But even in those cases where the discrepancy is not large enough to pose difficulties of this kind, it appears that a substantial part of all messenger RNA molecules is composed of nucleotide sequences that are not translated, or, if translated, not represented in the amino acids of the completed polypeptide chain. A second feature is that at least some translatable messengers have a high degree of secondary structure.[123, 145] In these two respects the cellular messenger ribonucleic

† Some progress has been made in the sequence analysis of the messenger RNA for immunoglobulin light chains.[144]

acids resemble the RNA of the MS2 bacteriophage in which the complete nucleotide sequence of one of the genes has been determined. This messenger sequence does contain untranslated regions and appears to have a very precise secondary and tertiary structure.[146] There is evidence that the secondary structure is of importance in ensuring faithful translation of bacteriophage f2 RNA in a cell-free system;[147] and it is therefore reasonable to suppose that secondary structure may have a similar importance in cellular messenger RNA. The function of the untranslated regions is not yet clear. Neither of these two properties is, however, specific enough to permit characterization of messenger RNA molecules as a class or identification of specific messenger ribonucleic acids in heterogeneous RNA preparations. A third property which appears to characterize messenger RNA molecules may, however, provide a general method for their identification and isolation: almost all of the messenger ribonucleic acids that have so far been examined contain long sequences of repeated adenylic acid residues.

6. Polyadenylic acid

The discovery that the nuclei of animal cells contained polyadenylic acid and an enzyme capable of synthesizing the polymer was made more than a decade ago;[148, 149] but like most important discoveries that do not fit easily into currently held doctrines, the original observation did not at once initiate a wave of exploratory activity. But when, with the development of techniques permitting the identification of specific messenger ribonucleic acids, it was found that a partially purified preparation of haemoglobin messenger RNA contained at one end a long sequence composed largely of adenylic acid residues,[150] a torrent of papers dealing with polyadenylic acid was released. These rapidly established that a long sequence of adenylic acid residues (between 50 and 200) was a feature of several reasonably well defined messenger ribonucleic acids and of some less well defined cytoplasmic RNA components that were assumed to have messenger function.[153–155] The polyadenylic acid is attached, apparently covalently, to the 3'-terminus of the messenger RNA molecules;[156, 157] and some evidence has been presented suggesting that the adenylic acid residues are added to the RNA after it has been transcribed from the DNA.[158] Histone messenger RNA appears to lack polyadenylic acid;[159] and it is not apparently found in the RNA of *E. coli*.[160] The function of the polyadenylic acid is at present ob-

scure. It has been proposed that it may be required for the transport of messenger RNA from nucleus to cytoplasm;[158,161] but
there is also evidence that it may be required for the initiation of
translation.[162] On the plausible assumption that messenger ribonucleic acids do contain polyadenylic acid and that most other families of RNA do not, techniques have been evolved to screen for RNA
molecules containing polyadenylic acid sequences. The most
promising of these exploits the ability of polyadenylic acid to bind
specifically to polythymidylic acid, so that RNA molecules containing polyadenylic acid can be isolated by their ability to bind to short
polymers of polythymidylic acid covalently linked to cellulose.[163]
This procedure has been used to purify biologically active messenger
RNA fractions and also to screen heterogeneous cellular preparations for putative messenger molecules. RNA fractions containing
polyadenylic acid have been found in the rapidly labelled
polydisperse nuclear RNA,[164] in RNA associated with cytoplasmic
polysomes[163, 164] and also in mitochondrial RNA.[165] When all the
polyribosomal RNA containing polyadenylic acid sequences is collected by adsorption to polythymidylic acid-cellulose and then
subjected to sucrose gradient sedimentation, the distribution shown
in Fig. 7 is obtained. If the presence of polyadenylic acid does
accurately identify messenger RNA, then this result indicates that,
as a class, messenger RNA in animal cells has a sedimentation

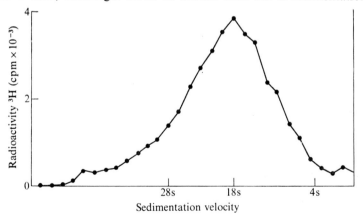

Sedimentation velocity

FIG. 7. Sedimentation behaviour of the RNA in polysomes that contains polyadenylic acid. This RNA was extracted from the polysomes in the cytoplasm of
HeLa cells by specific hybridization to polythymidylic acid-cellulose. The RNA
containing polyadenylic acid is heterogeneous in sedimentation, but the main
peak sediments at 18S. (From Nakazato and Edmonds.[164])

distribution more heterogeneous than, but largely coincident with, the 18S ribosomal RNA. This result may well explain a decade of failure to identify messenger RNA in the cytoplasm of animal cells by its sedimentation behaviour; and the fact that at least some well defined messenger ribonucleic acids clearly do contain polyadenylic acid also underlines the futility of past attempts to identify messenger RNA by its resemblance to DNA in overall base composition.

7. The stability of messenger RNA

One of the most serious obstacles to the application of the genetic operator model of Jacob and Monod to higher cells is the requirement of this model that the life of messenger RNA should be short. Enucleation and other experiments that I have described in Chapter 1 make it clear that the information for protein synthesis in the cytoplasm of eukaryotic cells is essentially stable, that is, the half-life of the messenger RNA is not notably short relative to the generation time of the cell. The application of the polythymidylic-cellulose technique for isolating RNA containing polyadenylic sequences has now provided some direct measurements of the half-life of cytoplasmic messenger ribonucleic acids in animal cells, at least in so far as they are identified by this technique. The whole class of cytoplasmic ribonucleic acids containing polyadenylic acid is stable. Although the values obtained for the mean half-life of these molecules show variations due to different experimental conditions, the lowest estimate for the mean half-life is 6 h[166] (but this is in the presence of actinomycin D, which is known to induce degradation of RNA in the cell), and the highest estimate is 2–3 days.[167] It is, in any case, clear that the cytoplasmic RNA containing polyadenylic acid does not turn over much more rapidly than once per cell generation.[168] This view of the stability of messenger RNA in animal cells is supported by experiments in which haemoglobin messenger RNA is injected into frog eggs or oocytes. The injected RNA is not degraded in the cytoplasm of the cell and supports the synthesis of haemoglobin for up to two weeks.[128, 169] These findings no doubt explain the failure of many workers in recent years to identify messenger RNA in animal cells by its rapid turnover.

Can it be accepted then that the messenger RNA of higher cells is stable, while the great bulk of the messenger RNA in bacteria is short-lived? I doubt it. No bacterial messenger RNA translatable in a cell-free system has yet been isolated (apart from the RNA of, or produced by, bacteriophages), and bacterial RNA appears not to contain any significant amount of polyadenylic acid.[160] Experiments of the kind described in the previous paragraph have not therefore been possible. On the other hand, the messenger ribonucleic acids of bacteria can readily be identified by the technique of DNA–RNA hybridization in a way that mammalian messenger ribonucleic acids cannot. In mammalian cells the extreme complexity of the genome has so far made it very difficult to use DNA–RNA hybridization techniques with any confidence in the identification of specific messenger ribonucleic acids; but in bacteria, where the specific genes can be incorporated into transducing bacteriophages, DNA preparations can be made which are greatly enriched for specific genes. Such preparations can be used in DNA–RNA hybridization experiments to identify specific bacterial messenger ribonucleic acids among the more limited family of such molecules that bacteria produce. DNA–RNA hybridization has been used to measure the life times of a number of specific messenger ribonucleic acids in bacterial cells, and the experiments have usually revealed that these messengers have a relatively short, although not uniformly short, half-life of a few minutes.[170–173] However, all these experiments involve procedures that produce acute changes in the metabolism of the cell. Either further transcription is stopped by the administration of antibiotics such as rifampicin, or the cell is infected with a virulent bacteriophage, or, more commonly, an exogenous inducer of the synthesis of a particular protein is removed from an induced culture and the rate of decay of the relevant messenger RNA then measured. I think there is no need to dwell on the possibility of artefactual degradation of RNA induced by rifampicin or virulent bacteriophages; but the technique of measuring the decay of a specific messenger after the removal of the relevant inducer requires comment. If, as now seems probable, a system of translational controls is superimposed on transcriptional controls even in the case of the classical inducible enzymes,[170] removal of the inducer may not only inhibit further transcription of the relevant genetic locus, it may also inhibit translation of the message, or, at least, greatly reduce the rate of its translation. Under such conditions, the message may decay *because* it is not translated or translated much less frequently. If this were so, the observed rate of decay of the message might not reflect its half-life under steady state conditions in which the inducer is constantly present. I know of no satisfactory measurements of the half-life of specific bacterial messengers under steady state conditions; and it therefore seems reasonable to suggest that attempts should be made to obtain such measurements before generalizations about the instability of bacterial messenger RNA can be finally accepted.

REFERENCES

1. JACOB, F. and MONOD, J. (1961). Genetic regulatory mechanisms in the synthesis of proteins. *J. molec. Biol.* **3**, 318.
2. HERSHEY, A. D. (1954). Conservation of nucleic acids during bacterial growth. *J. gen. Physiol.* **38**, 145.
3. LABAW, L. W., MOSLEY, V. M., and WYCKOFF, R. W. G. (1950). Radioactive studies of the phosphorus metabolism of *Escherichia coli. J. Bact.* **59**, 251.
4. SIMINOVITCH, L. S. and GRAHAM, A. F. (1956). Significance of ribonucleic acid and deoxyribonucleic acid turnover studies. *J. Histochem. Cytochem.* **4**, 508.
5. DAVERN, C. I. and MESELSON, M. (1960). The molecular conservation of ribonucleic acid during bacterial growth. *J. molec. Biol.* **2**, 153.
6. BELOZERSKY, A. N. and SPIRIN, A. S. (1958). A correlation between the compositions of deoxyribonucleic acid and ribonucleic acid. *Nature, Lond.* **182**, 111.
7. CHARGAFF, E. (1955). Isolation and composition of the deoxypentose nucleic acids and of the corresponding nucleoproteins. *The nucleic acids* (Eds. E. CHARGAFF and J. N. DAVIDSON), p. 307. Academic Press, New York.
8. MAGASANIK, B. (1955). Isolation and composition of the pentose nucleic acids and of the corresponding nucleoproteins. *The nucleic acids* (Eds. E. CHARGAFF and J. N. DAVIDSON), p. 373. Academic Press, New York.
9. BRENNER, S., JACOB, F., and MESELSON, M. (1961). An unstable intermediate carrying information from genes to ribosomes for protein synthesis. *Nature, Lond.* **190**, 576.
10. GROS, F., HIATT, H., GILBERT, W., KURLAND, C. G., RISEBROUGH, R. W., and WATSON, J. D. (1961). Unstable ribonucleic acid revealed by pulse labelling of *Escherichia coli. Nature, Lond.* **190**, 581.
11. ARONSON, A. I., BOLTON, E. T., BRITTEN, R. J., COWIE, D. B., DUERKSEN, J. D., MCCARTHY, B. J., MCQUILLEN, K., and ROBERTS, R. B. (1960). *Carnegie Institution of Washington Year Book* **59**, 229.
12. KITAZUME, Y., YČAS, M., and VINCENT, W. S. (1962). Metabolic properties of a ribonucleic acid fraction in yeast. *Proc. natn. Acad. Sci. U.S.A.* **48**, 265.
13. MIDGLEY, J. E. M. and MCCARTHY, B. J. (1962). The synthesis and kinetic behaviour of deoxyribonucleic acid-like ribonucleic acid in bacteria. *Biochim. biophys. Acta* **61**, 696.
14. BELLAMY, A. R. (1966). RNA synthesis in exponentially growing tobacco cells subjected to a step-down nutritional shift. *Biochim. biophys. Acta* **123**, 102.
15. LEVINTHAL, C., KEYNAN, A., and HIGA, A. (1962). Messenger RNA turnover and protein synthesis in *B. subtilis* inhibited by actinomycin D. *Proc. natn. Acad. Sci. U.S.A.* **48**, 1631.
16. HARRIS, H. (1964). Breakdown of nuclear ribonucleic acid in the presence of actinomycin D. *Nature. Lond.* **202**, 1301.

17. WIESNER, R., ACS, G., REICH, E., and SHAFIQ, A. (1965). Degradation of ribonucleic acid in mouse fibroblasts treated with actinomycin. *J. Cell Biol.* **27**, 47.
18. ACS, G., REICH, E., and VALANJU, S. (1963). RNA metabolism in *B. subtilis. Biochim. biophys. Acta* **76**, 68.
19. STEWART, G. H. and FARBER, E. (1968). The rapid acceleration of hepatic nuclear ribonucleic acid breakdown by actinomycin but not by ethionine. *J. biol. Chem.* **243**, 4479.
20. ARTMAN, M., SILMAN, N., and ENGELBERG, H. (1967). Pulse labelled RNA associated with ribosomes in *Escherichia coli. Nature, Lond.* **213**, 39.
21. FRY, M. and ARTMAN, M. (1968). Sedimentation behaviour of rapidly labelled RNA from *Escherichia coli. Nature, Lond.* **217**, 661.
22. FRY, M., ISRAELI-RECHES, M. and ARTMAN, M. (1972). Messenger RNA from normal and T4 phage-infected *Escherichia coli*: isolation and distribution. *Biochim. biophys. Acta* **281**, 365.
23. SEDAT, J., LYON, A., and SINSHEIMER, R. L. (1969). Purification of *Escherichia coli* pulse-labelled RNA by benzoylated DEAE-cellulose chromatography. *J. molec. Biol.* **44**, 415.
24. MONIER, R., NAONO, S., HAYES, D., HAYES, F., and GROS, F. (1962). Studies on the heterogeneity of messenger RNA from *E. coli. J. molec. Biol.* **5**, 311.
25. ISHIHAMA, A., MIZUNO, N., TAKAI, M., OTAKA, E., and OSAWA, S. (1962). Molecular and metabolic properties of messenger RNA from normal and T2-infected *Escherichia coli. J. molec. Biol.* **5**, 251.
26. ASANO, K. (1965). Size heterogeneity of T2 messenger RNA. *J. molec. Biol.* **14**, 71.
27. COHEN, S. S. (1949). Growth requirements of bacterial viruses. *Bact. Rev.* **13**, 1.
28. HARRIS, H. Unpublished data.
29. BRITTEN, R. J. and McCLURE, F. T. (1962). The amino acid pool in *Escherichia coli. Bact. Rev.* **26**, 292.
30. DALGARNO, L. and GROS, F. (1968). Completion of ribosomal particles in *Escherichia coli* during inhibition of protein synthesis. *Biochim. biophys. Acta* **157**, 52.
31. SANTER, M., RUEBUSH, T. K., BRUNT, J. V., OLDMIXON, E., HESS, R., PRIMAKOFF, P., and PALADE, P. (1968). Identification of a precursor pool of ribosome protein in *Escherichia coli. J. Bact.* **95**, 1355.
32. GIERER, L. and GIERER, A. (1968). Synthesis of ribosomal protein and formation of ribosomes in *Escherichia coli. J. molec. Biol.* **34**, 293.
33. MARCHIS-MOUREN, G., COZZONE, A., and MARVALDI, J. (1969). Ribosomal protein pools in *Escherichia coli. Biochim. biophys. Acta* **N31**, 232.
34. LANDY, A. and SPIEGELMAN, S. (1968). Exhaustive hybridization and its application to an analysis of the ribonucleic acid synthesized in T4-infected cells. *Biochemistry, N.Y.* **7**, 585.
35. KENNELL, D. (1968). Inhibition of host protein synthesis during infection of *Escherichia coli* by bacteriophage T4. I. Continued synthesis of host ribonucleic acid. *J. Virol.* **2**, 1262.
36. BERGSTRAND, A., ELIASSON, N.A., HAMMARSTEN, E., NORBERG, B., REICHARD, P., and VON UBISCH, H. (1948). Experiments with ^{15}N on purines from nuclei and cytoplasm of normal and regenerating liver. *Cold Spring Harb. Symp. quant. Biol.* **13**, 22.
37. HARRIS, H. (1963). Nuclear ribonucleic acid. *Prog. nucl. Acid. Res.* **2**, 20. Academic Press, New York.

38. CARO, L. G. and FORRO, F. (1961). Localization of macromolecules in *Escherichia coli. J. biophys. biochem. Cytol.* **9**, 555.
39. HARRIS, H., FISHER, H. W., RODGERS, A., SPENCER, T., and WATTS, J. W. (1963). An examination of the ribonucleic acids in the HeLa cell with special reference to current theory about the transfer of information from nucleus to cytoplasm. *Proc. R. Soc.* B **157**, 177.
40. CRAWLEY, J. C. W. and HARRIS, H. (1963). The fine structure of isolated HeLa cell nuclei. *Expl Cell Res.* **31**, 70.
41. LACOUR, L. F. (1964). Behaviour of nucleoli in isolated nuclei. *Expl Cell Res.* **34**, 239.
42. BONNER, J., HUANG, R.-C., and MAHESHWARI, N. (1961). The physical state of newly synthesized RNA. *Proc. natn. Acad. Sci. U.S.A.* **47**, 1548.
43. CHENG, P.-Y. (1961). Size of rapidly labelled ribonucleic acids in human amnion cells. *Biochim. biophys. Acta* **53**, 235.
44. HIATT, H. H. (1962). A rapidly labeled RNA in rat liver nuclei. *J. molec. Biol.* **5**, 217.
45. PERRY, R. P. (1962). The cellular sites of synthesis of ribosomal and 4*S* RNA. *Proc. natn. Acad. Sci. U.S.A.* **48**, 2179.
46. KIDSON, C., KIRBY, K. S., and RALPH, R. K. (1963). Isolation characteristics of rapidly labeled RNA from normal rat liver. *J. molec. Biol.* **7**, 312.
47. FENWICK, M. L. (1964). The fate of rapidly labelled ribonucleic acid in the presence of actinomycin in normal and virus-infected animal cells. *Biochim. biophys. Acta* **87**, 388.
48. ROBERTS, W. K. (1965). Studies on RNA synthesis in Ehrlich ascites cells. Extraction and properties of labelled RNA. *Biochim. biophys. Acta* **108**, 474.
49. SCHERRER, K. and DARNELL, J. E. (1962). Sedimentation characteristics of rapidly labelled RNA from HeLa cells. *Biochem. biophys. Res. Commun.* **7**, 486.
50. ATTARDI, G., PARNAS, H., HWANG, M., and ATTARDI, B. (1966). Giant-size rapidly labeled nuclear RNA and cytoplasmic messenger RNA in immature duck erythrocytes. *J. molec. Biol.* **20**, 145.
51. SCHERRER, K., MARCAUD, L., ZAJDELA, F., LONDON, I. M., and GROS, F. (1966). Patterns of RNA metabolism in a differentiated cell: a rapidly labelled, unstable 60S RNA with messenger properties in duck erythroblasts. *Proc. natn. Acad. Sci. U.S.A.* **56**, 1571.
52. WARNER, J. R., SOEIRO, R., BIRNBOIM, H. C., GIRARD, M. and DARNELL, J. E. (1966). Rapidly labelled HeLa cell nuclear RNA I. Identification by zone sedimentation of a heterogeneous fraction separate from ribosomal precursor RNA. *J. molec. Biol.* **19**, 349.
53. MAYO, V. S. and DE KLOET, S. R. (1971). Disaggregation of 'giant' heterogeneous nuclear RNA of mouse Ehrlich ascites cells by thermal denaturation in the presence of formaldehyde. *Biochim. biophys. Acta* **247**, 74.
54. BRAMWELL, M. E. (1972). A comparison of gel electrophoresis and density gradient centrifugation of heterogeneous nuclear RNA. *Biochim. biophys. Acta* **281**, 329.
55. RILEY, W. T. (1969). Polynucleotide chain lengths of rapidly labelled and ribosomal RNA of mammalian cells and *E. coli. Nature, Lond.* **222**, 446.
56. TAMAOKI, T. and LANE, B. G. (1967). The chain termini and alkali-stable dinucleotide sequences in rapidly labeled ribonucleates from L cells. *Biochemistry, N.Y.* **6**, 3583.
57. GOLDSTEIN, L. and PLAUT, W. (1955). Direct evidence for nuclear synthesis of cytoplasmic ribose nucleic acid. *Proc. natn. Acad. Sci. U.S.A.* **41**, 874.

58. WATTS, J. W. and HARRIS, H. (1959). Turnover of nucleic acids in a non-multiplying animal cell. *Biochem. J.* **72**, 147.

59. HARRIS, H. (1959). Turnover of nuclear and cytoplasmic ribonucleic acid in two types of animal cell, with some further observations on the nucleolus. *Biochem. J.* **73**, 362.

60. HARRIS, H. and WATTS, J. W. (1962). The relationship between nuclear and cytoplasmic ribonucleic acid. *Proc. R. Soc.* B **156**, 109.

61. WATTS, J. W. (1964). Turnover of nucleic acids in a multiplying animal cell. 2. Retention studies. *Biochem. J.* **93**, 306.

62. SCOTT, J. F., TAFT, E. B., and LETOURNEAU, N. W. (1962). Conservation of nucleic acids by Ehrlich ascites-tumour cells. *Biochim. biophys. Acta* **61**, 62.

63. ADAMS, D. H. (1966). The relationship between cellular nucleic acids in the developing rat cerebral cortex. *Biochem. J.* **98**, 636.

64. HOUSSAIS, J.-F. and ATTARDI, G. (1966). High molecular weight non-ribosomal-type nuclear RNA and cytoplasmic messenger RNA in HeLa cells. *Proc. natn. Acad. Sci. U.S.A.* **56**, 616.

65. SCHERRER, K., MARCAUD, L., ZAJDELA, F., BRECKENRIDGE, B., and GROS, F. (1966). Etude des RNA nucléaires et cytoplasmiques à marquage rapide dans les cellules érythropoiétiques aviaires différenciées. *Bull. Soc. Chim. biol.* **48**, 1037.

66. OWEN, M. (1967). Uptake of [^{3}H]uridine into precursor pools and RNA in osteogenic cells. *J. Cell Sci.* **2**, 39.

67. LOEB, J. N., HOWELL, R. R., and TOMKINS, G. M. (1965). Turnover of ribosomal RNA in rat liver. *Science, N.Y.* **149**, 1093.

68. EMERSON, C. P. (1971). Regulation of the synthesis and the stability of ribosomal RNA during contact inhibition of growth. *Nature, Lond. New Biol.* **232**, 101.

69. WEBER, M. J. (1972). Ribosomal RNA turnover in contact inhibited cells. *Nature, Lond. New Biol.* **235**, 58.

70. HARRIS, H. (1963). The breakdown of RNA in the cell nucleus. *Proc. R. Soc.* B **158**, 79.

71. SCOTT, J. F., KALTREIDER, H. B., BOEKER, F. A., and TAFT, E. B. (1964). Studies on the nuclear RNA of Ehrlich ascites tumour cells. *Fedn Proc. Fedn Am. Socs exp. Biol.* **23**, 168.

72. HARRIS, H. (1965). The short-lived RNA in the cell nucleus and its possible role in evolution. *Evolving genes and proteins* (Eds. V. BRYSON and H. J. VOGEL), p. 469, Academic Press, New York.

73. EDSTRÖM, J.-E. (1965). Chromosomal RNA and other nuclear RNA fractions. *Role of the chromosomes in development* (Ed. M. LOCKE), p. 137. Academic Press, New York.

74. BRUNS, G. P., FISCHER, S., and LOWY, B. A. (1965). A study of the synthesis and interrelationships of ribonucleic acids in duck erythrocytes. *Biochim. biophys. Acta* **95**, 280.

75. SOEIRO, R., BIRNBOIM, H. C., and DARNELL, J. E. (1966). Rapidly labelled HeLa cell nuclear RNA. *J. molec. Biol.* **19**, 362.

76. ATTARDI, G., PARNAS, H., and ATTARDI, B. (1970). Pattern of RNA synthesis in duck erythrocytes in relationship to the stage of cell differentiation. *Expl Cell Res.* **62**, 11.

77. LAZARUS, H. M. and SPORN, M. B. (1967). Purification and properties of a nuclear exoribonuclease from Ehrlich ascites tumour cells. *Proc. natn. Acad. Sci. U.S.A.* **57**, 1386.

78. SCHÜTZ, G., GALLWITZ, D., and SEKERIS, C. E. (1968). Rapidly labelled high molecular RNA from rat liver. *Eur. J. Biochem.* **4**, 149.

79. SOEIRO, R., VAUGHAN, M. H., WARNER, J. R., and DARNELL, J. E. (1968). The turnover of nuclear DNA-like RNA in HeLa cells. *J. Cell Biol.* **39**, 112.
80. KIJIMA, S. and WILT, F. H. (1969). Rate of nuclear ribonucleic acid turnover in sea urchin embryos. *J. molec. Biol.* **40**, 235.
81. ARONSON, A. I. and WILT, F. H. (1969). Properties of nuclear RNA in sea urchin embryos. *Proc. natn. Acad. Sci. U.S.A.* **62**, 186.
82. DANEHOLT, B. and SVEDHEM, L. (1971). Differential representation of chromosomal HRNA in nuclear sap. *Expl Cell Res.* **67**, 263.
83. FAKAN, S. and BERNHARD, W. (1971). Localization of rapidly and slowly labelled RNA as visualized by high resolution autoradiography. *Expl Cell Res.* **67**, 129.
84. BRANDHORST, B. P. and HUMPHREYS, T. (1972). Stabilities of nuclear and messenger RNA molecules in sea urchin embryos. *J. Cell Biol.* **53**, 474.
85. VOLKIN, E. and ASTRACHAN, L. (1956). Phosphorus incorporation in *Escherichia coli* ribonucleic acid after infection with bacteriophage T2. *Virology* **2**, 149.
86. SPENCER, T. (1962). The incorporation of [^{32}P]phosphate into the ribonucleic acid of HeLa cells and its relation to ribonucleic acid base composition. *Biochem. J.* **84**, 87P.
87. MARBAIX, G., BURNY, A., HUEZ, G., and CHANTRENNE, H. (1966). Base composition of messenger RNA from rabbit reticulocytes. *Biochim. biophys. Acta* **114**, 404.
88. HADJIOLOV, A. A., VENKOV, P. V., DOLAPCHIEV, L. B., and GENCHEV, D. D. (1967). The action of snake venom phosphodiesterase on liver ribosomal ribonucleic acids. *Biochim. biophys. Acta* **142**, 111.
89. TSANEV, R. G., MARKOV, G. G., and DESSEV, G. N. (1966). Incorporation of labelled precursors into the electrophoretic fractions of rat-liver ribonucleic acid. *Biochem. J.* **100**, 204.
90. BOYADJIEV, S. I. and HADJIOLOV, A. A. (1968). Fractionation and biosynthesis of ribonucleic acid of the rat adrenals. *Biochem. biophys. Acta* **161**, 341.
91. COOPER, H. L. and KAY, J. E. (1969). Differential extraction of nuclear and cytoplasmic RNA from intact lymphocytes. *Biochim. biophys. Acta* **174**, 503.
92. KAY, J. E. and COOPER, H. L. (1969). Rapidly labelled cytoplasmic RNA in normal and phytohaemagglutinin-stimulated human lymphocytes. *Biochim. biophys. Acta* **N31**, 62.
93. BILLING, R. J., INGLIS, A. M., and SMELLIE, R. M. S. (1969). The distribution of deoxyribonucleic acid-like ribonucleic acid in rat liver cells. *Biochem. J.* **113**, 571.
94. BRAMWELL, M. E. and HARRIS, H. (1967). The origin of the polydispersity in sedimentation patterns of rapidly labelled nuclear RNA. *Biochem. J.* **103**, 816.
95. ELLEM, K. A. O. and SHERIDAN, J. W. (1964). Tenacious binding of the bulk of the DNA-like RNA of metazoan cells to methylated albumin columns. *Biochem. biophys. Res. Commun.* **16**, 505.
96. BRAMWELL, M. E. (1970). Intranuclear accumulation of RNA resembling the smaller ribosomal RNA component. *J. Cell Sci.* **6**, 53.
97. DINGMAN, C. W., KAKEFUDA, T., and ARONOW, A. (1970). Rat liver cytoplasmic ribonucleic acids: some aspects of their localization and isolation. *Biochim. biophys. Acta* **224**, 114.
98. AAIJ, C., AGSTERIBBE, E., and BORST, P. (1971). A study of minor RNA components of rat liver microsomes. *Biochim. biophys. Acta* **246**, 233.

99. PLAGEMANN, P. G. W. (1969). RNA synthesis in exponentially growing rat hepatoma cells. I. A caution in equating pulse-labelled polyribosomal RNA with messenger RNA. *Biochim. biophys. Acta* **182**, 46.

100. PERRY, R. P. and KELLEY, D. E. (1968). Messenger RNA-protein complexes and newly synthesized ribosomal subunits: analysis of free particles and components of polyribosomes. *J. molec. Biol.* **35**, 37.

101. IVANYI, J. (1971). The 'informosome'-like particles of lymphoid cells. *Biochim. biophys. Acta* **238**, 303.

102. WARNER, J., RICH, A., and HALL, C. (1962). Electron microscope studies of ribosomal clusters synthesizing haemoglobin. *Science, N.Y.* **138**, 1399.

103. WARNER, J. R., KNOPF, P. M., and RICH, A. (1963). A multiple ribosomal structure in protein synthesis. *Proc. natn. Acad. Sci. U.S.A.* **49**, 122.

104. GIERER, A. (1963). Polypeptide synthesis in *Escherichia coli*. I. Ribosomes and the active complex. *J. molec. Biol.* **6**, 148.

105. RICH, A., WARNER, J. R., and GOODMAN, H. M. (1963). The structure and function of polyribosomes. *Cold Spring Harb. Symp. quant. Biol.* **28**, 269.

106. DUBIN, D. T. (1972). Mitochondrial ribonucleic acid from cultured animal cells. *J. biol. Chem.* **247**, 2662.

107. FUKAMACHI, S., BARTOOV, B., and FREEMAN, K. B. (1972). Synthesis of ribonucleic acid by isolated rat liver mitochondria. *Biochem. J.* **128**, 299.

108. HADJIOLOV, A. A. (1967). An endomessenger hypothesis on the mechanism of information transfer in animal cells. *J. theor. Biol.* **16**, 229.

109. HARRIS, H. (1968). *Nucleus and cytoplasm*. 1st edn., p. 107. Clarendon Press, Oxford.

110. FELLNER, P. and SANGER, F. (1968). Sequence analysis of specific areas of the 16S and 23S ribosomal RNAs. *Nature, Lond.* **219**, 236.

111. FELLNER, P., EHRESMANN, C., and EBEL, J. P. (1970). Nucleotide sequences present within the 16S ribosomal RNA of *Escherichia coli*. *Nature, Lond.* **225**, 26.

112. FELLNER, P. and EBEL, J. P. (1970). Observations on the primary structure of the 23S ribosomal RNA from *Escherichia coli*. *Nature, Lond.* **225**, 1131.

113. EHRESMANN, C., FELLNER, P., and EBEL, J. P. (1970). Nucleotide sequences of sections of 16S ribosomal RNA. *Nature, Lond.* **227**, 1321.

114. HAYES, F., HAYES, D., FELLNER, P., and EHRESMANN, C. (1971). Additional nucleotide sequences in precursor 16S ribosomal RNA from *Escherichia coli*. *Nature, Lond. New Biol.* **232**, 54.

115. FELLNER, P., EHRESMANN, C., STIEGLER, P., and EBEL, J. P. (1972). Partial nucleotide sequence of 16S ribosomal RNA from *E. coli*. *Nature, Lond. New Biol.* **239**, 1.

116. LAMFROM, H. (1961). Factors determining the specificity of hemoglobin synthesized in a cell-free system. *J. molec. Biol.* **3**, 241.

117. NIRENBERG, M. W. and MATTHAEI, J. H. (1961). The dependence of cell-free protein synthesis in *E. coli* upon naturally occurring or synthetic polyribonucleotides. *Proc. natn. Acad. Sci. U.S.A.* **47**, 1588.

118. NIRENBERG, M., CASKEY, T., MARSHALL, R., BRIMACOMBE, R., KELLOGG, D., DOCTOR, B., HATFIELD, D., LEVIN, J., ROTTMAN, F., PESTKA, S., WILCOX, M., and ANDERSON, F. (1966). The RNA code and protein synthesis. *Cold Spring Harb. Symp. quant. Biol.* **31**, 11.

119. NATHANS, D., NOTANI, G., SCHWARTZ, J. H., and ZINDER, N. D. (1962). Biosynthesis of the coat protein of coliphage f2 by *E. coli* extracts. *Proc. natn. Acad. Sci. U.S.A.* **48**, 1424.

120. NATHANS, D. (1965). Cell-free protein synthesis directed by coliphage MS2 RNA: synthesis of intact viral coat protein and other products. *J. molec. Biol.* **13**, 521.

121. LOCKARD, R. E. and LINGREL, J. B. (1969). The synthesis of mouse hemoglobin β chains in a rabbit reticulocyte cell-free system programmed with mouse reticulocyte 9S RNA. *Biochem. biophys. Res. Commun.* **37**, 204.

122. LOCKARD, R. E. and LINGREL, J. B. (1971). Identification of mouse haemoglobin messenger RNA. *Nature, Lond. New Biol.* **233**, 204.

123. LINGREL, J. B., LOCKARD, R. E., JONES, R. F., BURR, H. E., and HOLDER, J. W. (1971). Biologically active messenger-RNA for hemoglobin. *Ser. Haemat.* **4**, 37.

124. LOCKARD, R. E. and LINGREL, J. B. (1972). Mouse hemoglobin messenger ribonucleic acid. *J. biol. Chem.* **247**, 4174.

125. MATTHEWS, M. B., OSBORN, M., and LINGREL, J. B. (1971). Translation of globin messenger RNA in a heterologous cell-free system. *Nature, Lond. New Biol.* **233**, 206.

126. JONES, R. F. and LINGREL, J. B. (1972). Peptide analysis of the mouse hemoglobin messenger ribonucleic acid-directed products synthesized in mammalian and avian cell-free systems. *J. biol. Chem.* **247**, 7951.

127. GURDON, J. B., LANE, C. D., WOODLAND, H. R., and MARBAIX, G. (1971). Use of frog eggs and oocytes for the study of messenger RNA and its translation in living cells. *Nature, Lond.* **233**, 177.

128. LANE, C. D., MARBAIX, G., and GURDON, J. B. (1971). Rabbit haemoglobin synthesis in frog cells: the translation of reticulocyte 9S RNA in frog oocytes. *J. molec. Biol.* **61**, 73.

129. MARBAIX, G. and LANE, C. D. (1972). Rabbit haemoglobin synthesis in frog cells. II. Further characterization of the products of translation of reticulocyte 9S RNA. *J. molec. Biol.* **67**, 517.

130. SWAN, D., AVIV, H., and LEDER, P. (1972). Purification and properties of biologically active messenger RNA for a myeloma light chain. *Proc. natn. Acad. Sci. U.S.A.* **69**, 1967.

131. MACH, B., FAUST, C., and VASSALLI, P. (1973). Purification of 14S messenger RNA of immunoglobulin light chain that codes for a possible light chain precursor. *Proc. natn. Acad. Sci. U.S.A.* **70**, 451.

132. STEVENS, R. H. and WILLIAMSON, A. R. (1973). Isolation of messenger RNA coding for mouse heavy chain immunoglobulin. *Proc. natn. Acad. Sci. U.S.A.* **70**, 1127.

133. RHOADS, R. E., McKNIGHT, G. S., and SCHIMKE, R. T. (1971). Synthesis of ovalbumin in a rabbit reticulocyte cell-free system programmed with hen oviduct ribonucleic acid. *J. biol. Chem.* **246**, 7407.

134. MEANS, A. R., COMSTOCK, J. P., ROSENFELD, G. C., and O'MALLEY, B. W. (1972). Ovalbumin messenger RNA of chick oviduct: partial characterization, estrogen dependence, and translation *in vitro*. *Proc. natn. Acad. Sci. U.S.A.* **69**, 1146.

135. PALACIOS, R., SULLIVAN, D., SUMMERS, N. M., KIELY, M. L., and SCHIMKE, R. T. (1973). Purification of ovalbumin messenger ribonucleic acid by specific immunoadsorption of ovalbumin-synthesizing polysomes and millipore partition of ribonucleic acid. *J. biol. Chem.* **248**, 540.

136. O'MALLEY, B. W., ROSENFELD, G. C., COMSTOCK, J. P., and MEANS, A. R. (1972). Steroid hormone induction of a specific translatable messenger RNA. *Nature, Lond. New Biol.* **240**, 45.

The search for the messenger 75

137. JACOBS-LORENA, M., BAGLIONI, C., and BORUN, T. W. (1972). Translation of messenger RNA for histones from HeLa cells by a cell-free extract from mouse ascites tumor. *Proc. natn. Acad. Sci. U.S.A.* **69**, 2095.
138. BERNS, A. J. M., VAN KRAAIKAMP, M., BLOEMENDAL, H., and LANE, C. D. (1972). Calf crystallin synthesis in frog cells: the translation of lens-cell 14S RNA in oocytes. *Proc. natn. Acad. Sci. U.S.A.* **69**, 1606.
139. MATTHEWS, M. B., OSBORN, M., BERNS, A. J. M., and BLOEMENDAL, H. (1972). Translation of two messenger RNAs from lens in a cell free system from Krebs II ascites cells. *Nature, Lond. New Biol.* **236**, 5.
140. BERNS, A. J. M., STROUS, G. J. A. M., and BLOEMENDAL, H. (1972). Heterologous *in vitro* synthesis of lens α-crystallin polypeptide. *Nature, Lond. New Biol.* **236**, 7.
141. ROURKE, A. W. and HEYWOOD, S. M. (1972). Myosin synthesis and specificity of eukaryotic initiation factors. *Biochemistry* **11**, 2061.
142. SCHUTZ, G., BEATO, M., and FEIGELSON, P. (1973). Messenger RNA for hepatic tryptophan oxygenase: its partial purification, its translation in a heterologous cell-free system, and its control by glucocorticoid hormones. *Proc. natn. Acad. Sci. U.S.A.* **70**, 1218.
143. GAYE, P., HOUDEBINE, L., and DENAMUR, R. (1973). Isolation of active messenger RNA for α_s casein from bound polyribosomes of mammary gland. *Biochem. biophys. Res. Commun.* **51**, 637.
144. BROWNLEE, G. G., CARTWRIGHT, E. M., COWAN, N. J., JARVIS, J. M., and MILSTEIN, C. (1973). *Nature, Lond. New Biol.* **244**, 236.
145. WHITE, H. B., LAUX, B. E., and DENNIS, D. (1972). Messenger RNA structure: compatibility of hairpin loops with protein sequence. *Science, N.Y.* **175**, 1264.
146. MIN JOU, W., HAEGEMAN, G., YSEBAERT, M., and FIERS, W. (1972). Nucleotide sequence of the gene coding for the bacteriophage MS2 coat protein. *Nature, Lond.* **237**, 82.
147. LODISH, H. F. (1970). Secondary structure of bacteriophage f2 ribonucleic acid and the initiation of *in vitro* protein biosynthesis. *J. molec. Biol.* **50**, 689.
148. EDMONDS, M. and ABRAMS, R. (1960). Polynucleotide biosynthesis: formation of a sequence of adenylate units from adenosine triphosphate by an enzyme from thymus nuclei. *J. biol. Chem.* **235**, 1142.
149. EDMONDS, M. and ABRAMS, R. (1963). Isolation of a naturally occurring polyadenylate from calf thymus nuclei. *J. biol. Chem.* **238**, 1186.
150. LIM, L. and CANELLAKIS, E. S. (1970). Adenine-rich polymer associated with rabbit reticulocyte messenger RNA. *Nature, Lond.* **227**, 710.
151. MORRISON, M. R., GORSKI, J., and LINGREL, J. B. (1972). The separation of mouse reticulocyte 9S RNA into fractions of different biological activity by hybridization to polyU cellulose. *Biochem. biophys. Res. Commun.* **49**, 775.
152. STEVENS, R. H. and WILLIAMSON, A. L. (1972). Specific IgG mRNA molecules from myeloma cells in heterogeneous nuclear and cytoplasmic RNA containing poly A. *Nature, Lond.* **239**, 143.
153. LEE, S. Y., MENDECKI, J., and BRAWERMAN, G. (1971). A polynucleotide segment rich in adenylic acid in the rapidly labeled polyribosomal RNA component of mouse sarcoma 180 ascites cells. *Proc. natn. Acad. Sci. U.S.A.* **68**, 1331.
154. DARNELL, J. E., WALL, R., and TUSHINSKI, R. J. (1971). An adenylic acid-rich sequence in messenger RNA of HeLa cells and its possible relationship to reiterated sites in DNA. *Proc. natn. Acad. Sci. U.S.A.* **68**, 1321.

155. GREENBERG, J. R. and PERRY, R. P. (1972). Relative occurrence of poly-adenylic acid sequences in messenger and heterogeneous nuclear RNA of L cells as determined by polyuridylic acid-hydroxyapatite chromatography. *J. molec. Biol.* **72**, 91.

156. BURR, H. and LINGREL, J. B. (1971). Poly A sequences at the 3'-termini of rabbit globin mRNAs. *Nature, Lond. New Biol.* **233**, 41.

157. MOLLOY, G. R., SPORN, M. B., KELLEY, D. E., and PERRY, R. P. (1972). Localization of polyadenylic sequences in messenger ribonucleic acid of mammalian cells. *Biochemistry N.Y.* **11**, 3256.

158. DARNELL, J. E., PHILIPSON, L., WALL, R., and ADESNIK, M. (1971). Poly-adenylic acid sequences: role in the conversion of nuclear RNA into messenger RNA. *Science, N.Y.* **174**, 507.

159. ADESNIK, M. and DARNELL, J. E. (1972). Biogenesis and characterization of histone messenger RNA in HeLa cells. *J. molec. Biol.* **67**, 397.

160. PERRY, R. P., KELLEY, D. E., and LaTORRE, J. (1972). Lack of polyadenylic acid sequences in the messenger RNA of *E. coli. Biochem. biophys. Res. Commun.* **48**, 1593.

161. ADESNIK, M., SALDITT, M., THOMAS, W., and DARNELL, J. E. (1972). Evidence that all messenger RNA molecules (except histone messenger RNA) contain poly(A) sequences and that the poly(A) has a nuclear function. *J. molec. Biol.* **71**, 21.

162. ROSENFELD, M. G., ABRASS, J. B., and PERKINS, L. A. (1972). Cleavage of the polyadenylate-rich region of polyadenylate-rich RNA. *Biochem. biophys. Res. Commun.* **49**, 230.

163. EDMONDS, M., VAUGHAN, M. H., and NAKAZATO, H. (1971). Polyadenylic acid sequences in the heterogeneous nuclear RNA and rapidly-labelled polyribosomal RNA of HeLa cells: possible evidence for a precursor relationship. *Proc. natn. Acad. Sci. U.S.A.* **68**, 1336.

164. NAKAZATO, H. and EDMONDS, M. (1972). The isolation and purification of rapidly labeled polysome-bound ribonucleic acid on polythymidylate cellulose. *J. biol. Chem.* **247**, 3365.

165. AVADHAM, G., KUAN, M., VANDER LIGN, P., and RUTMAN, R. J. (1973). Polyadenylic acid sequences in mitochondrial RNA. *Biochem. biophys. Res. Commun.* **51**, 1090.

166. SINGER, R. H. and PENMAN, S. (1972). Stability of HeLa cell m RNA in actinomycin. *Nature, Lond.* **240**, 100.

167. MURPHY, W. and ATTARDI, G. (1973). Stability of cytoplasmic messenger RNA in HeLa cells. *Proc. natn. Acad. Sci. U.S.A.* **70**, 115.

168. GREENBERG, J. R. (1972). High stability of messenger RNA in growing cultured cells. *Nature, Lond.* **240**, 102.

169. GURDON, J. B., LINGREL, J. B., and MARBAIX, G. (1973). Message stability in injected frog oocytes: long life of mammalian α and β globin messages. *J. molec. Biol.* (in the press).

170. LAVALLÉ, R. and DE HAUWER, G. (1970). Tryptophan messenger translation in *Escherichia coli. J. molec. Biol.* **51**, 435.

171. SCHWARTZ, T., CRAIG, E., and KENNELL, D. (1970). Inactivation and de-gradation of messenger ribonucleic acid from the lactose operon of *Escherichia coli. J. molec. Biol.* **54**, 299.

172. MARRS, B. L. and YANOFSKY, C. (1971). Host and bacteriophage specific messenger RNA degradation in T_7-infected *Escherichia coli. Nature, Lond. New Biol.* **234**, 168.

173. FORSCHHAMMER, J., JACKSON, E. N., and YANOFSKY, C. (1972). Different half-lives of messenger RNA corresponding to different segments of the tryptophan operon of *Escherichia coli. J. molec. Biol.* **71**, 687.

4

Regulation in higher cells

ALL cellular events are subject to regulation. This platitude is worth uttering only because certain kinds of regulation have, over the last decade, taken up more than a fair share of the attention of experimenters, while other kinds, intrinsically no less interesting, have tended to be neglected. The genetic operator model for protein synthesis has naturally focussed attention on the control of transcription; and the behaviour of enucleate cells and cells in which transcription has been blocked by antibiotics has focussed attention on the control of translation. But it should be remembered that highly complex and precise forms of regulation can be achieved by mechanisms that do not operate either at the level of transcription or translation. For example, a self-sustaining regulatory cycle not dependent on either transcription or translation is seen in the circadian rhythm of photosynthesis. It has been shown in *Acetabularia* that this rhythm persists under constant illumination for more than 40 days after the removal of the nucleus;[1-3] it is thus not directly determined by transcription of nuclear genes. But the nucleus does exercise some control, for the phase of the photosynthetic rhythm differs in different cells and nuclear transplantation experiments demonstrate that the phase characteristic of the transplanted nucleus is imposed on the recipient cytoplasm within a few days.[3,4] A nuclear determinant does therefore exist, but it is not concerned with the immediate control of the oscillatory activity itself. The latter is not abolished by chloramphenicol, which inhibits translation by chloroplast ribosomes, or by puromycin, which inhibits translation by cytoplasmic ribosomes other than those contained in cytoplasmic organelles;[4,5] nor, in the enucleate cell, is it abolished by actinomycin in concentrations that inhibit the transcription of cytoplasmic DNA[4, 5] This precisely regulated oscillatory system is therefore governed by molecular interactions that do not depend on the concomitant synthesis of specific proteins. But even when a specific protein is synthesized in association with a particular event, for example, a morphological change, it does not always follow that the 'critical variable' in determining the morphogenetic event is the increase in concentration of the protein being studied.[6] Increased availability of substrate, or interactions of quite a different kind, might be more relevant. Nonetheless, a great deal of the experimental work on nucleo-cytoplasmic relationships has centred on the control of protein synthesis, so that a consideration of this problem must inevitably form a major part of any discussion of regulation in higher cells.

1. The control of translation

In dealing with translational control in bacteria I referred to the existence of translational repressors formally equivalent to the repressors that govern transcription at specific genetic loci. There is indirect evidence for the existence of translational repressors in higher cells also. Some of this evidence involves the use of inhibitors of transcription and hinges on the interpretation of the phenomenon of 'superinduction' of enzyme activity. A number of cases have been recorded in which an enzyme increases in activity when transcription is inhibited by actinomycin D or compounds acting in the same way.[7, 8] This paradoxical effect has been examined most thoroughly in the case of tyrosine aminotransferase in cultures of rat hepatoma cells. It has been demonstrated that the increase in enzyme activity is associated with net synthesis of the enzyme and cannot be accounted for simply by a reduction in the rate of enzyme degradation.[7, 9] The suggestion is that the stimulation of enzyme synthesis results from the decay of a labile translational repressor which requires continuous transcription for its maintenance.[10] Other interpretations are, of course, possible.[11] In the case of haemoglobin synthesis, more direct evidence for the existence of a translational repressor has been presented, and the repressor has been partially purified.[12] However, for both tyrosine aminotransferase and haemoglobin it is not clear how specific the translational repression is. Several enzymes show 'superinduction' in the presence of actinomycin D, so that a relatively non-specific effect on translation might be involved. In the case of haemoglobin, it has recently been shown that haem, with which the translational repressor interacts, also stimulates the synthesis of ovalbumin[13] and other proteins[14] in cell-free synthetic systems produced from cells other than reticulocytes. Soluble factors mediating the initiation of translation, peptide chain elongation and chain release have been studied intensively in bacteria, and some of these factors can discriminate between different classes of messenger RNA.[15, 16] There is evidence for the operation of similar factors in eukaryotic cells,[17–20] but it seems unlikely that there can be enough substances of this kind to permit the discrimination required to repress or stimulate the synthesis of one specific protein rather than another. As with transcription, the heart of the problem of translational control is specificity.

To have the required specificity, repressors or activators of the initiation of translation would need to be able to recognize sequences of nucleotides in RNA. As discussed in Chapter 2, proteins have been described which do recognize specific nucleotide sequences in RNA and govern its translation. There is also direct experimental evidence for translational control exercised by specific transfer ribonucleic acids. I have already described some features of the regulatory system controlling histidine biosynthesis in *Salmonella typhimurium*. In this operon, it is clear that pyrophosphate phosphoribosyltransferase, the first enzyme in the sequence, plays a crucial role in regulating the expression of the whole operon.[21, 22] Mutations in the feed-back sensitive site of this enzyme render the whole operon insensitive to repression by histidine.[23] It has recently been shown that mutations in histidyl-transfer RNA also render the operon insensitive to repression by histidine;[24] and histidyl-transfer RNA has been found to bind specifically, and with high affinity, to purified preparations of the pyrophosphate phosphoribosyltransferase.[25, 26] It is therefore possible to envisage repression of the operon by a complex of the histidyl-transfer RNA and the first enzyme acting together.[27] As mentioned previously, there is a good deal of evidence to suggest that the first enzyme in a metabolic sequence may play a decisive regulatory role in a number of other operons;[28] and, in the case of valine biosynthesis, it has been shown that threonine deaminase, the first enzyme in the sequence, interacts specifically with leucyl-transfer RNA.[29] In higher organisms it is known that structural mutations in enzymes may result in their overproduction;[30] and some observations do suggest a regulatory role for specific transfer ribonucleic acids.[31] The analysis in higher cells, however so far lacks the precision of the work on the histidine locus in bacteria.†

Any model for translational control that acts by regulating the release of polypeptide chains must, if the requirement for specificity

† See note on p. 108.

is to be met, involve the operation of mechanisms that can recognize one polypeptide chain from another while the chains are still attached to the translational machinery. All such models must therefore assume that the polypeptide chain can adopt some three dimensional configuration while it is still attached. The main advantage of models of this kind is that they place no restriction on the nature of the molecules with which the attached poypeptide can interact. Chain release could, in principle, be governed not only by macromolecules but also by small molecules.[32] For example, release of an enzyme could be blocked not only by interaction between the nascent polypeptide chain and another protein, but also by interaction between the polypeptide and the end product of the reaction catalyzed by the enzyme or the end product of the sequence of reactions to which the enzyme contributes an essential step. The rate of synthesis of the enzyme could thus be controlled directly by the ambient concentration of a relevant end product. This, of course, is a classical feedback circuit in which both sensitivity and specificity are ensured with the greatest possible economy, for no elements are required other than the enzyme itself and a critical end product. We know, in the case of the histidine operon, that mutations at the feed-back sensitive site in the first enzyme of the sequence render the operon insensitive to repression by histidine. This may, in the light of the experiments implicating histidyl-transfer RNA, mean that the transfer RNA binds to the first enzyme at the feed-back sensitive site; but it may also mean that the regulatory event involves interaction between the enzyme and histidine itself. It has been shown that histidine is strongly bound by the pyrophosphate phosphoribosyltransferase and that this binding produces a marked configurational change in the enzyme.[33] The enzyme bearing a mutation at the feed-back sensitive site does not undergo this configurational change even though it does bind histidine. One might envisage that the configurational change induced by histidine might block the release of the polypeptide and thus exercise a direct control over the expression of the whole operon. There is now good evidence in support of the view that a polypeptide can assume a three dimensional configuration capable of recognizing, or being recognized by, other molecules while it is still attached to the translational machinery. Antibodies to β-galactosidase can react with incomplete chains of the enzyme while they are still bound to ribosomes;[34, 35] and mutant forms of the enzyme carrying large deletions are still able to bind substrate.[36]

Translational control by means of transfer ribonucleic acids is unlikely to be a general mechanism for regulating the rate of synthesis of different proteins, if only because there are nothing like enough transfer ribonucleic acids in the cell to accommodate the number of proteins that must be regulated; and it is not easy to see how inhibition of polypeptide chain release by critical end products could operate in the case of nonenzyme proteins that do not have either substrates or end products. Yet another possibility that may be envisaged is that the rate of synthesis of different proteins is determined by the intrinsic structure of the different messenger ribonucleic acids themselves. It is now clear that messenger ribonucleic acids do have highly specific three dimensional structures, and it is possible that differences in these structures might ensure that some messenger ribonucleic acids are translated more rapidly or more frequently than others. In the case of haemoglobin synthesis it has been shown that the messenger ribonucleic acids for the alpha and beta globin chains are translated at different relative frequencies;[37] and it is possible that part of the explanation for the enormous range that one finds in the concentrations of different proteins in the cell might lie in intrinsic differences in the translatability of different messenger ribonucleic acids.

Finally, we come back to stability of messenger RNA as a determinant of translational control. I have presented reasons for believing that the great bulk of the messenger ribonucleic acids in animal cells are essentially stable. If this is so, regulation of protein synthesis by selective degradation of specific messengers is unlikely to be an important mechanism of translational control. This does not, of course, exclude the possibility that some particular messenger ribonucleic acid might be peculiarly susceptible to degradation and thus form an exception to the general rule; nor does it exclude the possibility that messenger ribonucleic acids might undergo degradation when, for some other reason, they cease to be translated. In higher cells, there is as yet no case in which it has been established that regulation of the synthesis of a specific protein is achieved by a mechanism which relies on degradation of the relevant messenger RNA.

This discussion of translational control is regrettably rather inconclusive. This is partly because our understanding of the structural basis of translation is still essentially schematic and partly because it is only very recently that efficient translation of natural cellular messengers in cell-free preparations has been achieved. It is reason-

able to expect that further purification of these messengers and detailed examination of the way in which they are translated will, in
due course, permit an informed choice to be made between the
various possibilities I have presented.

2. Control of 'transcription'

In principle, regulation of the transcription of DNA may operate
in two ways: by variation in the rate of synthesis of RNA at any
one genetic locus, or by variation in the number of active genes. It
is, of course, also possible that the intrinsic structure of some genes
may dictate a slower rate of transcription than that of other genes.
If this were the case, all genetic regulatory phenomena would have
to operate on a basis of intrinsically different transcription rates for
different genes. As I described in the preceding section, there is
evidence that different messenger ribonucleic acids may be translated at different rates, but we do not at present have any decisive
evidence on variation in the rate of transcription of different cellular
genes. There is no doubt, however, that genetic activity can be
regulated by both of the other mechanisms that have been mentioned:
by changes in the over-all rate of RNA transcription and by changes in
the amount of DNA transcribed. The over-all rate of RNA synthesis
on the genes is, like any other synthetic process, governed by the
general energy level in the cell, by the availability of the necessary
precursors, and by the concentrations of the enzymes involved. There
is no doubt that dramatic and rapid fluctuations in RNA synthesis can
occur in response to changes in the environment of the cell, often to
quite trivial changes. But this form of regulation does not greatly
illuminate the study of gene action. Once again, the real centre of
interest is in mechanisms that permit specificity of genetic regulation,
that is, permit the synthesis of RNA on some genes but not on
others.

It is, of course, immensely attractive to suppose that in higher
cells single genes or small groups of genes are switched on and off
by the interplay of specific activators and repressors operating in a
manner analogous to that described in bacteria. But there is as yet
no convincing evidence that gene-specific repressors or activators are
of importance in controlling genetic activity in higher cells; and there
is a good deal of evidence that suggests the operation of mechanisms
of a different kind. As pointed out in previous chapters, the genes
determining a sequence of metabolically related proteins in higher

PLATE 1

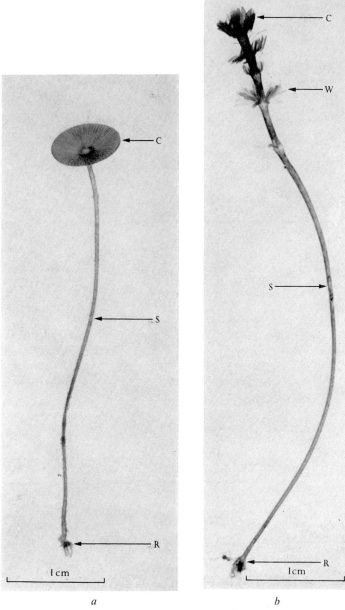

a   *b*

Two species of the giant unicellular alga *Acetabularia* showing differences in the morphology of the caps. These structures provide a mechanism for the formation and dissemination of the spores.

(*a*) *Acetabularia mediterranea.* (*b*) *Acetabularia crenulata.* C, cap; W, whorls, which are formed shortly before the development of the cap; S, stalk; R, rhizoid containing the single nucleus.

PLATE 2

The formation of a fruiting body in a culture of the slime mould *Dictyostelium discoideum*. The motile amoebae aggregate to form the fruiting body which is thus composed of many cells. Its function is essentially equivalent to that of the cap in *Acetabularia*. Some earlier stages in the process of fruiting body formation are shown on the left.

PLATE 3

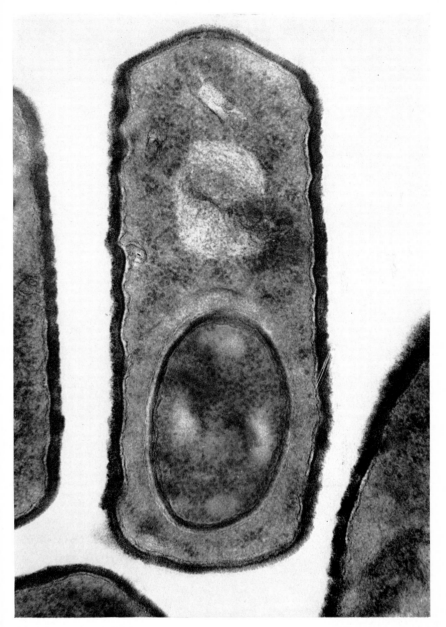

Spore formation in *Bacillus subtilis*. The spore is formed intracellularly. The cell contains a vegetative nucleus and a spore nucleus. (By courtesy of Dr. D. Kay.)

PLATE 4

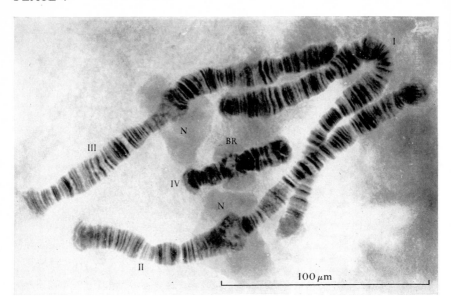

a

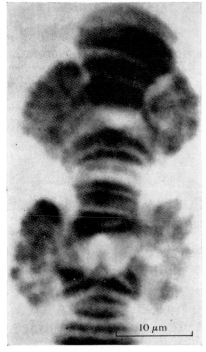

a. The polytene salivary gland chromosomes (I, II, III, IV) of *Chironomus tentans*. The nucleoli (N) and a large puff (Balbiani ring) (BR) are shown. (By courtesy of Prof. J.-E. Edström and Prof. E. Beermann.)

b. Two large puffs (Balbiani rings) on chromosome IV of the salivary gland of *Chironomus tentans*. (By courtesy of the late Dr. U. Clever.)

PLATE 5. (see opposite) Formation of specific puffs in isolated polytene chromosomes. (*a*) Chromosome II of *Chironomus thummi* isolated in the condensed state. (*b*) Differential dispersion of the same chromosome induced by changes in the electrolyte composition of the medium. Arrows show puffs formed at specific loci. L, left arm of chromosome; R, right arm; C, centromere. (By courtesy of Drs. M. Lezzi and M. Robert.)

b

PLATE 5

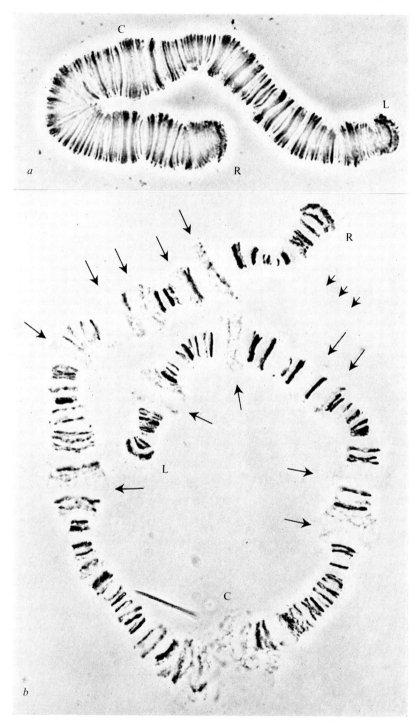

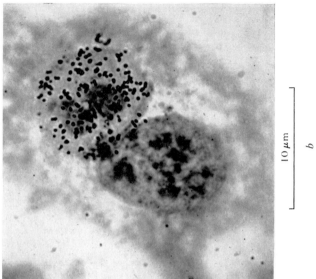

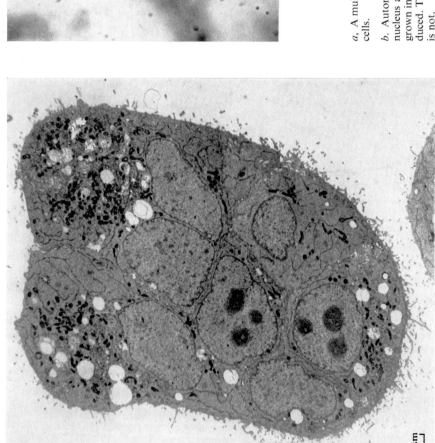

a, A multinucleate cell formed by the fusion of several HeLa cells.

b. Autoradiograph of a binucleate cell containing one HeLa nucleus and one Ehrlich nucleus. The HeLa cells had been grown in [³H] thymidine before the heterokaryons were produced. The HeLa nucleus is labelled and the Ehrlich nucleus is not.

PLATE 7

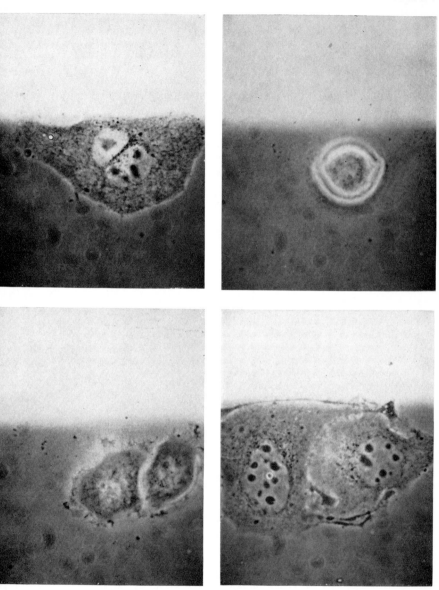

Four frames from a cinematographic sequence showing a HeLa-Ehrlich heterokaryon undergoing mitosis and giving rise to two hybrid mononucleate daughter cells.

PLATE 8

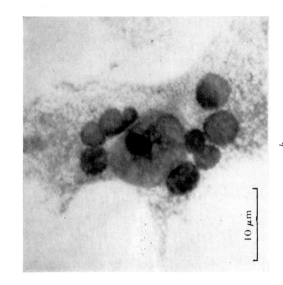

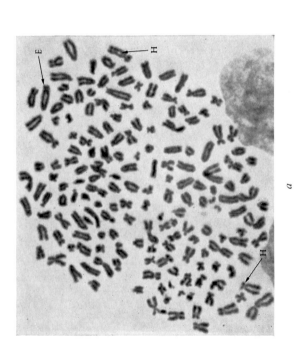

10 μm

a. A HeLa-Ehrlich hybrid at metaphase. This cell contains 181 chromosomes in proportions very close to those expected from the fusion of one modal Ehrlich cell and two modal HeLa cells. Arrows indicate two HeLa (H) and one Ehrlich (E) marker chromosomes.

b. A heterokaryon containing one HeLa nucleus and a number of rabbit macrophage nuclei.

organisms are not usually closely linked; dramatic fluctuations in enzyme concentration, necessitated by abrupt changes in nutrient supply, do not occur; and the great bulk of the cytoplasmic messenger ribonucleic acids are essentially stable. One would not therefore expect to see in higher cells a regulatory system functioning in the same way as that governing the synthesis of β-galactosidase in *E. coli*. What one does find is very different. Consider the following four cases in which there is direct evidence for selective suppression of transcription:

(1) Inactivation of the paternal set of chromosomes in the mealy bug, *Pseudococcus obscurus*.[38]

(2) Inactivation of individual sex chromosomes in some species of vertebrates.[39–41]

(3) Inactivation of 'condensed' or heterochromatic regions of interphase nuclei in some differentiated somatic cells of animals.[42, 43]

(4) Inactivation of 'unexpanded' bands or segments in the giant polytene chromosomes found in the glandular cells of certain insects.[44, 45]

The inactivation of the paternal set of chromosomes in the mealy bug and the inactivation of one of the X chromosomes in certain vertebrates appear to me to be incomplete manifestations of a more widespread phenomenon, namely, the complete elimination of some or all of the chromosomes of either the paternal or the maternal set. In the fungus gnat, *Sciara*, for example, the whole paternal set of chromosomes is eliminated in the male, which thus functions with only a maternal set of chromosomes.[46] In other related forms, the males develop from unfertilized eggs and thus contain only the maternal chromosomes.[47] It seems very likely that the inactivation of the paternal set of chromosomes in the mealy bug is simply another means of achieving the same end, and it is possible that inactivation is an evolutionary alternative to complete elimination. A similar argument probably holds for the inactivation of one of the X chromosomes in the females of certain vertebrates. In some insects, one or other of the sex chromosomes is normally eliminated early in development,[48] and a similar situation also exists in certain mammals[49] and marsupials[50, 51] in which the female develops with only one X chromosome. It again appears likely that inactivation, but retention, of the X represents an evolutionary alternative to its complete elimination.

It is, I think, obvious that these two cases of selective suppression of RNA synthesis can have nothing to do with cytoplasmic regulatory phenomena of the sort that I have been discussing in previous chapters. The inactivation of these chromosomes is usually permanent and inherited from one cell generation to the next; it may be virtually complete; it occurs, with minor exceptions, in all tissues of the body; and it involves only one of the two homologous chromosomes or chromosome sets. This form of chromosomal inactivation may have great evolutionary and ontogenetic significance, but it is difficult to conceive how it could play any direct role in controlling the rates of synthesis of individual cytoplasmic proteins.

Although a direct demonstration has been made in few cell types, it seems clear that other highly condensed heterochromatic regions in interphase nuclei also synthesize very much less RNA than the dispersed euchromatic regions.[42, 43] In certain highly differentiated cells, the process of differentiation involves a marked reduction in nuclear volume, and this is accompanied by visible condensation of large parts of the chromatin. In these condensed regions RNA synthesis is suppressed, and in some cases the nucleus may stop synthesizing RNA altogether. This process is best seen in the differentiation of the red blood cells in certain vertebrates, where progressive condensation of the chromatin is associated with progressive reduction of RNA synthesis as the cell assumes specialized morphological characteristics.[52] This form of nuclear differentiation appears to be a means of imposing a state of dormancy, or even reproductive death, on the specialized cell. Where the effect is reversible, as in the small lymphocyte or the fibrocyte of vertebrates, the cell nucleus enlarges again, and the condensed chromatin within it becomes dispersed, when the dormant cell resumes a high level of metabolic activity. Complete inactivation of the nucleus again appears to be an evolutionary alternative to its elimination: in mammals the whole nucleus is eliminated during differentiation of the erythrocyte;[53] in amphibians, birds, reptiles, and some other orders, the nucleus is retained but appears to be completely inactive.

Cells that are not in the process of becoming dormant may contain smaller condensed regions of chromatin (chromocentres) in addition to the one produced by the inactivated X chromosome.[54, 55] The formation of chromocentres is not a random event. A detailed analysis of the number and size of chromocentres in cultured animal cells has revealed that when two nuclei share the same cytoplasm, as in a binucleate cell, the pattern of chromocentres in them is very similar; but during the outgrowth of a clone of cells from a single parent cell diversity of chromocentre pattern is rapidly imposed. It has, moreover, been shown that this pattern, once imposed, undergoes little change during interphase. New patterns are imposed on the daughter cells at each mitosis. These findings suggest that a specific pattern of gene inactivation is imposed on the nucleus by the cell cytoplasm shortly after mitosis, that different cytoplasms impose different patterns, and that the pattern once imposed undergoes little change until the next mitosis.

If these chromocentres contain DNA that codes for specific proteins, it is clear that the formation of even the smallest chromocentre must involve the inactivation of a huge number of individual genes. We do not, at present, have any precise information about how much of the DNA in chromocentres does code for proteins. Heterochromatin is conventionally divided into two categories, constitutive and facultative.[56] Constitutive heterochromatin is said to be permanently inactive; it is commonly located at or near the centromeres of the chromosomes in metaphase preparations; and it is constant both in amount and distribution in virtually all the cells of any one organism. Facultative heterochromatin may be genetically active or inactive depending on the physiological state of the cell and on its developmental history. It has recently been shown that the constitutive heterochromatin seen in metaphase preparations contains a high proportion of 'simple sequence' or 'satellite' DNA, that is, DNA composed of a repetitive array of short and very similar, if not identical, nucleotide sequences.[57–59] This simple sequence DNA presumably does not code for protein, but it is by no means clear that constitutive heterochromatin does not contain any coding sequences. It has further been shown that the heterochromatic regions of interphase nuclei also contain a high proportion of simple sequence DNA.[60, 61] None the less, it seems unlikely that the chromocentres that one sees in interphase can correspond strictly to the constitutive heterochromatin found at or near the centromeres in metaphase preparations. Both the number of chromocentres and the total mass of condensed chromocentric material vary from cell to cell,[55] so that some facultative heterochromatin must be included in what is observed as the chromocentric complex. Facultative heterochromatin, since it is known to be genetically active under certain conditions, must contain some coding nucleotide sequences; indeed, there is no evidence to suggest that the nucleotide composition of facultative heterochromatin is any different from that of euchromatin. It is, in any case, difficult to see how the chromocentric system could form a basis for the transcriptional control of the synthesis of single specific proteins. Both the amount of genetic material inactivated in each chromocentre and the constancy of the inactivation throughout interphase argue against any close analogy between the formation of chromocentres and the switching on and off of single genes.

3. Puffs in polytene chromosomes

We now come to the one case that does, at least at first sight, appear to provide an adequate structural basis for the genetic operator model of protein synthesis: the giant polytene chromosomes of certain insects. These chromosomes are found in the larvae of many *Diptera* in the cells of glandular tissues, especially those derived from the gut. The salivary glands have been most extensively studied. The chromosomes in these glands are extraordinary for two reasons. The first is that they are grossly polytenic. Each chromosome contains thousands of identical parallel copies of the basic diploid genetic structure. The extent of polyteny may vary in different species, but for *Chironomus tentans* it has been estimated that each chromosome contains about 16 000 times the normal diploid amount of DNA.[62] This accounts for the huge size of these chromosomes and for the fact that structural details (vastly magnified by the existence of the polyteny) can be made out in them that cannot be resolved in normal diploid material. Not all the genes in the basic diploid set are apparently replicated to the same extent; it appears that the constitutive heterochromatic segments of the normal diploid chromosomes do not take part in the process of polytenization and thus have a minimal representation in the giant chromosomes.[63] The second unusual feature of these chromosomes is that they are visible as discrete condensed entities. Their physiological state thus resembles, not interphase, but a protracted and, since the cell does not divide, abortive prophase. It is difficult to know how far the observations made on the physiology of these extraordinary chromosomes can be extrapolated to normal diploid cells, but, if extrapolation is possible, the conditions that appear to provide the closest parallel are those stages of prophase in which the chromosomes are already condensed into discrete units, but in which some residual synthesis of RNA none the less takes place.

The bulk of the genetic material in the giant chromosomes is inactive. There are about 5000 identifiable (DNA) bands in the whole chromosome set in *Drosophila* or *Chironomus*,[64] but only about 300 of these bands have at any time been observed to synthesize RNA or to form 'puffs', the characteristic morphological change that the bands undergo when they are activated[44] (Plate 4*a*). The maximum number of loci that are active simultaneously is less than this: not more than about 200 bands have been seen to synthesize RNA at any one time. Measurements of the DNA content of the individual bands indicates that a band of average dimensions represents the polytenization of a primary unit that contains enough DNA to account for about 100 genes,[62] and many bands, of course, contain much more than the average amount of DNA. We are therefore dealing, even in these chromosomes, with the apparent activation and inactivation of relatively large units of genetic material. Detailed genetic analysis of specific deletions and translocations in *Drosophila* chromosomes has, however, established that, in general, there is only one essential functional gene, as defined by complementation tests, in each band. This gene occupies only a small fraction of the total extent of the band and is located at its proximal extremity, or possibly even in the adjacent interband (the region between two bands). No genetic function can be detected in other parts of the band.[64] It thus appears that the great bulk of the DNA in each band, even though autoradiographic studies show that it is transcribed into RNA, has no essential coding function. This rather surprising conclusion has generated a number of models that seek to provide some function for the excess DNA in the bands. These models are of two general kinds: those that postulate a tandem reiteration of the essential functional gene[65] and those that invoke some regulatory function for most of the band DNA. Models involving gene reiteration are not especially attractive because they require the operation of *ad hoc* mechanisms to rectify all mutations in the reiterated genes (since these mutations are without genetic consequences) and because they require that the degree of reiteration must be strictly and individually controlled for each gene (since the amount of DNA in each band remains remarkably constant). Regulatory models are at present too vague in molecular terms to permit detailed discussion; the most radical of these models proposes that the structural genes are in the interband regions and that the bands, which are the regions involved in puffing, are concerned only with regulating the expression of the DNA in the interbands.[66] Most of the DNA in the bands is none the less composed of 'unique', not 'repetitive', nucleotide sequences, that is, sequences that are represented in the DNA in a very limited number of copies.[67] We have no information about the mechanism by which interband DNA might be activated, but the activation of the bands clearly depends upon the existence of polyteny. The synthesis of RNA in each active band in controlled by the formation of a puff in which increasing numbers of identical polytenic copies of the same basic genetic unit are opened up and thus become accessible to the transcription machinery (Plate 4*b*). The degree of activity of each band is therefore determined by the number of polytenic copies that are available for transcription. It is difficult to see how a control mechanism that depends upon a polytenic chromosomal structure might operate in chromosomes that are not polytenic.

It has been contended that the pattern of puffing shows organ specificity,[68] but the evidence for this does not seem to be conclusive. It does indeed happen that the pattern of puffing may be different in the chromosomes of different tissues, but this pattern varies from animal to animal in the cells of any one tissue and also varies with the physiological state and the stage of development of the larva. When the physiological variation in puffing pattern is taken into account, very few, if any, puffs are found to be tissue-specific in the sense that they are found only in one particular tissue.[69] Some loci are found to be puffed throughout most stages of development, but others are puffed only at certain specific stages.[44, 45, 69, 70] In the salivary glands, the most intense puffing activity is seen just before the moulting periods, especially before the pupal moult during which metamorphosis occurs and the salivary glands break down. The puffing pattern associated with the pupal moult may persist even when the cells of the salivary glands have begun to undergo autolysis.

The phenotypic consequences of these various puffing patterns are far from clear. As I have already pointed out, only 200 to 300 bands are subject to puffing, and of these, many are more or less continuously puffed. There is evidence that in the salivary gland some of the puffs are involved in determining the synthesis of secretory proteins,[71–76] although none of this evidence is decisive. Some of the puffs in the giant cells of the foot pad of the fly may be involved in determining the secretion and maturation of the cuticle,[45] but the evidence in this case is even less direct. On the other hand, some experiments suggest that the proteins of the salivary secretion are not synthesized in the gland, but are simply extracted from the haemolymph.[77, 78] In *Sciara coprophila*, the maximal period of puff formation in the polytene chromosomes is not associated with either the appearance of any new proteins in the salivary secretion or the disappearance of any of the existing proteins.[79] In another sciarid, *Bradysia*, the polytene chromosomes in the salivary glands do not appear to undergo visible puffing at all.[80] The intense puffing activity associated with the moults has suggested the idea that some puffs might provide templates for the synthesis of the enymes or enzyme-containing lysosomes that destroy the gland at metamorphosis;[78, 81] and the possibility has also been considered that the puffs might be responsible for the production of substances that are required after metamorphosis. It is, of course, perfectly reasonable to suppose that some of the RNA made in the puffs does carry information for the synthesis of specific proteins, and there is good evidence that the RNA made in at least one large puff (Balbiani ring 2 in chromosome IV of *Chironomus tentans*) does find its way to the cytoplasm of the cell;[82] but the idea that the appearance and disappearance of a particular puff determine the onset and cessation of synthesis of a particular protein, in the manner proposed by the genetic operator model, is very difficult to accept. Even when the synthesis of RNA in the salivary glands of *Chironomus tentans* has been inhibited for 48 hours by the administration of actinomycin D, salivary proteins continue to be synthesized at the normal rate; and the specific cell granules associated with the salivary secretion in *Chironomus palli-divittatus* continue to be formed and, if depleted by pilocarpine, re-formed under these conditions.[83-85] The secretion of albumin by the salivary glands is also insensitive to the suppression of RNA synthesis by actinomycin D.[86] The messenger RNA in these salivary gland cells thus appears to be essentially stable, as it is in other eukaryotic cells, and one cannot therefore expect that regulation of the synthesis of specific proteins in the cell cytoplasm could be achieved by mechanisms that operate only at the level of DNA transcription.

4. The mechanisms that govern transcription

We have now to consider the mechanisms by which localized suppression of RNA synthesis in the chromosomes of eukaryotic cells is brought about. The genetic operator model of protein synthesis postulates a very high order of precision in the regulatory mechanisms that operate at the genetic level: single genes or small groups of genes are switched on and off. This type of model requires that the signals that pass from the cytoplasm to the genes must have a corresponding degree of specificity. They must be able to recognize one gene from another. None of the examples of regional control of transcription that I have described, not even the formation of puffs, appears to depend on cytoplasmic signals of high genetic specificity. Where a complete haploid set of chromosomes or one of the sex chromosomes is inactivated, it is clear that, if cytoplasmic signals are involved, they do not discriminate between one genetic locus and another, but must operate at an altogether different level. In the one case, the signals must merely distinguish between the paternal and the maternal set of chromosomes as a whole; and the inactivation of the paternal set cannot be due to the cumulative activity of a whole range of specific genetic repressors, since the great bulk of the genetic material is identical in both maternal and paternal chromosome sets. In the case of sex chromosome inactivation in eutherian mammals, the proposed cytoplasmic signals do not even distinguish between the paternal and the maternal X chromosome. Except in certain special cases,[87, 88] either one or other X chromosome is inactivated at random, and where there are more than two X chromosomes, all except one are inactivated.[41] The control mechanism is not concerned with inactivating any particular X chromosome or inactivating any fixed number of X chromosomes; it operates to ensure that only one X chromosome remains active. Indeed, translocations involving the X chromosome make it very improbable that inactivation of this chromosome involves mechanisms that recognize the genes within the chromosome. When a fragment of an X chromosome is translocated into an active autosomal region, the translocated fragment is always active;[89, 90] and when a fragment from a normally active autosome is translocated into an inactive X chromosome, the autosomal fragment is inactivated.[91-93] It is clear that the inactivation mechanisms are not concerned with what these genes are, but where they are. Moreover, X chromosome inactivation is not only permanent, it is heritable. Once a particular X chromosome is inactivated in a cell during early embryological development, the same X chromosome is inactivated in all the clonal descendants of that cell; and all attempts to reactivate an inactive X by cell fusion (a technique that I shall discuss in some detail in the next chapter) have so far failed.[94] Numerous models have been proposed to explain these remarkable features of X chromosome inactivation,[95] but none of them is convincing. Mechanisms that can achieve the stable inheritance of a specific pattern of gene inactivation may, of course, be relevant to the general question of how differentiated traits are inherited in cell populations. I shall return to this question when, in Chapter 6, I discuss differentiation.

The condensation and inactivation of large areas of chromatin during the terminal differentiation of certain specialized vertebrate cells appears to be connected with progressive reduction in the volume of the nucleus; and the appearance of smaller chromocentres in cells not undergoing terminal differentiation also appears to be related in some way to nuclear volume.[52, 96, 97] In these cases also, there can be little doubt that any cytoplasmic signals that might be operative act by ensuring the wholesale closure of very large areas of contiguous chromatin and not by inactivating single genes or small clusters of genes.

All these cases of localized genetic inactivation involve a visible change in the structure of the chromatin, a change that, for want of better information, we call condensation. Although the precise molecular changes underlying this process are at present totally obscure, some preliminary exploration has been done. It is clear that the condensed structure is dependent on the integrity of the proteins attached to the DNA, especially the histones; for, if the basic proteins are moved by polyanions, the condensed chromatin undergoes dispersion, and this change is associated with an increase in the capacity of the chromatin to support RNA synthesis.[98, 99] However, no qualitative or quantitative differences have been detected between the histones of active and inactive regions.[100-102] That histones cannot be specific gene repressors, as proposed some years ago, has, in any case, become obvious from studies of their structure: there is a rather limited number of different histones and the structure of some of them appears to be much the same throughout a very wide range of animal and plant cells.[103, 104] Secondary modifications of histones, such as phosphorylation or acetylation have been detected;[105-106] but these seem not to be immediate determinants of genetic activity or inactivity.[109, 110] Condensation of chromatin is accompanied by changes in its 'melting profile', condensed chromatin being less susceptible to denaturation by heat than dispersed chromatin;[111-113]

but the accessibility of the phosphate groups of the DNA to poly-cations seems not to be very different in condensed and dispersed chromatin.[114] However, condensed chromatin has a much reduced capacity to bind acridine orange and actinomycin D.[115-119] Indeed, there is a direct relationship between the capacity of chromatin to bind actinomycin D (under conditions that measure the specific binding of the antibiotic to DNA) and its ability to support the synthesis of RNA.[120] It thus appears that condensation induces specific conformational changes in the deoxyribonucleoprotein com-plex which result in restriction of the *accessibility* of the coding ele-ments of the DNA not only to macromolecules but also to relatively small molecules such as acridine orange or actinomycin D. It is difficult to avoid the conclusion that this restriction in accessibility applies also to some essential components of the transcription machi-nery. Condensed chromatin can be dispersed, with a concomitant increase in its ability to bind intercalating dyes, not only by removal of basic proteins, but also by changes in ionic environment.[121, 122] Both in the intact cell and in isolated nuclei, chromatin exhibits a marked sensitivity to the electrolyte composition of the ambient medium;[122, 123] and reversible condensation or dispersion can be produced by changes in the concentrations of either divalent or monovalent cations.[122] The picture that begins to emerge is that condensation of chromatin is produced by electrolyte interactions, and that selective condensation of different regions results from intrinsic regional differences in the structure of the chromatin itself. The crucial question is, of course, whether ionic effects of this kind could have the necessary discrimination to impose restrictions on transcription that are genetically specific. Recent studies on polytene chromosomes indicate that ion-mediated effects can be highly specific, specific enough, indeed, to achieve the activation or inactiva-tion of single genetic loci.

Polytene chromosomes are composed of chromatin in a generally condensed state punctuated by highly localized regions of dispersion (puffs) in which transcription of the DNA is permitted. It is now clear that the puffing pattern has a high degree of intrinsic structural stability and does not require to be maintained by a continuous flow of specific cytoplasmic signals.[124, 125] Nuclei divested of virtually all their cytoplasm by microsurgical procedures none the less main-tain specific puffing patterns;[124, 126] and replacement of most of the cytoplasm of a cell of one type with cytoplasm from a cell of a different type, showing a different puffing pattern, fails to induce any specific changes in the puffing pattern of the recipient cell.[127,128] Removal of the major part of a chromosome by surgical means does not significantly alter the puffing pattern of the remaining fragment. Polytene chromosomes can be removed from the cell nucleus altogether and, in a medium of appropriate electrolyte composition, will maintain their characteristic puffing pattern.[129] Such isolated chromosomes have been the subject of detailed investigations which indicate that the individual bands respond specifically to different electrolyte ratios: some bands are especially sensitive to changes in K ion concentration, others to changes in Na ion concentration.[129–131] Puffs can readily be produced at specific loci by alterations in the ionic composition of the medium (Plate 5). The ion concentrations required to produce most of these effects are within the ranges normally found in the cell nucleus,[129] and some of the puffs induced by ionic effects in isolated chromosomes or in isolated nuclei correspond exactly to those formed in the intact animal.[126, 129] Intranuclear cation concentrations in salivary gland and most other somatic cells are very high relative to those in the cytoplasm,[129,132,133] and there is evidence that cation levels in the cell nucleus do fluctuate under physiological conditions.[134,135] There is therefore every reason to believe that the puffing patterns produced by ionic effects in isolated chromosomes are not merely experimental artefacts, but are a reflection, although obviously not a completely faithful reflection, of events that take place in the intact cell. It is, in any case, clear that activation or inactivation of single genetic loci can be achieved by ionic effects, and that, for the structurally complex chromatin of higher cells, specificity of genetic regulation does not necessarily require a corresponding specificity of cytoplasmic signals.

Proteins other than histones are, of course, present in the chromatin of eukaryotic cells, and their function must also be considered. Apart from the enzymes responsible for replication and transcription of the DNA, none of these proteins has been adequately characterized, either chemically or functionally.[136] It is, in general, the case that dispersed and genetically active chromatin has a higher protein content than condensed and genetically inactive chromatin;[137, 138] and proteins have been shown to accumulate in the active bands of polytene chromosomes.[139] The proteins associated with genetically active regions no doubt represent a considerable mixture of different functional elements, including the polymerase enzymes themselves.

In a general way, some of them may be regarded as gene activators, but probably not in any highly specific sense. The accumulation of these proteins appears to be secondary to the structural changes that initially remove the restrictions on the accessibility of the DNA;[121] and there is no doubt that these restrictions can be removed without the intervention of extraneous proteins.

All this shows very little resemblance to the highly specific system of signals envisaged in the genetic operator model. For higher cells there is as yet no evidence for the existence of specific repressors and activators of single genes such as have been described in bacteria. If such mechanisms do operate in higher cells, their task must inevitably be much more difficult than it is in bacteria, for precise discrimination between a very much larger number of genes would be required. And the scope for specific repressors and activators would be more limited; for it is clear that the expression of a large part of the genetic material in higher cells is governed by mechanisms that operate in a quite different way. In considering any possible homology between the forms of genetic regulation that have been observed in higher cells and any similar processes that might exist in bacteria, one important fact must be taken into account. If the selective condensation of the chromatin in higher cells does indeed depend upon changes in electrolyte concentrations within the nucleus, it is not easy to see how any comparable mechanisms could operate in bacteria where there is no nuclear membrane and where the DNA is not bound to structural proteins, as it is in the chromatin of higher forms. There are, I think, no good grounds for supposing that anything resembling the phenomena that I have been discussing in this section exists in bacteria.

5. Control of the flow of information from the nucleus

Apart from the regulation of transcription and translation, one can envisage three other ways in which the expression of genetic information might be governed in higher cells. There could be mechanisms that regulate the release of templates from the DNA, mechanisms that regulate the passage of the templates across the nuclear membrane, and mechanisms that select for transport to the cytoplasm only a proportion of the templates made on the DNA. Studies in bacteria have suggested that the acts of translation and transcription may be closely coupled: more specifically, that when a template ceases to be translated it automatically ceases to be produced.[140] In disrupted bacterial preparations, electron micrographs show that the ribosomes become attached to the DNA when it is transcribed;[141] and labelling experiments confirm that the RNA synthesized on the DNA in such preparations is transferred to the attached ribosomes.[142] These observations have naturally lent support to the idea that in bacteria the ribosomes might be instrumental in detaching the messenger RNA from the DNA. As far as higher cells are concerned, this idea can hardly be entertained. The nucleus of higher cells contains very few, if any, completed ribosomes;[143-146] and those structures which might on morphological grounds be classed as some form of ribosome appear to be limited to the nucleolar areas.[147] There is no evidence for the existence of any appreciable number of completed ribosomes in close proximity to the bulk of the chromatin. While there is no reason to doubt that the rate of release of the RNA from the chromosome may be influenced by a variety of factors, there is, as far as I am aware, no information that suggests that there is anything selective about the mechanism of release. It is possible that there may be local variations in the rate of release of RNA from the chromosomes in different parts of the nucleus; but inhibition of the release of RNA can hardly be a general mechanism for regulating the expression of the genes. If it were, then inactive genes would have RNA attached to them as well as active genes. But measurement of the ratio of DNA to RNA in the nuclei of higher cells indicates that most of the DNA cannot have RNA attached to it.[148]

The permeability characteristics of the nuclear membrane have not yet been explored in great detail. Earlier work involving the measurement of potential differences across nuclear membranes suggested that in somatic cells, but not in oocytes, the membrane presented a barrier to free ion movement and thus provided a mechanism for generating the solute asymmetries that had been observed between nucleus and cytoplasm.[149,150] However, more recent experiments have indicated that both in oocytes and in somatic cells the diffusion of ions and metabolites of small molecular weight is essentially unhindered by the nuclear membrane and that the solute asymmetries between nucleus and cytoplasm must be explained by some form of cation binding.[151-153] However, for macromolecules the position appears to be more complex. Although many proteins are known to enter the nucleus from the cytoplasm, the rate at which they do so varies.[154] Proteins of particle size less than about 45 Å pass freely from cytoplasm to nucleus, but larger particles show a substantial delay at the nuclear membrane, and their rate of passage is roughly inversely proportional to particle size.[155] It is therefore to be assumed that high molecular weight ribonucleic acids, which have a particle size much greater than 45 Å, to say nothing of ribonucleoprotein complexes, would be subject to the restrictions that apply to larger proteins, and that special mechanisms must therefore exist to ensure their transport across the nuclear membrane. It is generally supposed that this transport occurs through the nuclear pores, but essentially nothing is known about the details of the process. The flow of protein across the nuclear membrane does show fluctuations in response to changes in physiological conditions,[156] so that it is possible to envisage the nuclear membrane exercising some form of general control over the flow of RNA from nucleus to cytoplasm; but it is difficult to see this membrane as a regulatory mechanism of high molecular specificity.

I have already discussed in Chapter 3 the remarkable fact that the rapidly labelled polydisperse RNA, which constitutes the great bulk of the RNA synthesized in the cell nucleus per unit time, appears to have a very short half-life and to be largely degraded within the cell nucleus. No satisfactory explanation for this rapid intranuclear RNA turnover has yet been provided. It has been suggested that the short-lived polydisperse RNA might play some intranuclear regulatory role, but no model has yet been proposed that plausibly accounts for the very unusual physical and metabolic properties of this RNA. Little purpose is served in discussing at length schemes that, at present, are purely conjectural. Another possibility is that newly formed messenger RNA must be shielded in some way from intranuclear degradation, either by secondary modification, or by coaptation with protein, or both, before it can be transferred to the cytoplasm of the cell. The limiting factor in the transfer of information from nucleus to cytoplasm might then be not the synthesis of messenger RNA, but its 'engagement' by mechanisms that shield it from intranuclear degradation. Much of the RNA degraded within the nucleus could then be messenger RNA molecules, or precursors of messenger RNA, that have failed to be engaged by the stabilizing mechanisms that ensure their transport to the cytoplasm. On this view, one would expect to find variations in intranuclear RNA turnover under different physiological or cultural conditions, and one would expect some roughly reciprocal relationship between the amount of RNA degraded in the cell nucleus and the amount transferred to the cytoplasm of the cell. These expectations are in fact fulfilled. The flow of RNA to the cell cytoplasm is much more sensitive to changes in external conditions than is the synthesis of RNA in the cell nucleus; and those cells in which there is no *net* RNA synthesis, or in which the flow of RNA to the cell cytoplasm has been inhibited, are the ones in which one finds that virtually all the RNA made in the cell nucleus undergoes intranuclear degradation.[157-162] Moreover, it appears that under certain conditions much less of the rapidly labelled nuclear RNA may be degraded than is commonly observed.[163]

However, this interpretation of intranuclear RNA turnover does meet a difficulty in the amount of RNA that appears to be degraded under most experimental conditions. While arguments based on what might or might not be economic for the cell are almost invariably inconclusive, it would none the less be surprising if the mechanisms that engaged messenger RNA for transfer to the cytoplasm normally functioned at such a low level of efficiency. I do not think they do. The experiments that have been done to measure the extent of intranuclear RNA turnover all involve pulse-chase procedures in which either the medium itself or its composition are changed between pulse and chase. The measurements are therefore made not while the cells are under steady state conditions, such as might be found during logarithmic growth, but under conditions in which cell metabolism is undergoing an acute perturbation. These are precisely the conditions under which one observes inhibition or reduction of the flow of RNA to the cytoplasm and under which one would therefore expect to see an increase in intranuclear RNA turnover. It is thus possible that the intranuclear RNA degradation seen in pulse-chase experiments might be a gross exaggeration of what one would find under steady state conditions. Because the breakdown products of intranuclear RNA turnover are re-utilized in the synthesis of new RNA molecules, it is extremely difficult to get a good estimate of how much nuclear RNA undergoes breakdown under steady state conditions. Nothing that I have said is, however, intended to preclude the possibility that some of the RNA molecules that break down in the cell nucleus might be something other than messenger RNA or a precursor of messenger RNA. It seems probable, for example, that some non-coding sequences of DNA are transcribed; but, as I have already pointed out, we do not at present have more than conjectural notions about what function intranuclear non-messenger RNA molecules might have.

If one accepts that messenger RNA does have to be shielded from intranuclear degradation in some way before it can be transferred to the cytoplasm of the cell, the question of mechanism arises. The obvious mechanism that comes to mind is one in which the newly formed messenger RNA is coupled in some way to protein. This idea finds support in numerous observations which suggest that messenger RNA is present in the cell in the form of ribonucleoprotein complexes. As mentioned in Chapter 3, it has also been suggested that polyadenylic acid sequences might be added to messenger RNA molecules after their transcription, and that this posttranscriptional modification might be essential for the transfer of the messenger RNA from nucleus to cytoplasm. The addition of polyadenylic acid alone is unlikely to protect the messenger RNA from intranuclear degradation, for the degradative enzymes involved are apparently exonucleases that degrade polyadenylic acid perfectly well.[164, 165] However, it is possible that the polyadenylic acid sequences may act indirectly, for example by facilitating in some way the attachment of proteins.

6. Regulation by means of enzyme degradation

Because there is little turnover of protein in bacteria during exponential growth,[166–168] the possibility that enzyme levels might be regulated by mechanisms that govern the rate of enzyme degradation has, until very recently, been given scant attention. But in bacteria that are not growing exponentially and in both animal and plant cells, which grow exponentially only in exceptional circumstances, substantial turnover of protein does take place.[169–176] In general it appears that there is a correlation between molecular weight and protein catabolism, larger proteins being degraded more rapidly than smaller ones,[177] but there is, in addition, some regional heterogeneity. Membrane proteins, for example, seem to be degraded more rapidly than most.[178] Decisive evidence has been obtained that intracellular enzyme concentrations in higher cells can be determined by variations not only in the rate of enzyme synthesis but also in the rate of enzyme breakdown.[179–183] The most detailed studies of this question are those of Schimke and his colleagues on arginase and tryptophan pyrrolase levels in liver cells.[179, 180] These enzymes undergo an easily measurable turnover within the cell and, in both cases, the intracellular enzyme level rises when the substrate of the enzyme, arginine or tryptophan, is supplied. Schmike and his colleagues have shown that the increase in enzyme level produced by the administration of substrate is due in large part to a reduction in the rate of enzyme degradation: the enzyme is stabilized by its substrate. It seems probable that stabilization by substrate will prove to be a phenomenon of quite general importance in the regulation of enzyme levels in higher cells, for an interaction of this sort provides an additional control mechanism that is not only completely specific, but also highly flexible.

REFERENCES

1. SWEENEY, B. M. and HAXO, F. T. (1961). Persistence of a photosynthetic rhythm in enucleated *Acetabularia*. *Science, N.Y.* **134**, 1361.
2. SCHWEIGER, E., WALLRAFF, H. G., and SCHWEIGER, H. G. (1964). Endogenous circardian rhythm in cytoplasm of *Acetabularia*. *Science, N.Y.* **146**, 658.
3. SCHWEIGER, E., WALLRAFF, H. G., and SCHWEIGER, H. G. (1964). Über tagesperiodsche Schwankungen der Sauerstoffbilanz kernhaltiger und kernloser *Acetabularia mediterranea*. *Z. Naturf.* **19b**, 499.
4. SCHWEIGER, H. G. (1971). Circadian rhythms: subcellular and biochemical aspects. *Proc. Int. Symp. Circadian Rhythmicity* (Wageningen, 1971), p. 157.
5. SWEENEY, B. M., TUFFLI, C. F., and RUBIN, R. H. (1967). The circadian rhythm in photosynthesis in *Acetabularia* in the presence of actinomycin D, puromycin and chloramphenicol. *J. gen. Physiol.* **50**, 647.
6. WRIGHT, B. E. (1973). *Critical variables in differentiation*. Prentice-Hall, New Jersey.
7. TOMKINS, G. M., LEVINSON, B. B., BAXTER, J. D., and DETHLEFSEN, L. (1972). Further evidence for posttranscriptional control of inducible tyrosine aminotransferase synthesis in cultured hepatoma cells. *Nature, Lond. New Biol.* **239**, 9.
8. DEANGELO, A. B. and FUJIMOTO, G. I. (1973). Translational control of specific uterine protein synthesis after estrogen induction. *Proc. natn. Acad. Sci. U.S.A.* **70**, 18.
9. THOMPSON, E. B., GRANNER, D. K., and TOMKINS, G. M. (1970). Superinduction of tyrosine aminotransferase by actinomycin D in rat hepatoma (HTC) cells. *J. molec. Biol.* **54**, 159.
10. LEVINSON, B. B., TOMKINS, G. M., and STELLWAGEN, R. H. (1971). The regulation of tyrosine aminotransferase synthesis. *J. biol. Chem.* **246**, 6297.
11. PALMITER, R. D. and SCHIMKE, R. T. (1973). Regulation of protein synthesis in the chick oviduct III. Mechanism of ovalbumin 'superinduction' by actinomycin D. *J. biol. Chem.* **248**, 1502.
12. GROSS, M. and RABINOWITZ, M. (1973). Partial purification of a translational repressor mediating hemin control of globin synthesis and implication of results on the site of inhibition. *Biochem. biophys. Res. Commun.* **50**, 832.
13. RHOADS, R. E., MCKNIGHT, S., and SCHIMKE, R. T. (1973). Quantitative measurement of ovalbumin messenger ribonucleic acid activity. Localization in polysome, induction by estrogen, and effect of actinomycin D. *J. biol. Chem.* **248**, 2031.

14. BEUZARD, Y., RODVIEN, R., and LONDON, I. M. (1973). Effect of hemin on the synthesis of hemoglobin and other proteins in mammalian cells. *Proc. natn. Acad. Sci. U.S.A.* **70**, 1022.

15. LEE-HUANG, S. and OCHOA, S. (1971). Messenger discriminating species of initiation factor F_3. *Nature, Lond. New Biol.* **234**, 236.

16. GRONER, Y., POLLACK, Y., BERISSI, H., and REVEL, M. (1972). Cistron specific translation control protein in *Escherichia coli*. *Nature, Lond. New Biol.* **239**, 16.

17. ZASLOFF, M. and OCHOA, S. (1971). A supernatant factor involved in initiation complex formation with eukaryotic ribosomes. *Proc. natn. Acad. Sci. U.S.A.* **68**, 3059.

18. KAEMPFER, R. and KAUFMAN, J. (1972). Translational control and haemoglobin synthesis by an initiation factor required for recycling of ribosomes and for their binding to messenger RNA. *Proc. natn. Acad. Sci. U.S.A.* **69**, 3317.

19. PALMITER, R. D. (1972). Regulation of protein synthesis in the chick oviduct II. Modulation of polypeptide elongation and initiation rates by estrogen and progesterone. *J. biol. Chem.* **247**, 6770.

20. CHONG-CHENG, C. and OLIVER, I. T. (1972). A translational control mechanism in mammalian protein synthesis modulated by cyclic adenosine monophosphate. Translational control of tyrosine aminotransferase synthesis in neonatal rat liver. *Biochemistry, N.Y.* **11**, 2547.

21. BRENNER, M. and AMES, B. N. (1971) The histidine operon and its regulation. *Metabolic regulation* (ed. H. J. Vogel), p. 349. Academic Press, New York and London.

22. KOVACH, J. S., PHANG, J. M., FERENCE, M., and GOLDBERGER, R. F. (1969). Studies on repression of the histidine operon. II. The role of the first enzyme in control of the histidine system. *Proc. natn. Acad. Sci. U.S.A.* **63**, 481.

23. ROTHMAN-DENES, L. and MARTIN, R. G. (1971). Two mutations in the first gene of the histidine operon of *Salmonella typhimurium* affecting control. *J. Bact.* **106**, 227.

24. SINGER, C. E., SMITH, G. R., CORTESE, R., and AMES, B. N. (1972). Mutant tRNA ineffective in repression and lacking two pseudouridine modifications. *Nature, Lond. New Biol.* **238**, 72.

25. KOVACH, J. S., PHANG, J. M., BLASI, F., BARTON, R. W., BALLESTEROS-OLMO, A., and GOLDBERGER, R. F. (1970). Interaction between histidyl transfer ribonucleic acid and the first enzyme for histidine biosynthesis in *Salmonella typhimurium*. *J. Bact.* **104**, 787.

26. VOGEL, T., MEYERS, M. KOVACH, J. S., and GOLDBERGER, R. F. (1972). Specificity of interaction between the first enzyme for histidine biosynthesis and aminoacylated histidine transfer ribonucleic acid. *J. Bact.* **112**, 126.

27. KOVACH, J. S., BALLESTEROS, A. O., MEYERS, M., SORIA, M., and GOLD-BERGER, R. F. (1973). A *cis/trans* test of the effect of the first enzyme for histidine biosynthesis on regulation of the histidine operon. *J. Bact.* **114**, 351.

28. CLINE, A. L. and BOCK, R. M. (1966). Translational control of gene expression. *Cold Spring Harb. Symp. quant. Biol.* **31**, 321.

29. HATFIELD, G. W. and BURNS, R. O. (1970). Specific binding of leucyl transfer RNA to an immature form of L-threonine deaminase: its implications in repression. *Proc. natn. Acad. Sci. U.S.A.* **66**, 1027.

30. YOSHIDA, A. (1970). Amino acid substitution (histidine to tyrosine) in a glucose-6-phosphate dehydrogenase variant (G6PD Hektoen) associated with over-production. *J. molec. Biol.* **52**, 483.

31. ILAN, J., ILAN, J., and PATEL, N. (1970). Mechanism of gene expression in *Tenebrio molitor. J. biol. Chem.* **245**, 1275.
32. GRUBER, M. and CAMPAGNE, R. N. (1965). Regulation of protein synthesis: an alternative to the repressor–operator hypothesis. *Proc. K. ned. Akad. Wet. Ser. C* **68**, 1.
33. BLASI, F., ALOJ, S. M., and GOLDBERGER, R. F. (1971). Effect of histidine on the enzyme which catalyzes the first step of histidine biosynthesis in *Salmonella typhimurium. Biochemistry, N.Y.* **10**, 1409.
34. HAMLIN, J. and ZABIN, I. (1972). *β*-Galactosidase: immunological activity of ribosome-bound, growing polypeptide chains. *Proc. natn. Acad. Sci. U.S.A.* **69**, 412.
35. VILLAREJO, M., ZAMENHOF, P. J., and ZABIN, I. (1972). *β*-Galactosidase. *In vivo* complementation. *J. biol. Chem.* **247**, 2212.
36. VILLAREJO, M. R. and ZABIN, I. (1973). Affinity chromatography of *β*-galactosidase fragments. *Nature, Lond. New Biol.* **242**, 50.
37. LODISH, H. F. (1971). Alpha and beta globin messenger ribonucleic acid. Different amounts and rates of initiation of translation. *J. biol. Chem.* **246**, 7131.
38. BERLOWITZ, L. (1965). Correlation of genetic activity, heterochromatization, and RNA metabolism. *Proc. natn. Acad. Sci. U.S.A.* **53**, 68.
39. EVANS, H. J., FORD, C. E., LYON, M. F., and GRAY, J. (1965). DNA replication and genetic expression in female mice with morphologically distinguishable X chromosomes. *Nature, Lond.* **206**, 900.
40. COMINGS, D. E. (1966). Uridine-5-^{3}H radioautography of the human sex chromatin body. *J. Cell Biol.* **28**, 437.
41. HAMERTON, J. L. (1968). Significance of sex chromosome derived heterochromatin in mammals. *Nature, Lond.* **219**, 910.
42. LITTAU, V. C., ALLFREY, V. G., FRENSTER, J. H., and MIRSKY, A. E. (1964). Active and inactive regions of nuclear chromatin as revealed by electron microscope autoradiography. *Proc. natn. Acad. Sci. U.S.A.* **52**, 93.
43. HSU, T. C. (1962). Differential rate in RNA synthesis between euchromatin and heterochromatin. *Expl Cell Res.* **27**, 332.
44. PELLING, C. (1964). Ribonukleinsäure-Synthese der Riesenchromosomen. *Chromosoma* **15**, 71.
45. WHITTEN, J. M. (1969). Coordinated development in the foot pad of the fly *Sarcophaga bullata* during metamorphosis: changing puffing patterns of the giant cell chromosomes. *Chromosoma* **26**, 215.
46. CROUSE, H. V. (1943). Translocations in *Sciara*. Their bearing on chromosome behavior and sex determination. *Univ. Missouri agric. expl Stn Res. Bull.* No. 379, p. 1.
47. BROWN, S. W. (1964). Automatic frequency response in the evolution of male haploidy and other coccid chromosome systems. *Genetics, Princeton* **49**, 797.
48. SWANSON, C. P. (1958). *Cytology and cytogenetics*, pp. 331–5. Macmillan, London.
49. OHNO, S., JAINCHILL, J., and STENIUS, C. (1963). The creeping vole (*Microtus oregoni*) as a gonosomic mosaic. I. The OY/XY constitution of the male. *Cytogenetics* **2**, 232.
50. HAYMAN, D. L. and MARTIN, P. G. (1965). Sex chromosome mosaicism in the marsupial genera isoodon and perameles. *Genetics, Princeton* **52**, 1201.
51. HAYMAN, D. L., MARTIN, P. G., and WALLER, P. F. (1969). Parallel mosaicism of supernumerary chromosomes and sex chromosomes in *Echymipera kalabu* (Marsupialia). *Chromosoma*, **27**, 371.

52. CAMERON, I. L. and PRESCOTT, D. M. (1963). RNA and protein metabolism in the maturation of the nucleated chicken erythrocyte. *Expl. Cell Res.* **30**, 609.
53. SKUTELSKY, E. and DANON, D. (1967). An electron microscopic study of nuclear elimination from the late erythroblast. *J. Cell Biol.* **33**, 625.
54. MITTWOCH, U. (1967). Barr bodies in relation to DNA values and nuclear size in cultured human cells. *Cytogenetics* **6**, 38.
55. ABERCROMBIE, M. and STEPHENSON, E. M. (1969). Observations on chromocentres in cultured mouse cells. *Nature, Lond.* **222**, 1250.
56. BROWN, S. W. (1966). Heterochromatin. *Science, N.Y.* **151**, 417.
57. PARDUE, M. L. and GALL, J. G. (1970). Chromosomal localisation of mouse satellite DNA. *Science, N.Y.* **168**, 1356.
58. JONES, K. W. (1970). Chromosomal and nuclear location of mouse satellite DNA in individual cells. *Nature, Lond.* **225**, 912.
59. WALKER, P. M. B. (1971). The 'repetitive' DNA in higher organisms. *Progr. Biophys. molec. Biol.* (eds. J. A. V. Butler and D. Noble) **23**, 145. Pergamon Press, London.
60. YASMINEH, W. G. and YUNIS, J. J. (1970). Localization of mouse satellite DNA in constitutive heterochromatin. *Expl. Cell Res.* **59**, 69.
61. YUNIS, J. J. and YASMINEH, W. G. (1970). Satellite DNA in constitutive heterochromatin of the guinea pig. *Science, N.Y.* **168**, 263.
62. EDSTRÖM, J.-E. (1965). Chromosomal RNA and other nuclear RNA fractions. *Role of the chromosomes in development* (ed. M. LOCKE), p. 137. Academic Press, New York.
63. RUDKIN, G. T. (1965). Nonreplicating DNA in giant chromosomes. *Genetics, Princeton* **52**, 470.
64. BEERMANN, W. (1972). Chromomeres and genes. *Developmental studies on giant chromosomes* (ed. W. BEERMANN), p. 1. Springer-Verlag, Berlin.
65. CALLAN, H. G. (1967). The organization of genetic units in chromosomes. *J. Cell Sci.* **2**, 1.
66. CRICK, F. H. C. (1971). General model for the chromosomes of higher organisms. *Nature, Lond.* **234**, 25.
67. DICKSON, E., BOYD, J., and LAIRD, C. D. (1971). Sequence diversity of polytene chromosome DNA from *Drosophila hydei*. *J. molec. Biol.* **61**, 615.
68. BEERMANN, W. (1952). Chromomerenkonstanz und spezifische Modifikationen der Chromosomenstruktur in der Entwicklung und Organdifferenzierung von *Chironomus tentans*. *Chromosoma* **5**, 139.
69. CLEVER, U. (1966). Gene activity patterns and cellular differentiation. *Am. Zoologist* **6**, 33.
70. ASHBURNER, M. (1972). Puffing patterns in *Drosophila melanogaster* and related species. *Developmental studies on giant chromosomes* (ed. W. BEERMANN), p. 101. Springer-Verlag, Berlin.
71. BEERMANN, W. (1961). Ein Balbiani-Ring als Locus einer Speicheldrüsenmutation. *Chromosoma* **12**, 1.
72. PANITZ, R. (1967). Funktionelle Veränderungen an Riesenchromosomen nach Behandlung mit Giberellinen. *Biol. Zbl.* **86**, Suppl., p. 147.
73. BAUDISCH, W. and PANITZ, R. (1968). Kontrolle eines biochemischen Merkmals in den Speicheldrüsen von *Acricotopus lucidus* durch einen Balbiani-Ring. *Expl. Cell Res.* **49**, 470.
74. GROSSBACH, U. (1968). Cell differentiation in the salivary glands of *Camptochironomus tentans* and *C. pallidivittatus*. *Annls zool. Fenn.* **5**, 37.

75. GROSSBACH, U. (1969). Chromosomen-Aktivität und biochemische Zell-differenzierung in den Speicheldrüsen von *Camptochironomus*. *Chromosoma* **28**, 136.

76. WOBUS, U., PANITZ, R., and SERFLING, E. (1970). Tissue specific gene activities and proteins in the *Chironomus* salivary gland. *Molec. gen. Genet.* **107**, 215.

77. DOYLE, D. and LAUFER, H. (1969). Sources of larval salivary gland secretion in the dipteran *Chironomus tentans*. *J. Cell Biol.* **40**, 61.

78. LAUFER, H. and NAKASE, Y. (1965). Developmental studies of the dipteran salivary gland. II. DNAase activity in *Chironomus thummi*. *J. Cell Biol.* **25**, 97.

79. BEEN, A. C. and RASCH, E. M. (1972). Cellular and secretory proteins of the salivary glands of *Sciara coprophila* during the larval-pupal transformation. *J. Cell Biol.* **55**, 420.

80. DA CUNHA, A. B., MORGANTE, J. S., PAVAN, C., and GARRIDO, M. C. (1969). Studies on cytology and differentiation in Sciaridae. III. Nuclear and cytoplasmatic differentiation in the salivary glands of *Bradysia* sp. *Stud. Genet.* **5**, 1. University of Texas.

81. SCHIN, K. S. and CLEVER, U. (1965). Lysosomal and free acid phosphatase in salivary glands of developing *Chironomus tentans* larvae. *Science, N.Y.* **150**, 1053.

82. DANEHOLT, B. and HOSICK, H. (1973). Evidence for transport of 75S RNA from a discrete chromosome region via nuclear sap to cytoplasm in *Chironomus tentans*. *Proc. natn. Acad. Sci. U.S.A.* **70**, 442.

83. CLEVER, U., STORBECK, I., and ROMBALL, C. G. (1969). Chromosome activity and cell function in polytenic cells. I. Protein synthesis at various stages of larval development. *Expl Cell Res.* **55**, 306.

84. CLEVER, U. (1969). Chromosome activity and cell function in polytenic cells. II. The formation of secretion in the salivary glands of *Chironomus*. *Expl Cell Res.* **55**, 317.

85. CLEVER, U., BULTMANN, H., and DARROW, J. M. (1969). The immediacy of genomic control in polytenic cells. *Problems in Biology: RNA in Development* (ed. E. W. HANLY), p. 403. University of Utah Press, Salt Lake City, U.S.A.

86. DOYLE, D. and LAUFER, H. (1969). Requirements of ribonucleic acid synthesis for the formation of salivary gland specific proteins in larval *Chironomus tentans*. *Expl Cell Res.* **57**, 205.

87. GUSTAVSSON, J., FRACCARO, M., TIEPOLO, L., and LINDSTEN, J. (1968). Presumptive X-autosome translocation in a cow: preferential inactivation of the normal X chromosome. *Nature, Lond.* **218**, 183.

88. HAMERTON, J. L., GIANNELLI, F., COLLINS, F., HALLETT, J., FRYER, A., McGUIRE, V. M., and SHORT, R. V. (1969). Non-random X-inactivation in the female mule. *Nature, Lond.* **222**, 1277.

89. LYON, M. F., SEARLE, A. G., FORD, C. E., and OHNO, S. (1964). A mouse translocation suppressing sex-linked variegation. *Cytogenetics* **3**, 306.

90. OHNO, S. and LYON, M. F. (1965). Cytological study of Searle's X-autosome translocation in *Mus musculus*. *Chromosoma* **16**, 90.

91. OHNO, S. and CATTANACH, B. M. (1962). Cytological study of an X-autosome translocation in *Mus musculus*. *Cytogenetics* **1**, 129.

92. CATTANACH, B. M. and ISAACSON, J. H. (1967). Controlling elements in the mouse X chromosome. *Genetics, Princeton* **57**, 331.

93. FRANCKE, U. and NESBITT, M. (1971). Cattanach's translocation: cytological characterization by quinacrine mustard staining. *Proc. natn. Acad Sci. U.S.A.* **68**, 2918.

94. MIGEON, B. R. (1972). Stability of X chromosomal inactivation in human somatic cells. *Nature, Lond.* **239**, 87.

95. LYON, M. F. (1971). Possible mechanisms of X chromosome inactivation. *Nature, Lond. New Biol.* **232**, 229.

96. MITTWOCH, U., LELE, K. P., and WEBSTER, W. S. (1965). Relationship of Barr bodies, nuclear size and deoxyribonucleic acid value in cultured human cells. *Nature, Lond.* **205**, 477.

97. MITTWOCH, U. (1968). Nuclear sizes in a human diploid/triploid cell culture. *Nature, Lond.* **219**, 1074.

98. MILLER, G. J., BERLOWITZ, L., and REGELSON, W. (1972). Chromatin and histones in hen erythrocyte nuclei. *Expl Cell Res.* **71**, 409.

99. ARNOLD, E. A., YAWN, D. H., BROWN, D. G., WYLLIE, R. C., and COFFEY, D. S. (1972). Structural alteration in isolated rat liver nuclei after removal of template restriction by polyanions. *J. Cell Biol.* **53**, 737.

100. COMINGS, D. E. (1967). Histones of genetically active and inactive chromatin. *J. Cell Biol.* **35**, 699.

101. GOROVSKY, M. A. and WOODARD, J. (1967). Histone content of chromosomal loci active and inactive in RNA synthesis. *J. Cell Biol.* **33**, 723.

102. PALLOTTA, D., BERLOWITZ, L., and RODRIGUEZ, L. (1970). Histones of genetically active and inactive chromatin in mealy bugs. *Expl. Cell Res.* **60**, 474.

103. JOHNS, E. W. (1969). The histones, their interactions with DNA, and some aspects of gene control. *Ciba Foundation symposium on homeostatic regulators* (eds. G. E. W. WOLSTENHOLME and J. KNIGHT), p. 128. Churchill, London.

104. JOHNS, E. W. (1972). Histones, chromatin structure and RNA synthesis. *Nature, Lond. New Biol.* **237**, 87.

105. ORD, M. G. and STOCKEN, L. A. (1965). Histones of rat liver and thymus. *Biochem. J.* **98**, 5p.

106. STEVELY, V. S. and STOCKEN, L. A. (1966). Phosphorylation of rat-thymus histone. *Biochem. J.* **100**, 20c.

107. POGO, B. G. T., ALLFREY, V. G., and MIRSKY, A. E. (1966). RNA synthesis and histone acetylation during the course of gene activation in lymphocytes. *Proc. natn. Acad. Sci. U.S.A.* **55**, 805.

108. POGO, B. G. T., ALLFREY, V. G., and MIRSKY, A. E. (1967). The effect of phytohemagglutinin on ribonucleic acid synthesis and histone acetylation in equine leukocytes. *J. Cell Biol.* **35**, 477.

109. OLIVER, D., BALHORN, R., GRANNER, D., and CHALKLEY, R. (1972). Molecular nature of F_1 histone phosphorylation in cultured hepatoma cells. *Biochemistry, N.Y.* **11**, 3921.

110. CLEVER, U. and ELLGAARD, E. G. (1970). Puffing and histone acetylation in polytene chromosomes. *Science, N.Y.* **169**, 373.

111. RIGLER, R., KILLANDER, D., BOLUND, L., and RINGERTZ, N. R. (1969). Cytochemical characterization of deoxyribonucleoprotein in individual cell nuclei. *Expl. Cell Res.* **55**, 215.

112. RIGLER, R. and KILLANDER, D. (1969). Activation of deoxyribonucleoprotein in human leucocytes stimulated by phytohemagglutinin. *Expl Cell Res.* **54**, 171.

113. RINGERTZ, N. R., GLEDHILL, B. L., and DARZYNKIEWICZ, Z. (1970). Changes in deoxyribonucleoprotein during spermiogenesis in the bull. *Expl Cell Res.* **62**, 204.
114. ITZHAKI, R. F. and COOPER, H. K. (1973). Similarity of chromatin from different tissues. *J. molec. Biol.* **75**, 119.
115. KILLANDER, D. and RIGLER, R. (1969). Activation of deoxyribonucleoprotein in human leucocytes stimulated by phytohemagglutinin. *Expl Cell Res.* **54**, 163.
116. RINGERTZ, N. R. and BOLUND, L. (1969). Actinomycin binding capacity of deoxyribonucleoprotein. *Biochim. biophys. Acta* **174**, 147.
117. DARZYNKIEWICZ, Z., BOLUND, L., and RINGERTZ, N. R. (1969). Actinomycin binding of normal and phytohaemagglutinin stimulated lymphocytes. *Expl Cell Res.* **55**, 120.
118. RINGERTZ, N. R., DARZYNKIEWICZ, Z., and BOLUND, L. (1969). Actinomycin binding properties of stimulated human lymphocytes. *Expl Cell Res.* **56**, 411.
119. DARZYNKIEWICZ, Z., GLEDHILL, B. L., and RINGERTZ, N. R. (1969). Changes in deoxyribonucleoprotein during spermiogenesis in the bull. *Expl Cell Res.* **58**, 435.
120. WONG, K.-Y., PATEL, J., and KRAUSE, M. O. (1971). RNA synthesis and chromatin structure in mammalian cells. *Expl. Cell Res.* **69**, 456.
121. RINGERTZ, N. R. and BOLUND, L. (1969). 'Activation' of hen erythrocyte deoxyribonucleoprotein. *Expl Cell Res.* **55**, 205.
122. OLINS, D. E. and OLINS, A. L. (1972). Physical studies of isolated eucaryotic nuclei. *J. Cell Biol.* **53**, 715.
123. PEDERSON, T. and ROBBINS, E. (1970). RNA synthesis in HeLa cells. *J. Cell Biol.* **47**, 734.
124. KROEGER, H. (1967). Hormones, ion balances and gene activity in dipteran chromosomes. *Endocrine genetics*, Proc. Symp., Cambridge, 1966 (ed. S. G. SPICKETT). *Mem. Soc. Endocr.* **15**, 55.
125. KROEGER, H. and LEZZI, M. (1966). Regulation of gene action in insect development. *A. Rev. Ent.* **11**, 1.
126. LEZZI, M. (1966). Induktion eines Ecdyson-aktivierbaren Puff in isolierten Zellkernen von *Chironomus* durch KCl. *Expl. Cell Res.* **43**, 571.
127. KROEGER, H. (1963). Experiments on the extranuclear control of gene activity in dipteran polytene chromosomes. *J. Cell comp. Physiol.* **62**, Suppl. I, 45.
128. KROEGER, H. (1964). Zellphysiologische Mechanismen bei der Regulation von Genaktivitäten in den Riesenchromosomen von *Chironomus thummi*. *Chromosoma* **15**, 36.
129. LEZZI, M. and ROBERT, M. (1972). Chromosomes isolated from unfixed salivary glands of *Chironomus*. *Result. Probl. Cell Different.* **4**, 35.
130. LEZZI, M. and GILBERT, L. I. (1970). Differential effects of K^+ and Na^+ on specific bands of isolated polytene chromosomes of *Chironomus tentans*. *J. Cell Sci.* **6**, 615.
131. LEZZI, M. and KROEGER, H. (1966). Aufnahme von ^{22}Na in die Zellkerne der Speicheldrüsen von *Chironomus thummi*. *Z. Naturf.* **21b**, 274.
132. SIEBERT, G., LANGENDORF, H., HANNOVER, R., NITZ-LITZOW, D., PRESSMAN, B. C., and MOORE, C. (1965). Untersuchungen zur Rolle des Natrium-Stoffwechsels im Zellkern der Rattenleber. *Hoppe-Seyler's Z. physiol. Chem.* **343**, 101.
133. SIEBERT, G. (1966). Gewinnung und Funktion isolierter Zellkerne. *Z. klin. Chem.* **3**, 13.

134. MUIR, C. and WHITLEY, J. E. (1972). Variation in the nuclear sodium concentration of newt oocytes during maturation. *J. Cell Sci.* **10**, 335.

135. KROEGER, H. (1966). Potentialdifferenz und Puff-muster. Elektrophysiologische und cytologische Untersuchungen an den Speicheldrüsen von *Chironomus thummi. Expl Cell Res.* **41**, 64.

136. SPELSBERG, T. C., WILHELM, J. A., and HNILICA, L. S. (1972). Nuclear proteins in genetic restriction. II. The nonhistone proteins in chromatin. *Sub-cell. Biochem.* **1**, 107.

137. BOLUND, L., RINGERTZ, N. R., and HARRIS, H. (1969). Changes in the cytochemical properties of erythrocyte nuclei reactivated by cell fusion. *J. Cell Sci.* **4**, 71.

138. BOLUND, L., DARZYNKIEWICZ, Z., and RINGERTZ, N. R. (1969). Growth of hen erythrocyte nuclei undergoing reactivation in heterokaryons. *Expl Cell Res.* **56**, 406.

139. BERENDES, H. O. (1972). The control of puffing in *Drosophila hydei. Result. Probl. Cell Different.* **4**, 181.

140. STENT, G. S. (1964). The operon: on its third anniversary. *Science, N.Y.* **144**, 816.

141. BLADEN, H. A., BYRNE, R., LEVIN, J. G., and NIRENBERG, M. W. (1965). An electron microscopic study of a DNA-ribosome complex formed *in vitro. J. molec. Biol.* **11**, 78.

142. JONES, O. W., DIECKMANN, M., and BERG, P. (1968). Ribosome-induced dissociation of RNA from an RNA polymerase DNA-RNA complex. *J. molec. Biol.* **31**, 177.

143. CRAWLEY, J. C. W. and HARRIS, H. (1963). The fine structure of isolated HeLa cell nuclei. *Expl. Cell Res.* **31**, 70.

144. HOLTZMAN, E., SMITH, I., and PENMAN, S. (1966). Electron microscopic studies of detergent-treated HeLa cell nuclei. *J. molec. Biol.* **17**, 131.

145. ROGERS, M. E. (1968). Ribonucleoprotein particles in the amphibian oocyte nucleus. Possible intermediates in ribosome synthesis. *J. Cell Biol.* **36**, 421.

146. MONNERON, A. and MOULÉ, Y. (1968). Etude ultrastructurale de particles ribonucléoprotéiques nucléaires isolées à partir du foie de rat. *Expl Cell Res.* **51**, 531.

147. BERNHARD, W. (1966). Ultrastructural aspects of the normal and pathological nucleolus in mammalian cells. *Natn. Cancer Inst. Monogr.* No. 23, p. 13.

148. McLEISH, J. (1963). Quantitative relationships between deoxyribonucleic and ribonucleic acid in isolated plant nuclei. *Proc. R. Soc.* B **158**, 261.

149. LOEWENSTEIN, W. R. and KANNO, Y. (1963). The electrical conductance and potential across the membrane of some cell nuclei. *J. Cell Biol.* **16**, 421.

150. LOEWENSTEIN, W. R., KANNO, Y., and ITO, S. (1966). Permeability of nuclear membranes. *Ann. N.Y. Acad. Sci.* **137**, 708.

151. HOROWITZ, S. B. and FENICHEL, I. R. (1970). Analysis of sodium transport in the amphibian oocyte by extractive and radioautographic techniques. *J. Cell Biol.* **47**, 120.

152. HOROWITZ, S. B. (1972). The permeability of the amphibian oocyte nucleus *in situ. J. Cell Biol.* **54**, 609.

153. KOHEN, E., SIEBERT, G., and KOHEN, C. (1971). Transfer of metabolites across the nuclear membrane. *Hoppe-Seyler's Z. physiol. Chem.* **352**, 927.

154. GURDON, J. B. (1970). Nuclear transplantation and the control of gene activity in animal development. *Proc. Roy. Soc.* B **176**, 303.

155. PAINE, P. L. and FELDHERR, C. M. (1972). Nucleocytoplasmic exchange of macromolecules. *Expl. Cell Res.* **74**, 81.
156. FELDHERR, C. M. (1970). Nuclear permeability during different physiological states. *J. Cell Biol.* **47**, 60a.
157. WATTS, J. W. and HARRIS, H. (1959). Turnover of nucleic acids in a non-multiplying animal cell. *Biochem. J.* **72**, 147.
158. HARRIS, H. (1959). Turnover of nuclear and cytoplasmic ribonucleic acid in two types of animal cell, with some further observations on the nucleolus. *Biochem. J.* **73**, 362.
159. BRUNS, G. P., FISCHER, S., and LOWY, B. A. (1965). A study of the synthesis and interrelationships of ribonucleic acids in duck erythrocytes. *Biochim. biophys. Acta* **95**, 280.
160. ATTARDI, G., PARNAS, H., HWANG, M., and ATTARDI, B. (1966). Giant-size rapidly labeled nuclear RNA and cytoplasmic messenger RNA in immature chick erythrocytes. *J. molec. Biol.* **20**, 145.
161. HARRIS, H. (1964). Breakdown of nuclear ribonucleic acid in the presence of actinomycin D. *Nature, Lond.* **202**, 1301.
162. PERRY, R. P. (1963). Selective effects of actinomycin D on the intracellular distribution of RNA synthesis in tissue culture cells. *Expl Cell Res.* **29**, 400.
163. RUBINSTEIN, L. and CLEVER, U. (1972). Chromosome activity and cell function in polytenic cells. V. Developmental changes in RNA synthesis and turnover. *Devl Biol.* **27**, 519.
164. LAZARUS, H. M. and SPORN, M. B. (1967). Purification and properties of a nuclear exoribonuclease from Ehrlich ascites tumour cells. *Proc. natn. Acad. Sci. U.S.A.* **57**, 1386.
165. MOLLOY, G. R., SPORN, M. B., KELLEY, D. E., and PERRY, R. P. (1972). Localization of polyadenylic sequences in messenger ribonucleic acid of mammalian cells. *Biochemistry, N.Y.* **11**, 3256.
166. HOGNESS, D. S., COHN, M., and MONOD, J. (1955). Studies on the induced synthesis of β-galactosidase: the kinetics and mechanism of sulphur incorporation. *Biochim. biophys. Acta* **16**, 99.
167. ROTMAN, B. and SPIEGELMAN, S. (1954). On the origin of the carbon in the induced synthesis of β-galactosidase in *Escherichia coli. J. Bact.* **68**, 419.
168. KOCH, A. L. and LEVY, H. R. (1955). Protein turnover in growing cultures of *Escherichia coli. J. biol. Chem.* **217**, 947.
169. HARRIS, H. and WATTS, J. W. (1958). Turnover of protein in a non-multiplying animal cell. *Nature, Lond.* **181**, 1582.
170. MANDELSTAM, J. (1958). Turnover of protein in growing and non-growing populations of *Escherichia coli. Biochem. J.* **69**, 110.
171. EAGLE, H., PIEZ, K. A., FLEISCHMAN, R., and OYAMA, V. I. (1959). Protein turnover in mammalian cell cultures. *J. biol. Chem.* **234**, 592.
172. MANDELSTAM, J. (1960). The intracellular turnover of protein and nucleic acids and its role in biochemical differentiation. *Bact. Rev.* **24**, 289.
173. RIGHETTI, P., LITTLE, E. P., and WOLF, G. (1971). Reutilization of amino acids in protein synthesis in HeLa cells. *J. biol. Chem.* **246**, 5724.
174. KLEVECZ, R. R. (1971). Rapid protein catabolism in mammalian cells is obscured by reutilization of amino acids. *Biochem. biophys. Res. Commun.* **43**, 76.
175. KEMP, J. D. and SUTTON, D. W. (1971). Protein metabolism in cultured plant tissues. Calculation of an absolute rate of protein synthesis, accumulation and degradation in tobacco callus *in vivo. Biochemistry, N.Y.* **10**, 81.
176. GLASS, R. D. and DOYLE, D. (1972). On the measurement of protein turnover in animal cells. *J. biol. Chem.* **247**, 5234.

177. DEHLINGER, P. J. and SCHIMKE, R. T. (1970). Effect of size on the relative rate of degradation of rat liver soluble proteins. *Biochem. biophys. Res. Commun.* **40**, 1473.
178. BOSMANN, H. B. (1972). Half lives of enzyme activities in an L5178Y mouse leukaemic cell. *J. Cell Sci.* **10**, 153.
179. SCHIMKE, R. T. (1964). The importance of both synthesis and degradation in the control of arginase levels in rat liver. *J. biol. Chem.* **239**, 3808.
180. SCHIMKE, R. T., SWEENEY, E. W., and BERLIN, C. M. (1964). An analysis of the kinetics of rat liver tryptophan pyrrolase induction: the significance of both enzyme synthesis and degradation. *Biochem. biophys. Res. Commun.* **15**, 214.
181. AURICCHIO, F., MARTIN, D., and TOMKINS, G. (1969). Control of degradation and synthesis of induced tyrosine aminotransferase studied in hepatoma cells in culture. *Nature, Lond.* **224**, 806.
182. SILPANANTA, P. and GOODRIDGE, A. G. (1971). Synthesis and degradation of malic enzyme in chick liver. *J. biol. Chem.* **246**, 5754.
183. ZIELKE, H. R. and FILNER, P. (1971). Synthesis and turnover of nitrate reductase induced by nitrate in cultured tobacco cells. *J. biol. Chem.* **246**, 1772.
184. STEVENS, R. H. and WILLIAMSON, A. R. (1973). Translational control of immunoglobulin synthesis. I. Repression of heavy chain synthesis. *J. molec. Biol.* **78**, 505.
185. STEVENS, R. H. and WILLIAMSON, A. R. (1973). Translational control of immunoglobulin synthesis. II. Cell-free interaction of myeloma immunoglobulin with messenger RNA. *J. molec. Biol.* **78**, 517.

† It has recently been shown that immunoglobulin heavy chains bind to a specific region of their messenger RNA and inhibit its translation in a cell-free system.[184, 185] This effect appears to be similar to the 'autoregulation' of translation described in Ch. 2.

5
Cell fusion

1. The formation of interspecific hybrid cells

THE work that I propose to review in this chapter bears on three of the central problems with which I have been concerned: (1) the nature and specificity of the cytoplasmic signals that regulate RNA synthesis in somatic cell nuclei; (2) the mechanism by which suppression of nuclear RNA synthesis is achieved; (3) the mechanism by which genetic information is transferred from the nucleus to the cytoplasm. This work began in 1965 with an experiment that I made in collaboration with J. F. Watkins.[1] We showed that an animal virus, killed by irradiation with ultraviolet light, could be used to fuse together cells derived from mouse and man to produce artificial man–mouse hybrid cells. The idea of using viruses in this way has its origins in observations that go back for more than a century.[2] Many diseases have long been known to be associated with lesions in which multinucleate cells are found. In the medical literature of the nineteenth century there is a protracted and vigorous controversy about the mode of formation of these cells. Multinucleate cells are commonly found in the lesions produced by certain pathogenic viruses and, during the last decade, it has become clear that in at least some cases the virus produces the multinucleate cell by fusing single cells together. It was thus a very small step to attempt to see whether a virus could be used to fuse together cells of different kinds, and whether the resulting hybrid cells, if they were formed, would survive. And since the survival of the hybrid cells might be jeopardized by infection with a living virus, the virus was killed before the cells were treated with it. In the event, it turned out that viruses, inactivated by ultraviolet light, could be used to provide a general method for fusing together both differentiated and undifferentiated cells from different species and even different orders of vertebrates.[3,4] The resulting interspecific hybrid cells survived for long periods and, in many cases, proved capable of indefinite multiplication.[5, 6] They thus offered interesting possibilities for the study of nucleo-cytoplasmic relationships and lent themselves to experiments of a kind that had not hitherto been feasible. Some of these experiments I now propose to discuss.

The virus used in this work was the 'Sendai' virus, a member of the para-influenza group of myxoviruses. Sendai virus was chosen because it had been shown by Okada[7] that animal tumour cells in suspension could be rapidly fused together by high concentrations of this virus. The virus was irradiated with doses of ultraviolet light that reduced its infectivity by at least 10^6; but the dead virus retained its ability to fuse cells together. The two cell types studied in the first instance were the HeLa cell (a cell of human origin that has been grown for many years in artificial culture) and the Ehrlich ascites cell (a tumour that grows as a cell suspension in the peritoneal cavity of the mouse). These two cell types were chosen for a number of technical reasons, but mainly because their nuclei were easily distinguishable on morphological grounds. When a suspension containing a mixture of the two cell types is treated with the dead virus under appropriate conditions the cells clump together, and electron micrographs of these clumps show the virus particles trapped among the interdigitations of the microvilli on the surfaces of the cells.[8] When the virus-treated cells are incubated at 37°C the cell surfaces at points of contact between the cells fuse together so that small cytoplasmic bridges are formed. These bridges increase in number and in extent until eventually the cytoplasms of neighbouring cells coalesce, so that multinucleate cells containing varying numbers of nuclei are formed (Plate 6*a*).

When these multinucleate cells are introduced into a culture chamber they adhere to the floor of the chamber, or to coverslips introduced into it, and within 3 or 4 h spread out over the surface of the glass. Stained preparations then reveal that many of the cells contain two sorts of nuclei, one having the characteristics of HeLa nuclei, the other those of Ehrlich nuclei. In order to confirm that these multinucleate cells were indeed heterokaryons (that is to say, that they contained nuclei of different kinds), a population of HeLa cells was grown in the presence of tritiated thymidine until virtually all the cell nuclei were labelled; and a suspension containing these labelled HeLa cells and unlabelled Ehrlich cells was treated with the virus. The resulting multinucleate cells were then allowed to spread out over glass coverslips and autoradiographs were made of fixed and suitably extracted preparations. These autoradiographs showed that the multinucleate cells contained both labelled and unlabelled nuclei; the labelled nuclei clearly resembled HeLa nuclei and the unlabelled nuclei clearly resembled Ehrlich nuclei (Plate 6*b*). There was thus no doubt that hybrid cells containing both human and murine nuclei had been formed under the influence of the virus.

2. Synthesis of macromolecules in fused cells

It was then of interest to see what these fused cells were capable of doing. Would they synthesize protein, RNA, and DNA, and would they undergo mitosis? Exposure of the fused cells to tritiated leucine reveals that they do synthesize protein, and the labelling seen in autoradiographs of such cells is not obviously different in distribution or intensity from that seen in neighbouring mononucleate cells. When the fused cells are exposed for a few minutes to a tritiated precursor of RNA, autoradiographs show that in heterokaryons both sets of nuclei are labelled. It is therefore clear that in these heterokaryons the genes of both mouse and man are transcribed. More prolonged incubation with radioactive RNA precursors results in labelling of the cytoplasmic RNA. The pattern of RNA synthesis in the heterokaryons is thus no different from that seen in normal animal cells except that both the human and the murine nuclei contribute to the process. Labelling with tritiated thymidine shows that both sets of nuclei also synthesize DNA. Initially, synthesis of DNA does not occur synchronously in all the nuclei of a multinucleate cell, but an increasing measure of synchrony is progressively imposed. Synchronization of DNA synthesis is readily achieved in multinucleate cells containing nuclei of the same type and also in some heterokaryons containing nuclei of different types; but, in certain cases, fusion of cells of widely different origin may be associated with persistent asynchrony of DNA synthesis in the heterokaryon. Synchronization of DNA synthesis is usually more complete in cells containing only two nuclei than in those containing higher numbers.[9–11]

3. Formation and behaviour of mononucleate hybrid cells

Although multinucleate cells produced by cell fusion may, under favourable conditions, remain alive for several weeks, their continued reproduction is conditional upon the formation of daughter cells that contain a single nucleus. This process may be achieved in a variety of ways, but all of them are mediated by the fusion of the individual nuclei in the multinucleate cell into larger units. This fusion takes place at mitosis. In binucleate cells, synchronous mitosis of the two nuclei is commonly associated with the formation of a single spindle. All the chromosomes become aligned along a single metaphase plate, and division of the cell produces two mononucleate daughters that contain within one nucleus the chromosomes of both parent cells (Plate 7). Other forms of mitosis are also seen, especially tripolar and tetrapolar mitosis, which give rise to variable numbers of daughter cells, some of which may be binucleate. In other cases, the nuclei in the heterokaryon may enter mitosis, but cell division may not occur. Post-mitotic reconstitution may then gather all the chromosomes of the cell into a single very large nucleus, or two nuclei may be formed, each containing both the parental sets of chromosomes. Where heterokaryons contain more than two nuclei, irregular and abortive mitosis becomes increasingly common, but daughter cells containing more than two parental chromosome sets are sometimes produced. There are thus several ways in which a heterokaryon can generate daughter cells in which a single nucleus contains genetic components from both parents.

These hybrid mononucleate daughter cells also synthesize protein, RNA, and DNA and may in turn undergo mitosis. At metaphase they show, in varying proportions, the chromosomal complements of the two parent cells (Plate 8*a*). Many of these mononucleate daughter cells are capable of indefinite multiplication, and, over a wide range, species differences in the parent cells do not appear to affect the ability of the daughter cells to multiply. Mononucleate hybrid cells capable of indefinite multiplication have now been produced from crosses between cells of the most remotely distant vertebrate species.[6] These experiments show that cells from different species may be perfectly compatible with each other when they are amalgamated into a single unit. It thus appears that in the cells of vertebrates there are, in general, no *intracellular* mechanisms for the recognition of incompatibility similar to those responsible for the recognition and destruction of tissue or organ grafts exchanged between different individuals. Not only do the cytoplasms of these different cells fuse amicably together, but their nuclei also; and after nuclear fusion has taken place the composite cell carries out its functions in a completely integrated way.

4. Fusion of differentiated cells

Hybrid cells of the type I have been describing are formed by the fusion of two cells each of which is normally capable of RNA synthesis, DNA synthesis, and multiplication; but cells in which the synthesis of RNA or DNA or both is partially or wholly suppressed can also be fused together. Cells that show restrictions in their ability to synthesize one or other nucleic acid may be fused with each other or with cells that show no such restrictions. These specialized types of heterokaryon have been particularly useful in the analysis of the cytoplasmic stimuli that regulate RNA synthesis in animal cell nuclei and the mechanisms by which this regulation is brought about. Three highly differentiated animal cells were chosen for special study. These were the rabbit macrophage, the rat lymphocyte, and the hen erythrocyte. Macrophages are motile, phagocytic cells, whose main function is the removal of debris from the tissues of the body. These cells can be obtained in large numbers from the peritoneal cavity of the rabbit after certain experimental procedures. They commonly have an oval or kidney-shaped nucleus. The macrophages that one obtains from the peritoneal cavity of the rabbit all synthesize RNA, but they do not, either in the peritoneal cavity or *in vitro*, synthesize DNA or undergo mitosis.[12] The lymphocyte is a small cell with a dense compact nucleus and very little cytoplasm. In the rat, almost pure populations of lymphocytes can be obtained by cannulation of the thoracic duct. These small lymphocytes synthesize variable amounts of RNA: when exposed for an hour to high concentrations of a radioactive RNA precursor some of the cells synthesize so little RNA that the amount of radioactivity incorporated is barely detectable, while other cells incorporate easily measureable amounts of radioactivity under the same conditions.[13] Small lymphocytes do not normally synthesize DNA or undergo mitosis; but they can be induced to resume the synthesis of DNA and to undergo mitosis when they are exposed to certain antigenic stimuli.[14] The small lymphocyte then becomes transformed into a cell that plays a crucial role in the immune responses of the body. Whereas mammalian erythrocytes normally eliminate their nuclei during the process of maturation, the red blood cells of birds, amphibians, reptiles, and certain other orders of vertebrate retain their nuclei throughout the life cycle of the cell. In the hen, these nucleated erythrocytes, when mature, synthesize very little, if any, RNA;[15] they do not synthesize DNA or undergo mitosis. They are thus 'end-cells':

after a variable period of circulation in the blood they are removed
and destroyed. It was of interest in the first instance to determine,
especially in the case of the nucleated erythrocyte, to what extent
these changes produced by differentiation were reversible. Could
the inert or partially inactive cell be induced to resume the synthesis
of RNA or DNA or both, if it was incorporated in a heterokaryon
together with a cell that synthesized both RNA and DNA in the
normal way?

By varying the ratio of the two cell types used and the concentration of inactivated virus, the average number of nuclei per heterokaryon and the proportion of each kind of nucleus can, over a
certain range, be controlled. Plate 8*b* shows a heterokaryon produced
by fusing one HeLa cell with nine rabbit macrophages; and Plate 9*a*
shows a heterokaryon produced by fusing three HeLa cells with two
rat lymphocytes. When HeLa-rabbit macrophage heterokaryons are
exposed for short periods to tritiated RNA precursors, suitably fixed
and extracted autoradiographs reveal that both sets of nuclei in the
heterokaryon synthesize RNA; and more prolonged exposure to
these precursors results, as usual, in labelling of cytoplasmic RNA.
It is thus clear that in these heterokaryons, as in the HeLa-Ehrlich
heterokaryons, both sets of nuclei contribute to the synthesis of the
cell's RNA. Since both the HeLa cell and the macrophage normally
synthesize RNA, this result is not unexpected. Of greater interest,
however, is the fact that when these heterokaryons are exposed to
tritiated thymidine, the macrophage nuclei as well as the HeLa
nuclei become labelled. Twenty-four hours after cell fusion, an hour's
exposure to tritiated thymidine may label as many as 80 per cent of
the macrophage nuclei in the heterokaryons. It is therefore clear
that the inability of the macrophage to synthesize DNA, and hence
replicate its genetic material, is reversible: DNA synthesis is resumed
in the macrophage nucleus when the macrophage is fused with a
HeLa cell.

An essentially similar result is obtained with HeLa-rat lymphocyte
heterokaryons. A 20-min exposure of these cells to tritiated uridine
labels virtually all the HeLa and all the lymphocyte nuclei in them.
Since about half of the small lymphocytes in the thoracic duct are not
labelled by even an hour's exposure to high concentrations of radioactive RNA precursors, it is probable that many of the lymphocyte
nuclei in the heterokaryons have been induced to resume, or at least
greatly increase, the synthesis of RNA. And when HeLa-lymphocyte

PLATE 9

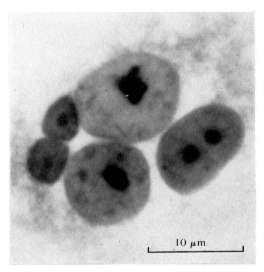

a. A heterokaryon containing three HeLa nuclei and two rat lymphocyte nuclei.

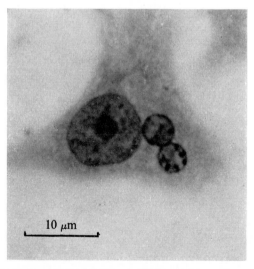

b. A heterokaryon containing one HeLa nucleus and two chick erythrocyte nuclei.

PLATE 10

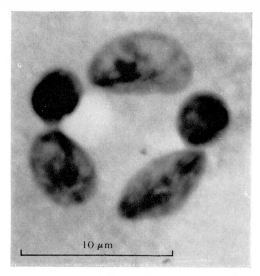

a. A heterokaryon containing three rabbit macrophrage nuclei and two rat lymphocyte nuclei, which are smaller and stain more deeply. Note the peripheral distribution of the nuclei in the cell.

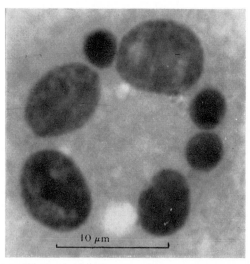

b. A heterokaryon containing four rabbit macrophage nuclei and three hen erythrocyte nuclei. Note the peripheral distribution of the nuclei in the cell.

PLATE 11

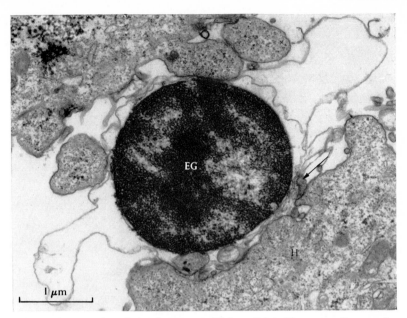

a. An erythrocyte ghost (EG) adherent to a HeLa cell (H). The arrow shows a virus particle wedged between the two cell membranes.

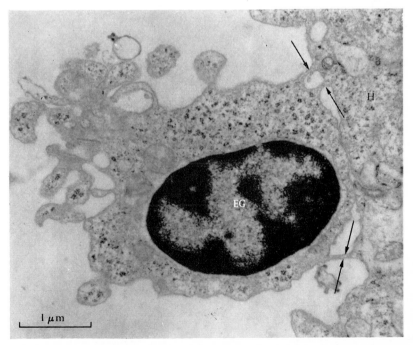

b. Tenuous cytoplasmic bridges, shown by arrows, formed between an erythrocyte ghost (EG) and a HeLa cell (H). The cytoplasm of the HeLa cell, which can be distinguished by its characteristic array of ribosomes, has flowed into the erythrocyte ghost.

PLATE 12

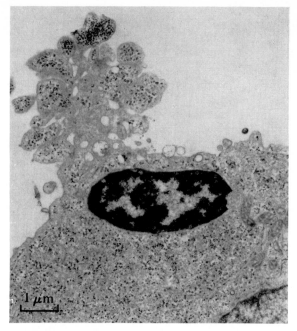

a. An erythrocyte nucleus passing into the cytoplasm of a HeLa cell.

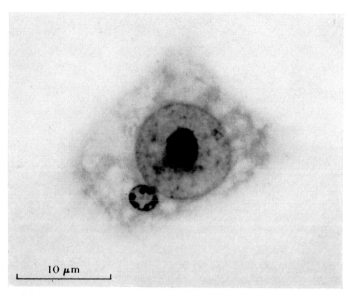

b. A heterokaryon containing one HeLa nucleus and one hen erythrocyte nucleus. The erythrocyte nucleus is highly contracted and its chromatin is condensed. 'Nuclear bodies', which are areas of extreme condensation in the chromatin, are seen.

heterokaryons are exposed to tritiated thymidine, not only the HeLa nuclei but also the lymphocyte nuclei are found to be synthesizing DNA. The results obtained with HeLa-hen erythrocyte heterokaryons (Plate 9*b*) are even more striking. Mature hen erythrocytes incorporate radioactive precursors into RNA only in trace amounts; to reveal this incorporation prolonged exposure of autoradiographs is required. There is no evidence that they incorporate radioactive precursors into DNA at all under normal conditions. However, when HeLa-hen erythrocyte heterokaryons are exposed to tritiated uridine for as little as 15–20 min, not only the HeLa nuclei, but also the majority of the erythrocyte nuclei are found to be synthesizing easily measurable amounts of RNA. It can therefore be concluded that in these heterokaryons the erythrocyte nuclei, which are normally virtually inert, have been induced to resume genetic activity. Labelling with tritiated thymidine reveals that many of the hen erythrocyte nuclei in the heterokaryons have also been induced to resume the synthesis of DNA.[10] Since, among nucleated cells, bird erythrocytes represent perhaps the most extreme form of differentiation seen in vertebrates, one is probably justified in concluding that, so long as the cell retains its nucleus, all restrictions on nucleic acid synthesis imposed by the process of differentiation are reversible.

It might, however, be supposed that these dormant or partially inactive .nuclei resume the synthesis of RNA and DNA in the heterokaryon not because they now find themselves in the cytoplasm of a cell that instructs its nuclei to synthesize RNA and DNA, but because they find themselves in *foreign* cytoplasm: the resumption of activity might be regarded as a non-specific reaction to 'foreignness'. This idea can be tested in a number of ways, one of which is to study the behaviour of heterokaryons made by fusing these differentiated cells with each other. Thus, for example, heterokaryons may be formed by fusing together rabbit macrophages and rat lymphocytes or rabbit macrophages and hen erythrocytes. The nuclei are then in foreign or partially foreign cytoplasm; but the heterokaryons differ from those made with HeLa cells in that neither of the parent cells normally synthesizes DNA. Such heterokaryons might therefore be expected to reveal whether the resumption of DNA synthesis in the dormant nucleus is determined simply by foreignness of the cytoplasm in the heterokaryon, or whether other factors are involved.

Plate 10*a* shows a heterokaryon containing three rabbit macrophage nuclei and two rat lymphocyte nuclei; and Plate 10*b* shows a heterokaryon containing four rabbit macrophage nuclei and three hen erythrocyte nuclei. It will be seen that the nuclei in these cases are distributed as a rosette at the periphery of the cells. This peripheral distribution of nuclei in certain types of multinucleate cell was first discussed by Langhans,[16] and when such cells are found in pathological conditions they are commonly referred to as 'Langhans' giant cells. This peculiar morphology appears to be characteristic of multinucleate cells in which the macrophage is the dominant cell type. When macrophage-lymphocyte heterokaryons are exposed to tritiated uridine, both sets of nuclei are found to be synthesizing RNA, thus showing that in these cells both sets of genes are again active. Both sets of nuclei in macrophage-erythrocyte heterokaryons also synthesize RNA, which indicates that rabbit macrophage cytoplasm, as well as HeLa cytoplasm, will induce the dormant hen erythrocyte nuclei to resume genetic activity. But none of these heterokaryons synthesizes DNA or undergoes mitosis: they may be exposed to tritiated thymidine at any time after cell fusion, but none of their nuclei becomes labelled. On the other hand, if chick embryo fibroblasts are fused with erythrocytes from the same embryo, the erythrocyte nuclei in the heterokaryons resume the synthesis of DNA even though they are not now in foreign cytoplasm. It is therefore clear that these dormant nuclei resume the synthesis of DNA in heterokaryons not because they are introduced into foreign cytoplasm, but because they are introduced into cytoplasm that instructs its nuclei to synthesize DNA; and when an erythrocyte nucleus is introduced into the cytoplasm of a macrophage, which normally synthesize RNA but not DNA, then the erythrocyte nucleus is induced to synthesize RNA but not DNA.

The results of these experiments with differentiated cells are summarized in Table 1, from which it will be seen that certain general principles emerge. (1) If either of the parent cells normally synthesizes RNA, then RNA synthesis will take place in both types of nuclei in the heterokaryon. (2) If either of the parent cells normally synthesizes DNA, then DNA synthesis will take place in both types of nuclei in the heterokaryon. (3) If neither of the parent cells normally synthesizes DNA, then no synthesis of DNA takes place in the heterokaryon. The regulation of nucleic acid synthesis in the heterokaryon is thus essentially unilateral: whenever a cell that synthesizes a particular nucleic acid is fused with one that does not the active cell initiates this synthesis in the inactive partner. In no case

TABLE 1

Synthesis of RNA and DNA in heterokaryons

	RNA	DNA
Cell type		
HeLa	+	+
rabbit macrophage	+	0
rat lymphocyte	+	0
hen erythrocyte	0	0
Cell combination in heterokaryon		
HeLa-HeLa	+ +	+ +
HeLa-rabbit macrophage	+ +	+ +
HeLa-rat lymphocyte	+ +	+ +
HeLa-hen erythrocyte	+ +	+ +
rabbit macrophage-rabbit macrophage	+ +	00
rabbit macrophage-rat lymphocyte	+ +	00
rabbit macrophage-hen erythrocyte	+ +	00

0, No synthesis in any nuclei; 00, no synthesis in any nuclei of either type; +, synthesis in some or all nuclei; + +, synthesis in some or all nuclei of both types.

does the inactive cell suppress synthesis in the active partner, even in those heterokaryons, like the HeLa-macrophage heterokaryon shown in Plate 8*b*, in which a number of inactive cells are fused with one active cell. In the terminology currently used to describe similar effects in bacteria, the synthesis of RNA and DNA in this situation may be said to be under 'positive control'.

5. The nature of the cytoplasmic signals

In considering the nature of the cytoplasmic signals that 'turn on' nucleic acid synthesis in these inactive or partially inactive nuclei, the heterokaryons containing hen erythrocyte nuclei are of special importance. All the other heterokaryons that I have described are produced by the simple fusion of the two parent cells and thus contain the nuclei and the cytoplasms of both parents. This is not, in general, the case for heterokaryons in which one of the parents is a nucleated erythrocyte. Sendai virus is a haemolytic virus, and at the high concentrations used to promote cell fusion it induces haemolysis of the red cells, so that their cytoplasmic contents are lost. The haemolysed red cells, which consist of little more than a cell nucleus and a leaky cell membrane, are referred to as erythrocyte ghosts. When mixed suspensions of hen erythrocytes and human or mouse tissue culture cells are treated with the virus, electron micrographs show the erythrocyte ghosts and the other cells stuck together in mixed clumps; and virus particles may be seen between the adjacent cell surfaces (Plate 11*a*). Under the influence of the virus, bridges are formed in the usual way between the membrane of the tissue culture cell and that of the erythrocyte ghost, and through these bridges the cytoplasm of the human or mouse cell flows to fill the space vacated by the cytoplasmic contents of the red cell itself (Plate 11*b*). Progressive dissolution of the contiguous regions of the apposed cell membranes eventually permits the red cell nucleus to be incorporated completely into the cytoplasm of the other cell (Plate 12*a*, *b*). In this case, therefore, the heterokaryon is formed essentially by transplantation of the erythrocyte nucleus, divested of its own cytoplasm, into the cytoplasm of the human or mouse cell.

The very fact that interspecific hybrid cells may function in a perfectly integrated way at once tells us something of importance about the mechanisms that regulate gene activity. We can be confident that the signals that the hybrid cytoplasm transmits to the genes of one of the species in the hybrid cell do not represent false signals to the genes of the other species. If such false signals were given, the end result would be a progressive disorganization of cell metabolism. But we know that some interspecific hybrid cells actually multiply more vigorously than either of their parent cells; so we can dismiss the idea that the signals emanating from the hybrid cytoplasm are misunderstood by either set of genes. And this must mean either that each set of genes reacts only to signals from its own cytoplasmic components, or that the signals that the hybrid cytoplasm transmits to the genes produce the same effect on both sets of genes. The demonstration that erythrocyte nuclei can be introduced into other cells without any appreciable contribution of erythrocyte cytoplasm permits us to decide which of these two alternatives is correct. The experiments I have already described make it clear that reactivation of the hen erythrocyte nucleus does not require the activity of hen cytoplasm. Erythrocyte nuclei, freed of their own cytoplasm by the haemolytic action of the Sendai virus, can be reactivated in the cytoplasm of cells from a wide variety of animal species, ranging from mouse to man; and frog erythrocyte nuclei can also be reactivated in these cells.[2] It is thus obvious that these nuclei *do* respond to signals emanating from grossly foreign cytoplasm. The remarkable integration of interspecific hybrid cells cannot therefore be due to the fact that each set of genes responds only to signals from its own cytoplasmic components. The reactivation of hen erythrocyte nuclei in human or mouse cytoplasm involves not only the resumption of nucleic acid synthesis, but also, as I shall show later, the ordered synthesis of specific proteins determined by these nuclei. We can therefore conclude that the signals emanating from human or mouse cytoplasms are understood perfectly well by hen nuclei. In short, these cytoplasmic signals are not species-specific.

The outstanding morphological event associated with the reactivation of the erythrocyte nucleus is a massive increase in volume.[17] While accurate measurements of nuclear volume are difficult, it is likely that there is at least a twenty- to thirtyfold increase.[18] This expansion of the nucleus is accompanied by dispersion of its highly condensed chromatin (Plates 12*b* and 13*a*). If these heterokaryons are exposed for a few minutes to a radioactive RNA precursor, it can be shown by autoradiographic methods that the amount of RNA synthesized per unit time in the reactivated erythrocyte nucleus is directly related to the degree of enlargement it has undergone (Plate 13*b*). As shown in Fig. 8, the amount of RNA synthesized by the erythrocyte nucleus is a simple function of its volume; and those erythrocyte nuclei that have not undergone enlargement do not synthesize RNA. The increase in volume of the nucleus is not simply due to the ingress of water; there is at least a fourfold to sixfold increase in dry mass, which is largely accounted for by an increase in protein content.[18] If the erythrocytes are irradiated with a large dose of ultraviolet light before the heterokaryons are made, synthesis of RNA and DNA in the erythrocyte nuclei is largely suppressed; but the irradiated nuclei none the less undergo enlargement in the usual way.[17] This means that the increase in volume that the erythrocyte nuclei undergo on reactivation is not the consequence of the increased synthesis and accumulation of RNA and DNA; enlargement of the nucleus and the concomitant dispersion of its condensed chromatin are the cardinal events and the progressive increase in the synthesis of nucleic acid is secondary. When they enlarge in the heterokaryon, erythrocyte nuclei in which RNA synthesis has been suppressed by ultraviolet irradiation show much the same increase in dry mass as unirradiated nuclei.[19] The irradiated nuclei cannot be synthesizing their own proteins under these conditions, so that the increase in dry mass that the erythrocyte nuclei undergo on reactivation must be due very largely to a flow of proteins from the cytoplasm into these nuclei. These proteins are, of course, human or mouse proteins, as the case may be, but they are none the less able to do whatever they need to do in the chick nucleus. Indeed, it has been shown by immunological techniques that chick erythrocyte nuclei reactivated in human cells accumulate human nuclear and nucleolar antigens at the appropriate sites.[20, 21] Until the chick nucleus determines the synthesis of chick proteins in the heterokaryon, we must regard it as operating, and operating perfectly well, in an environment composed for the most part of foreign proteins.

The dispersion of the chromatin that takes place as the erythrocyte nuclei enlarge is associated with the characteristic structural changes

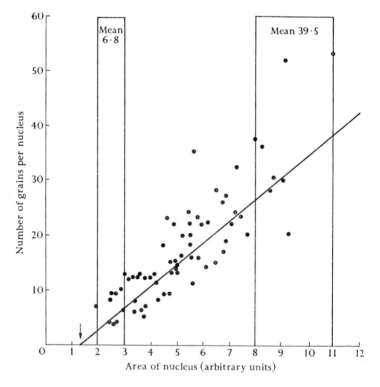

FIG. 8. The relationship between the maximum cross-sectional area of erythrocyte nuclei (a measure of their volume) in heterokaryons and the number of grains overlying these nuclei in autoradiographs. The cells were exposed for 20 min to [³H] uridine. The arrow indicates the mean cross-sectional area of unenlarged erythrocyte nuclei.

that I described in the previous chapter. The melting profile of the chromatin shows a progressive increase in its susceptibility to heat denaturation,[18] and its affinity for intercalating dyes and for actinomycin also increases. Even before replication of DNA begins, there is at least a fourfold rise in the amount of acridine orange that the chromatin can bind, and the amount of dye bound rises still further as nuclear enlargement proceeds.[18] These changes again reflect the increased accessibility of the coding elements of the DNA; and it is difficult to avoid the conclusion that as dispersion of the chromatin makes more of the DNA accessible, so more of it is transcribed. Some of the changes that the erythrocyte nuclei undergo when they are reactivated in heterokaryons can be mimicked in erythrocyte ghosts if these are treated under certain conditions with agents that chelate divalent cations.[18, 22] It therefore seems likely that in these erythrocyte nuclei, as in the nuclei of other eukaryotic cells, transcription of the DNA is determined, at least in part, by interactions between the chromatin and its electrolyte environment. If this is so, it is not surprising that chick erythrocyte nuclei can be reactivated in the cytoplasm of cells from widely different species; for, on this view, the signals that pass to the chick nuclei from the foreign cytoplasm would be of a quite general kind likely to be common to all vertebrate cells.

6. Transfer of information from nucleus to cytoplasm: evidence from the behaviour of reactivated erythrocyte nuclei

Heterokaryons in which one of the parent cells is a nucleated erythrocyte present an unparalleled opportunity to examine the whole process by which genetic information is expressed in mammalian cells. The erythrocyte nucleus is initially in a completely repressed state, and its reactivation takes place slowly enough to permit piecemeal dissection of the process. The reactivated nuclei can be re-isolated from the heterokaryon at any time, and the nature of the RNA that they are making can be examined. The passage of RNA from the reactivated nuclei to the cytoplasm of the cell can be monitored; and the relationship between the transcription of genes and the synthesis of proteins specified by these genes can be determined. In short, the whole process of information transfer can be analysed in these heterokaryons with a degree of precision that is hardly attainable in any other biological system. In this section, I shall present the results of such an analysis.

In studying the synthesis of any protein that might be determined by the chick erythrocyte nucleus reactivated in human or mouse cytoplasm, the first requirement is to show that the protein being examined is chick, and not human or mouse, protein. It was for this reason that the first proteins chosen for investigation in these heterokaryons were species-specific surface antigens.[23] These antigens can be detected on the surface of cells in culture with great sensitivity and complete specificity by the technique of immune haemadsorption,[24,25] an application of the mixed antiglobulin reaction.[26] Sensitized red cells serve as the marker, and specific antiserum binds these red cells to surfaces bearing the appropriate antigens, but not to others. There is no cross-reaction, at suitable dilutions of anti-serum, between chick surface antigens and human or mouse antigens, so that, in these heterokaryons, adsorbed red cells indicate the presence of chick-specific antigens.

Since the formation of these heterokaryons involves the fusion of the recipient cell with the erythrocyte ghost, membrane components derived from the erythrocyte are present in the surface of the heterokaryon immediately after fusion.[8] Immune haemoadsorption reveals the presence of the chick-specific antigens (Plate 14*a*). The behaviour of these antigens during the first few days after cell fusion presents an interesting paradox. Since the chick erythrocyte nuclei undergo reactivation during this period and synthesize large amounts of RNA, one might have expected that the amount of chick-specific antigen on the surface of the heterokaryon would increase. Instead, it was found that these antigens gradually disappeared from the cell surface and, by the fourth day after fusion, could not be detected at all in the great majority of the cells (Plate 14*b*). Analysis of this phenomenon revealed that the disappearance of the chick-specific antigens initially present on the surface of the heterokaryons was due to their progressive displacement by human or mouse antigens that continued to be produced by the human or mouse cells into which the erythrocyte nuclei had been introduced. During this period the erythrocyte nuclei, although they synthesized large amounts of RNA, did not determine the appearance of any new chick-specific antigens on the surface of the heterokaryon; nor did they influence the rate of disappearance of the chick-specific antigens introduced by the process of cell fusion.

In one important respect the reactivation of the erythrocyte nuclei during the first two or three days after cell fusion is incomplete. Although these nuclei undergo great enlargement and resume the synthesis of RNA and DNA, they do not develop normal nucleoli (Plate 13*a*, *b*). On the third, and occasionally on the second, day after cell fusion, some erythrocyte nuclei develop small structures which, under the light microscope, appear to be rudimentary nucleoli; but the prominent nucleoli characteristic of tissue cells in culture are not seen. Since the erythrocytes are taken from normal animals, there is no reason to suspect a genetic defect in this respect. One might therefore suppose either that the human or mouse cytoplasm is, in some unidentified way, an inadequate environment for the chick erythrocyte nucleus, or that these heterokaryons do not survive long enough as multinucleate cells to permit the nucleolus to develop fully in the erythrocyte nucleus. Within four days of cell fusion virtually all the heterokaryons enter mitosis which, in one way or another, results in the disappearance of the erythrocyte nuclei as separate bodies. In order to permit development of the erythrocyte nuclei within the heterokaryons for a longer period, the recipient cells were therefore subjected to an appropriate dose of gamma radiation. The irradiated cells continued to grow for up to 3 weeks without undergoing mitosis and thus permitted the further development of the erythrocyte nuclei as discrete entities. In these irradiated cells, nucleoli began to appear in the erythrocyte nuclei on the third day after cell fusion and became progressively larger. By the eleventh day, more than 80 per cent of the erythrocyte nuclei contained one or two readily identifiable nucleoli (Plate 15). Chick-specific antigens could be detected on the surface of virtually all these irradiated heterokaryons immediately after cell fusion and for about 24 hours thereafter. These antigens were then progressively eliminated in the usual way and, by the sixth day, no chick-specific antigen could be detected in any of the cultures. On the eighth day, however, traces of chick-specific antigen began to reappear in some of the cells: the antigen was first observed on the tips of elongated cytoplasmic processes. On succeeding days, increasing numbers of cells showed the presence of the antigen, which could now be detected all over the periphery of the cells. The amount of antigen per cell, as judged by the intensity of the haemadsorption reaction, continued to increase until, by the eleventh day, most of the heterokaryons showed strong haemadsorption over the whole of their periphery. The intensity of the haemadsorption greatly exceeded that seen in heterokaryons immediately after cell fusion. This sequence of events is illustrated in Plates 14*a*, *b* and 15 and plotted, as a function of time, in Fig. 9.

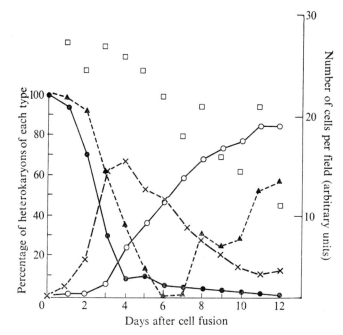

FIG. 9. Reappearance of chick-specific antigens on the surface of heterokaryons made by fusing irradiated mouse cells with erythrocytes from adult birds. The relationships between the enlargement of the erythrocyte nucleus, the development of nucleoli within it, and the disappearance and reappearance of the chick-specific surface antigens are shown. □, Total number of cells; ●, heterokaryons with unenlarged erythrocyte nuclei; ×, heterokaryons with enlarged erythrocyte nuclei, but no visible nucleoli; ○, heterokaryons with enlarged erythrocyte nuclei containing visible nucleoli; ▲, heterokaryons showing chick-specific surface antigens.

When the same experiment was done with erythrocytes from 12-day-old chick embryos, essentially similar results were obtained, except that the whole process took place more rapidly. Nucleoli began to appear in the erythrocyte nuclei on the second day after fusion, and the *de novo* appearance of chick-specific surface antigens took place before the antigens introduced during cell fusion were completely eliminated (Fig. 10). When erythrocytes from even younger chick embryos were used, the appearance of nucleoli and of new surface antigens occurred even sooner. In all cases, there was a clear correlation between the speed with which the nucleoli developed and the time at which the species-specific antigens re-appeared on the surface of the cells. These experiments thus indicated that chick

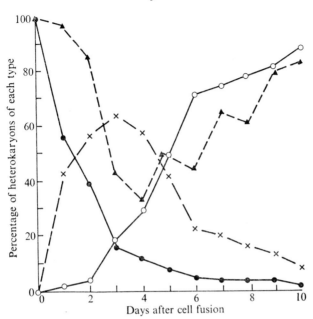

FIG. 10. Reappearance of chick-specific antigens on the surface of heterokaryons made by fusing irradiated mouse cells with chick embryo erythrocytes. The relationships between the enlargement of the erythrocyte nucleus, the development of nucleoli within it, and the disappearance and reappearance of the chick-specific surface antigens are shown. ●, Heterokaryons with unenlarged erythrocyte nuclei; ×, heterokaryons with enlarged erythrocyte nuclei, but no visible nucleoli; ○, heterokaryons with enlarged erythrocyte nuclei containing visible nucleoli; ▲, heterokaryons showing chick-specific surface antigens.

erythrocyte nuclei, operating in the cytoplasm of cells from widely different animal species, were capable of determining the appearance of chick-specific surface antigens in these cells; but the reactivated erythrocyte nuclei did not determine the appearance of these antigens until they developed nucleoli.

Since these species-specific antigens were only detected when they appeared at the surface of the cell, the possibility existed that there might be a lag between the time of their synthesis and the time of their detection by the haemadsorption technique. If this lag were considerable, the antigens might well have been synthesized before the appearance of nucleoli in the erythrocyte nuclei. In that case, the observed association between the appearance of the nucleoli and the appearance of the surface antigens might simply be fortuitous. It was therefore obviously necessary to examine the behaviour of other proteins that might be determined by the erythrocyte nucleus, and especially soluble proteins that did not form part of a larger structural organization. A soluble enzyme was the obvious choice, and the enzyme inosinic acid pyrophosphorylase, which catalyzes the condensation of hypoxanthine with phosphoribosyl pyrophosphate, was chosen for study.[27] The enzyme is essential for the incorporation of hypoxanthine into nucleic acid and may thus be assayed either directly in a cell homogenate or indirectly in the intact cell by measuring the incorporation of labelled hypoxanthine. This enzyme was chosen because a line of mouse cells was available that lacked inosinic acid pyrophosphorylase activity (A_9 cells).[28]

When A_9 cells were exposed to tritiated hypoxanthine and then subjected to appropriate autoradiography, only a trivial amount of radioactivity was found to be incorporated into nucleic acid. When erythrocyte nuclei were introduced into irradiated A_9 cells, the heterokaryons also initially showed very little incorporation of hypoxanthine. The enlargement and reactivation of the erythrocyte nuclei produced no change in this respect, until nucleoli made their appearance in the erythrocyte nuclei. When this occurred, the ability of the heterokaryons to incorporate hypoxanthine showed a sharp increase, and autoradiographs began to show RNA labelling in many of the cells. This sequence of events is illustrated in Plate 16*a*, *b*. On further cultivation, the ability of the heterokaryons to incorporate hypoxanthine and the number of erythrocyte nuclei showing nucleoli continued to rise *pari passu* (Fig. 11). At all times, those heterokaryons in which the erythrocyte nuclei had not yet developed nucleoli showed no significant increase in hypoxanthine incorporation (Fig. 12). Direct assay of the enzyme in cell homogenates confirmed the findings obtained in intact cells by autoradiographic procedures. Very little inosinic acid pyrophosphorylase activity was initially detected in the heterokaryons, but when nucleoli began to appear in the erythrocyte nuclei, the enzyme activity rose sharply and continued to rise as the development of nucleoli proceeded (Fig. 13). Electrophoretic examination of the enzyme formed in the heterokaryons confirmed that it was chick, and not mouse, inosinic acid pyrophosphorylase.[29]

Other enzyme markers behaved in the same way. When the erythrocyte nuclei were introduced into mutant cells that were triply defective, lacking inosinic acid pyrophosphorylase, adenylic

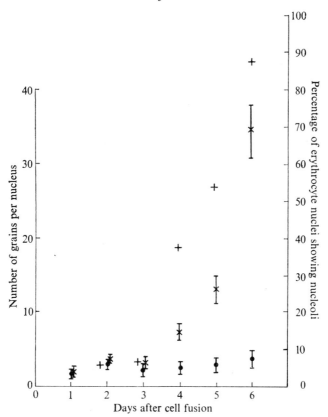

F<small>IG</small>. 11. The development of inosinic acid pyrophosphorylase activity in A$_9$-chick erythrocyte heterokaryons, as measured by their ability to incorporate tritiated hypoxanthine into nucleic acid. The incorporation of hypoxanthine in the heterokaryons is initially only marginally greater than that in A$_9$ cells alone; but when the erythrocyte nuclei develop nucleoli, this incorporation increases markedly. ●, A$_9$ cells; ×, heterokaryons; + erythrocyte nuclei showing nucleoli.

acid pyrophosphorylase and nucleoside permease, the missing enzymes again made their appearance within the one cell when nucleoli appeared in the erythrocyte nuclei.[30] Diphtheria toxin provided another species-specific marker. Mouse cells are at least a hundred thousand times more resistant to the toxin than chick cells, so that, at an appropriate concentration, susceptibility to the toxin may be used as a species-specific marker. Mouse cells into which chick erythrocyte nuclei were introduced remained insensitive to the destructive action of the toxin until nucleoli developed in the

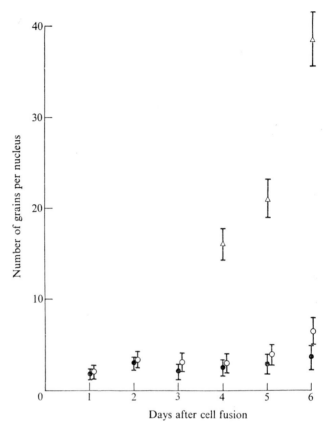

FIG. 12. A comparison between A₉-chick erythrocyte heterokaryons in which the erythrocyte nuclei have developed nucleoli and those in which they have not. The former show a marked increase in their ability to incorporate tritiated hypoxanthine; the latter are not much different from A₉ cells alone. ●, A₉ cells; △, erythrocyte nuclei showing nucleoli; ○, erythrocyte nuclei not showing nucleoli.

erythrocyte nuclei, but after this point, the heterokaryons became progressively more susceptible.[31] It was thus clear that a correlation existed between the time at which the reactivated erythrocyte nuclei developed nucleoli and the time at which chick-specific proteins began to be made in the hybrid cell.

It was clearly of overriding importance to determine what kind of RNA was made in the erythrocyte nuclei before and after they developed nucleoli. A technique was therefore devised to permit re-isolation of the nuclei from the heterokaryons and separation of

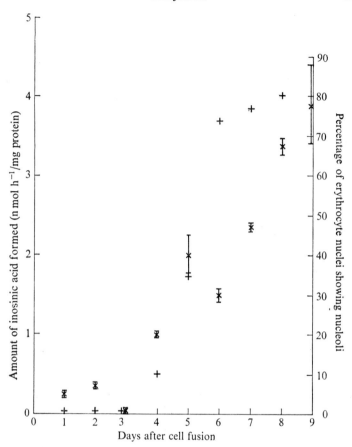

FIG. 13. The development of inosinic acid pyrophosphorylase activity in A₉-chick erythrocyte heterokaryons, as measured by direct assay of the cell homogenate. There is a marked increase in enzyme activity when the erythrocyte nuclei in the heterokaryons develop nucleoli. ×, inosinic acid pyrophosphorylase activity; +, erythrocyte nuclei showing nucleoli.

the reactivated erythrocyte nuclei from the human or mouse nuclei.[23,32] The heterokaryons were exposed to radioactive RNA precursors at various times after cell fusion, and the RNA synthesized in the two sorts of nuclei was examined by sucrose gradient centrifugation. It was found that while the human or mouse nuclei in the heterokaryon synthesized both rapidly labelled polydisperse RNA and the normal 28S and 16S RNA components, the erythrocyte nuclei, before the appearance of nucleoli, synthesized only poly-

Cell fusion

disperse RNA: normal 28S and 16S RNA began to be synthesized by these nuclei only when they developed nucleoli. Autoradiographic studies showed that the 'polydisperse' RNA made by the erythrocyte nuclei before development of nucleoli was synthesized, *grosso modo*, all over the nucleus and must therefore have contained the products of a very large number of genes. The RNA analysis thus posed a further paradox: polydisperse RNA of high molecular weight, representing the activity of a very large number of genes, was synthesized by the erythrocyte nuclei for several days without determining the synthesis of species-specific proteins; but when the erythrocyte nuclei developed nucleoli and began to make RNA of ribosomal type, proteins specified by these nuclei began to be synthesized.

There appeared to be three possible explanations for these observations. The first was that there might be species-specific restrictions on the translation of RNA, in particular that mouse or human ribosomes might not be able to translate the RNA made on chick genes. The whole corpus of experiments on interspecific hybrid cells argues against this idea. For example, man–mouse hybrid cells can be constructed in which the great majority of the human chromosomes are rapidly eliminated, and cell lines can be derived in which a single human chromosome is retained in an otherwise entirely mouse chromosome set.[33] Proteins specified by genes on this residual human chromosome are synthesized in the mouse cell, and genes on a number of different single human chromosomes have been shown to be expressed under these conditions.[34-36] But these man–mouse hybrid cells synthesize only mouse, not human 28S ribosomal RNA.[37,38] Chick–mouse hybrid cells can be made which contain only fragments of chick genetic material, too small to be detected in conventional chromosome preparations; but genes located in these fragments can determine the synthesis of chick-specific proteins in the cytoplasm of these otherwise completely mouse cells.[39, 40] Again, the chick–mouse hybrids synthesize only mouse, not chick, 28S ribosomal RNA. It therefore seems unlikely that mouse ribosomes are unable to translate chick messenger RNA, a conclusion that, in any case, finds strong support in experiments with cell-free and other systems which also show absence of species-specificity in the translation of RNA.[41-44]

A second possibility was that the association between the appearance of nucleoli in the reactivated erythrocyte nuclei and the onset

PLATE 13

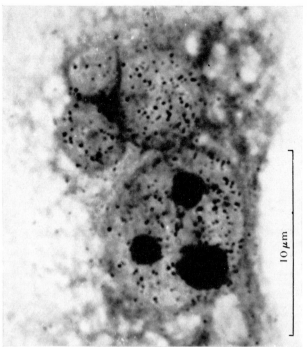

b

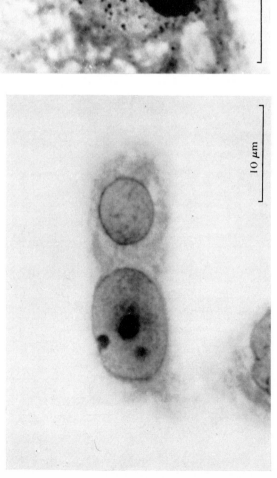

a

a. A heterokaryon containing one HeLa nucleus and one hen erythrocyte nucleus 24 hours after cell fusion. The erythrocyte nucleus has undergone enlargement, the chromatin has become more dispersed and the 'nuclear bodies' are no longer visible.

b. Autoradiograph of a heterokaryon exposed for 20 min to [³H] uridine. The cell contains one HeLa nucleus and three hen erythrocyte nuclei in various stages of englargement. All the nuclei are synthesizing RNA. Note that the labelling of the erythrocyte nuclei increases as they enlarge.

PLATE 14

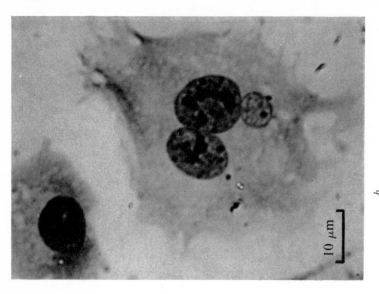

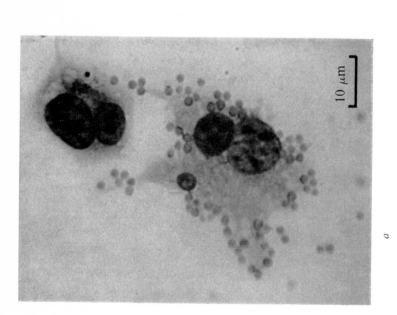

a. A heterokaryon containing two mouse nuclei and one hen erythrocyte nucleus, 18 h after cell fusion. The haemadsorption reaction reveals the presence of hen-specific antigens on the surface of the cell.

b. A heterokaryon containing two mouse nuclei and one hen erythrocyte nucleus, 5 days after cell fusion. The erythrocyte nucleus has been reactivated, but the absence of any haemadsorption shows that the hen-specific antigens are no longer present on the surface of the cell. The erythrocyte nucleus shows a small nucleolus.

PLATE 15

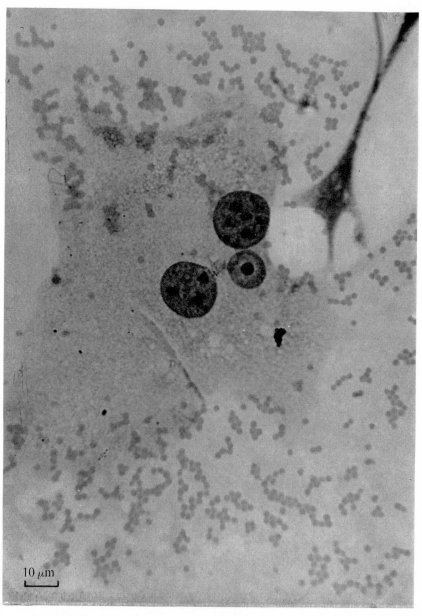

10 μm

A heterokaryon containing two irradiated mouse nuclei and one hen erythrocyte nucleus, 11 days after cell fusion. This is now a typical radiation giant cell. The reactivated erythrocyte nucleus has a prominent nucleolus, and hen-specific antigens have reappeared on the surface of the cell.

PLATE 16

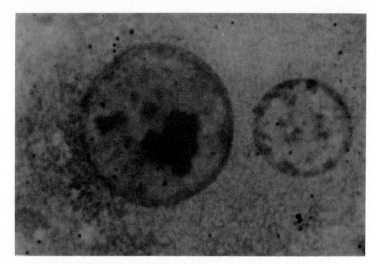

a. Autoradiograph of an A₉-chick erythrocyte heterokaryon in which the erythrocyte nucleus has been reactivated but has not yet developed a nucleolus. The cell has been exposed for 4 h to tritiated hypoxanthine, but there is still very little incorporation of label.

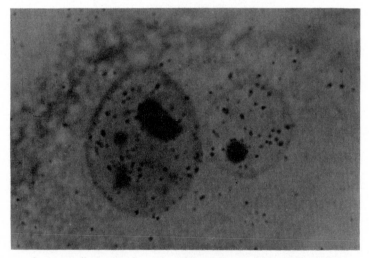

b. Autoradiograph of an A₉-chick erythrocyte heterokaryon in which the erythrocyte nucleus shows early development of the nucleolus. The cell has been exposed for 4 h to tritiated hypoxanthine. Both the A₉ and the erythrocyte nucleus are now clearly labelled. The cell has acquired the ability to incorporate hypoxanthine into nucleic acid.

of chick-specific protein synthesis was essentially fortuitous. It could be argued that these two processes happened to occur simultaneously, but that they were not functionally related. Experiments were therefore done to test this proposition.[45] If the association between the development of the nucleolus in the reactivated erythrocyte nucleus and the onset of synthesis of chick specific proteins was fortuitous, then one would expect that inactivation of the nucleolus *after* the synthesis of chick-specific proteins had been established would be without effect on this synthesis. Three chick-specific markers were examined to see whether their synthesis, once established in the heterokaryon, was affected by inactivation of the nucleolus in the chick erythrocyte nucleus. The nucleolus and other areas of the erythrocyte nucleus were inactivated by irradiation with a beam of ultraviolet light, the dose delivered being enough to produce a greater than 90 per cent suppression of nucleic acid synthesis at the irradiated site. Five groups of heterokaryons, each containing one reactivated chick erythrocyte nucleus and one mouse nucleus, were compared: unirradiated cells; cells in which an extranucleolar region of the erythrocyte nucleus was inactivated; cells in which one of two nucleoli in the erythrocyte nucleus was inactivated; cells in which a solitary nucleolus in the erythrocyte nucleus was inactivated; and cells in which the whole erythrocyte nucleus was inactivated. Fig. 14 shows the results obtained with heterokaryons in which the chick erythrocyte nuclei were reactivated in A_9 cells. In these heterokaryons, as previously described, the development of nucleoli in the reactivated erythrocyte nuclei coincides with the onset of synthesis of chick inosinic acid pyrophosphorylase. The level of enzyme activity rises until about the seventh day after cell fusion and thereafter remains steady. The various parts of the erythrocyte nuclei were irradiated with the microbeam after the maximal level of enzyme activity had been attained. The enzyme was assayed as before by measuring the incorporation of tritiated hypoxanthine into RNA. It will be seen that cells in which an extranucleolar region of the erythrocyte nucleus and those in which one of two nucleoli in the erythrocyte nucleus had been irradiated were indistinguishable from unirradiated cells in their subsequent ability to incorporate tritiated hypoxanthine into RNA. But cells in which a solitary nucleolus in the erythrocyte nucleus had been irradiated progressively lost the ability to incorporate hypoxanthine; by the fourth or fifth day after irradiation they showed levels of inosinic acid pyrophosphorylase compar-

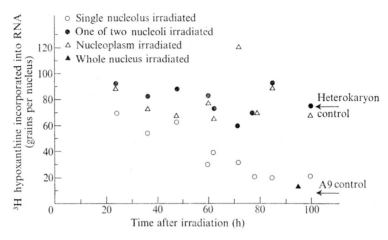

FIG. 14. Decay of inosinic acid pyrophosphorylase activity in A₉-chick erythro-cyte heterokaryons after selective irradiation of parts of the erythrocyte nucleus with an ultraviolet microbeam. ○, a solitary nucleolus in the erythrocyte nucleus irradiated; ●, one of two nucleoli in the erythrocyte nucleus irradiated; △, an extranucleolar area in the erythrocyte nucleus irradiated; ▲, the whole erythro-cyte nucleus irradiated. Cells were irradiated with the microbeam at zero time. The controls are unirradiated heterokaryons and A₉ cells. Chick inosinic acid pyrophosphorylase activity decays when a solitary nucleolus in the erythrocyte nucleus is inactivated. (From Deák *et al.*[45])

able to those found in A₉ cells or in heterokaryons in which the whole of the erythrocyte nucleus had been irradiated. This experiment demonstrates that even after the heterokaryon has developed the ability to synthesize chick inosinic acid pyrophosphorylase, inactiva-tion of the erythrocyte nucleolus (where the erythrocyte nucleus contains only one such structure) results in decay of the synthetic system. That this system does not decay when an extranucleolar region of the erythrocyte nucleus is irradiated, or when only one of two nucleoli in the erythrocyte nucleus is irradiated, provides an adequate control for the specificity of the irradiation. Essentially similar results were obtained for chick-specific surface antigens and for sensitivity to diphtheria toxin. Inactivation of a solitary nucleolus in the erythrocyte nucleus, but not one of two nucleoli or an extra-nucleolar area, resulted in the disappearance of these chick-specific markers also.

It might still be argued that the genes for all these markers were by chance situated at the nucleolar site and were therefore inactivated directly by the microbeam. The fact that the synthesis of the chick-specific markers is unaffected when only one of two nucleoli in the erythrocyte nucleus is inactivated makes this highly improbable; for it would then be necessary to propose that for each marker a structural gene is present at both nucleolar sites and that the gene in the unirradiated nucleolar region compensates for the loss of its partner. It has, in any case, been shown that the genes determining the synthesis of species-specific surface antigens are widely distributed throughout the chromosome set.[33] It is clear that the association between the development of the nucleolus in the erythrocyte nucleus and the onset of synthesis of chick-specific markers is not fortuitous: some function located at, or close to, the nucleolus is required for the full expression of the structural genes.

The third possibility was the obvious one that the nucleolus, in addition to its involvement in the synthesis of ribosomal RNA, might in some way control the flow of other families of RNA, including messenger RNA, to the cytoplasm of the cell. This idea was also tested by experiments in which nuclei or nucleoli were inactivated by the ultraviolet microbeam.[46,47] If, before they developed nucleoli, the erythrocyte nuclei were unable to transfer the RNA that they synthesized to the cytoplasm of the cell, then 'anucleolate' erythrocyte nuclei in heterokaryons in which the human or mouse nuclei had been inactivated by the microbream would not be expected to contribute to cytoplasmic RNA labelling when the cells were exposed to a radioactive RNA precursor. Heterokaryons containing a single mouse nucleus and up to four reactivated erythrocyte nuclei were selected for study. The mouse nuclei were inactivated by the microbeam, and the level of cytoplasmic RNA labelling in the irradiated cells was measured after they had been exposed to a radioactive RNA precursor for periods up to 6 hours. In the same cultures normal mononucleate mouse cells in which the nucleus had also been inactivated by the microbeam served as controls, since, even in mononucleate cells, a low level of cytoplasmic RNA labelling persists after the nucleus has been irradiated. It was found that during the period in which the erythrocyte nuclei had not yet developed nucleoli, the level of cytoplasmic labelling in heterokaryons in which the mouse nucleus had been inactivated was indistinguishable from that in normal mononucleate mouse cells in which the nucleus had been inactivated (Fig. 15). This was the case even in cells that contained several reactivated erythrocyte nuclei which collectively synthesized very large amounts of RNA as judged by the

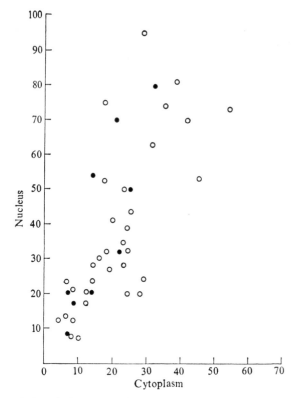

FIG. 15. Relationship between nuclear grain counts and cytoplasmic grain counts in heterokaryons and in single mouse cells. The heterokaryons contained one mouse nucleus and up to four chick erythrocyte nuclei that had been reactivated but had not yet developed nucleoli. The mouse nucleus was inactivated by ultraviolet light both in the heterokaryons and in the single mouse cells. The cells were exposed to a radioactive RNA precursor for 6 h. The ratio of nuclear to cytoplasmic RNA labelling in the heterokaryons in which the mouse nucleus had been inactivated was no different from that in the single mouse cells in which the nucleus had been inactivated. The reactivated erythrocyte nuclei, although they synthesize large amounts of RNA, do not make any detectable contribution to cytoplasmic RNA labelling at this stage. ○, heterokaryons; ●, single mouse cells.

intensity of nuclear labelling in autoradiographs. It thus appeared that, prior to the development of nucleoli, the reactivated erythrocyte nuclei, although they synthesized large amounts of RNA continuously for some days, did not transfer detectable amounts of this RNA to the cytoplasm of the cell. A similar experiment, done at a stage when the erythrocyte nuclei had developed nucleoli, showed, as expected,

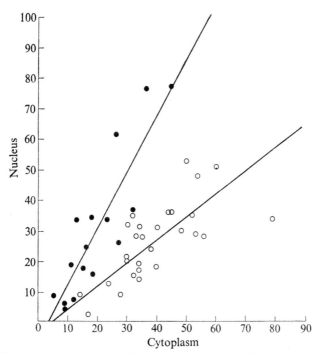

FIG. 16. A similar experiment to that shown in Fig. 15, but done at a stage when the erythrocyte nuclei had developed well defined nucleoli. The cytoplasmic labelling in the heterokaryons is now decisively greater than in the single mouse cells. The erythrocyte nuclei are making a substantial contribution to cytoplasmic RNA labelling. ○, heterokaryons; ●, single mouse cells.

a much higher level of cytoplasmic labelling than that found in the irradiated mononucleate cells (Fig. 16). Plates 17*a*, *b* show the levels of cytoplasmic RNA labelling in an unirradiated heterokaryon and in a heterokaryon in which the mouse nucleus was inactivated before the erythrocyte nuclei had developed nucleoli. It will be seen that the erythrocyte nuclei continue to synthesize RNA but make no contribution to cytoplasmic RNA labelling. There is thus a strong resemblance between the reactivated erythrocyte nuclei before they develop nucleoli and the nuclei of specialized cells in which there is little or no *net* RNA synthesis.[48-50] In both cases synthesis of nuclear RNA continues, but almost all of this RNA undergoes intranuclear degradation.

The question, of course, at once arises whether the flow of RNA from nucleus to cytoplasm would be stopped by inactivation of the nucleolus in cells in which net synthesis of RNA was taking place in the normal way. The nucleoli and non-nucleolar regions in the nuclei of epithelial cells growing *in vitro* were therefore given increasing doses of irradiation by means of the ultraviolet microbeam, and the effect on cytoplasmic RNA labelling was examined. Three groups of cells were compared: those in which a solitary nucleolus was inactivated; those in which one of two nucleoli in the one nucleus was inactivated and those in which an extranucleolar region, chosen at random, was inactivated. The results are shown in Fig. 17. It will be seen that progressive inactivation of an extranucleolar region produces progressive reduction in cytoplasmic RNA labelling, but the effect is small: a maximum reduction of about 20 per cent is reached after 6 seconds of irradiation. When one of two nucleoli in the one nucleus is irradiated a large reduction in cytoplasmic RNA labelling is observed, but this does not exceed 50 per cent, and again a maximum effect is produced after 6 seconds of irradiation. But when the nucleus contains only one nucleolus, inactivation of this structure results in a greater than 90 per cent reduction in cytoplasmic RNA labelling, and, in this case, the level of labelling does not reach a plateau after 6 seconds of irradiation but continues to fall still further as the duration of radiation is prolonged. The conditions of labelling in these experiments were such that about half of the radioactivity in the cytoplasmic RNA was in non-ribosomal components, including transfer RNA. It can therefore be concluded that inactivation of the nucleolus, where the nucleus contains only one such structure, not only inhibits the flow of ribosomal RNA to the cytoplasm, but also profoundly depresses the flow of non-ribosomal RNA. The nuclei in which nucleolar activity has been completely inactivated thus resemble reactivated erythrocyte nuclei at the stage before the development of nucleoli: in both cases the flow of RNA from nucleus to cytoplasm is reduced to very low levels. These measurements of radioactive RNA flow do not, of course, delineate the contribution made by messenger RNA to the total cytoplasmic RNA labelling; but the fact that inactivation of a solitary nucleolus in a cell nucleus also results in decay of the synthesis of proteins specified by that nucleus makes it very difficult to avoid the conclusion that messenger RNA is among the non-ribosomal RNA components whose flow to the cytoplasm is inhibited by nucleolar inactivation.

It thus appears that the nucleolus is indeed the seat of some

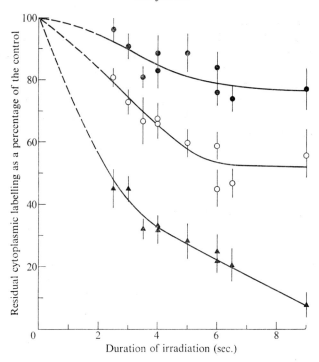

Fig. 17. Effect of irradiation of the nucleolus on cytoplasmic RNA labelling. Different parts of the cell nucleus were given increasing doses of irradiation with the ultraviolet microbeam. ●, cells in which an extranucleolar region was irradiated; ○, cells in which one nucleolus of two in the same nucleus was irradiated; ▲, cells in which a solitary nucleolus was irradiated. Inactivation of a solitary nucleolus reduces total cytoplasmic RNA labelling to very low levels. In these experiments about half of the radioactivity in cytoplasmic RNA was in non-ribosomal components. Inactivation of the nucleolus thus inhibits the flow of non-ribosomal as well as ribosomal RNA to the cytoplasm. (From Deák.[47])

general mechanism that controls the flow from nucleus to cytoplasm, not only of the RNA made at the nucleolar site, but also of RNA made elsewhere in the nucleus. The problem that now remains is to determine how this control is achieved. The reciprocal relationship that appears to exist between the amount of RNA degraded within the nucleus and the amount transported to the cytoplasm does suggest that the control mechanism operates, at least in part, by shielding the newly formed messenger RNA from intranuclear degradation. As mentioned previously, this might be achieved by linking the messenger RNA to protein. Proteins accumulate in very high concentration in the nucleolus, although they do not appear to be synthesized there;[51,52] and one might speculate, for want of evidence, that the nucleolus may play some special role in bringing messenger RNA and the necessary proteins together. If, as has been proposed, the addition of polyadenylic acid sequences to messenger RNA is required to ensure its transport to the cell cytoplasm, the nucleolus might be involved in some way in this process, although, again, there is as yet no evidence for this notion either. Finally, it is possible that nascent ribosomes or ribosomal subunits might ferry the newly formed messenger RNA to the cytoplasm of the cell. For this there is a little circumstantial evidence. In insect salivary gland cells it has been shown that ribosomal RNA, although apparently made at nucleolar sites, attaches to other regions of the chromosomes before passing to the cytoplasm.[53,54] It is difficult to see what ribosomal RNA might be doing on these chromosomes unless it was involved in some way in the expression of genes located there. It is tempting to suppose that as the ribosomal RNA becomes associated with ribosomal proteins, one or other of the ribosomal subunits, perhaps the smaller, picks up the newly formed messenger RNA and shields it from degradation. It has been shown in cell-free preparations that the attachment of ribosomes to artificial messenger RNA does shield it from degradation by exonucleases of the type thought to be responsible for intranuclear RNA degradation.[55, 56] This scheme, although tenuously based, is attractive for two reasons. First, it explains why absence or inactivation of the nucleolus results in the failure of structural genes to be expressed; and second, it explains the remarkable fact that, in situations that have been critically examined, stimuli that produce an increased flow of messenger RNA to the cell cytoplasm also produce an increased flow of ribosomal RNA.[57-60]

REFERENCES

1. HARRIS, H. and WATKINS, J. F. (1965). Hybrid cells from mouse and man: artificial heterokaryons of mammalian cells from different species. *Nature, Lond.* **205**, 640.
2. HARRIS, H. (1966). Hybrid cells from mouse and man: a study in genetic regulation. *Proc. R. Soc.* B **166**, 358.
3. HARRIS, H. (1965). Behaviour of differentiated nuclei in heterokaryons of animal cells from different species. *Nature, Lond.* **205**, 640.
4. HARRIS, H., WATKINS, J. F., FORD, C. E., and SCHOEFL, G. I. (1966). Artificial heterokaryons of animal cells from different species. *J. Cell Sci.* **1**, 1.

5. HARRIS, H., WATKINS, J. F., CAMPBELL, G. LE M., EVANS, E. P. and FORD, C. E. (1965). Mitosis in hybrid cells derived from mouse and man. *Nature, Lond.* **207,** 606.
6. HARRIS, H. (1970). *Cell fusion,* p. 19. Clarendon Press, Oxford.
7. OKADA, Y. (1958). The fusion of Ehrlich's tumor cells caused by H. V. J. virus *in vitro. Biken's J.* **1,** 103.
8. SCHNEEBERGER, E. E. and HARRIS, H. (1966). An ultrastructural study of interspecific cell fusion induced by inactivated Sendai virus. *J. Cell Sci.* **1,** 401.
9. JOHNSON, R. T. and HARRIS, H. (1969). DNA synthesis and mitosis in fused cells. I. HeLa homokaryons. *J. Cell Sci.* **5,** 603.
10. JOHNSON, R. T. and HARRIS, H. (1969). DNA synthesis and mitosis in fused cells. II. HeLa-chick erythrocyte heterkaryons. *J. Cell Sci.* **5,** 625.
11. JOHNSON, R. T. and HARRIS, H. (1969). DNA synthesis and mitosis in fused cells III. HeLa-Ehrlich heterokaryons. *J. Cell Sci.* **5,** 645.
12. WATTS, J. W. and HARRIS, H. (1959). Turnover of nucleic acids in a non-multiplying animal cell. *Biochem. J.* **72,** 147.
13. GOWANS, J. L. and KNIGHT, E. J. (1964). The route of re-circulation of lymphocytes in the rat. *Proc. R. Soc.* B **159,** 257.
14. GOWANS, J. L., McGREGOR, D. D., COWEN, D. M., and FORD, C. E. (1962). Initiation of immune responses by small lymphocytes. *Nature, Lond.* **196,** 651.
15. CAMERON, I. L. and PRESCOTT, D. M. (1963). RNA and protein metabolism in the maturation of the nucleated chicken erythrocyte. *Expl. Cell Res.* **30,** 609.
16. LANGHANS, T. (1968). Ueber Riesenzellen mit wandständigen Kernen in Tuberkeln und die fibröse Form des Tuberkels. *Virchows Arch. path. Anat. Physiol.* **42,** 382.
17. HARRIS, H. (1967). The reactivation of the red cell nucleus. *J. Cell Sci.* **2,** 23.
18. BOLUND, L., RINGERTZ, N. R., and HARRIS, H. (1969). Changes in the cytochemical properties of erythrocyte nuclei reactivated by cell fusion. *J. Cell Sci.* **4,** 71.
19. BOLUND, L., DARZYNKIEWICZ, Z., and RINGERTZ, N. R. (1969). Growth of hen erythrocyte nuclei undergoing reactivation in heterokaryons. *Expl. Cell Res.* **56,** 406.
20. RINGERTZ, N. R., CARLSSON, S.-A., EGE, T., and BOLUND, L. (1971). Detection of human and chick nuclear antigens in nuclei of chick erythrocytes during reactivation in heterokaryons with HeLa cells. *Proc. natn. Acad. Sci. U.S.A.* **68,** 3228.
21. EGE, T., CARLSSON, S.-A., and RINGERTZ, N. R. (1971). Immune micro-fluorimetric analysis of the distribution of species specific nuclear antigens in HeLa chick erythrocyte heterokaryons. *Expl Cell Res.* **69,** 472.
22. RINGERTZ, N. R. and BOLUND, L. (1969). Activation of hen erythrocyte deoxyribonucleoprotein. *Expl. Cell Res.* **55,** 205.
23. HARRIS, H., SIDEBOTTOM, E., GRACE, D. M., and BRAMWELL, M. E. (1969). The expression of genetic information: a study with hybrid animal cells. *J. Cell Sci.,* **4,** 499.
24. WATKINS, J. F. and GRACE, D. M. (1967). Studies on the surface antigens of interspecific mammalian cell heterokaryons. *J. Cell Sci.* **2,** 193.
25. ESPMARK, J. H. and FAGRAEUS, A. (1965). Identification of the species of origin of cells by mixed haemadsorption: a mixed antiglobulin reaction applied to monolayer cell cultures. *J. Immun.* **94,** 530.
26. COOMBS, R. R. A., MARKS, J., and BEDFORD, D. (1956). Specific mixed agglutination: mixed erythrocyte-platelet antiglobulin reaction for the detection of platelet antibodies. *Br. J. Haemat.* **2,** 84.

27. HARRIS, H. and COOK, P. R. (1969). Synthesis of an enzyme determined by an erythocyte nucleus in a hybrid cell. *J. Cell Sci.* **5**, 121.
28. LITTLEFIELD, J. W. (1964). Three degrees of guanylic acid-inosinic acid pyrophosphorylase deficiency in mouse fibroblasts. *Nature, Lond.* **203**, 1142.
29. COOK, P. R. (1970). Species specificity of an enzyme determined by an erythrocyte nucleus in an interspecific hybrid cell. *J. Cell Sci.* **7**, 1.
30. CLEMENTS, G. B. (1972). Ph. D. Thesis, University of Glasgow.
31. DENDY, P. R. and HARRIS, H. (1973). Sensitivity to diphtheria toxin as a species-specific marker in hybrid cells. *J. Cell Sci.* **12**, 831.
32. FISHER, H. W. and HARRIS, H. (1962). The isolation of nuclei from animal cells in culture. *Proc. R. Soc.* B **156**, 521.
33. WEISS, M. C. and GREEN, H. (1967). Human–mouse hybrid cell lines containing partial complements of human chromosomes and functioning human genes. *Proc. natn. Acad. Sci. U.S.A.* **58**, 1104.
34. MIGEON, B. R. and MILLER, C. S. (1968). Human–mouse somatic cell hybrids with single human chromosome (group E): link with thymidine kinase activity. *Science, N.Y.* **162**, 1005.
35. MILLER, O. J., ALLDERDICE, P. W., MILLER, D. A., BREG, W. R., and MIGEON, B. R. (1971). Assignment of human thymidine kinase gene locus to chromosome 17 by identification of its distinctive quinacrine fluorescence in a man–mouse somatic hybrid. *Science, N.Y.* **173**, 244.
36. BOONE, C., CHEN, T.-R., and RUDDLE, F. H. (1972). Assignment of three human genes to chromosomes (LDH-A to 11, TK to 17, and IDH to 20) and evidence for translocation between human and mouse chromosomes in somatic cell hybrids. *Proc. natn. Acad. Sci. U.S.A.* **69**, 510.
37. ELICEIRI, G. L. and GREEN, H. (1969). Ribosomal RNA synthesis in human–mouse hybrid cells. *J. molec. Biol.* **41**, 253.
38. BRAMWELL, M. E. and HANDMAKER, S. D. (1971). Ribosomal RNA synthesis in human–mouse hybrid cells. *Biochim. biophys. Acta* **232**, 580.
39. SCHWARTZ, A. G., COOK, P. R., and HARRIS, H. (1971). Correction of a genetic defect in a mammalian cell. *Nature, Lond. New Biol.*, **230**, 5.
40. BOYD, Y. L. and HARRIS, H. (1973). Correction of genetic defects in mammalian cells by the input of small amounts of foreign genetic material. *J. Cell Sci.* In press.
41. LOCKARD, R. E. and LINGREL, J. B. (1969). The synthesis of mouse hemoglobin β-chains in rabbit reticulocyte cell-free system programmed with mouse reticulocyte 9s RNA. *Biochem. biophys. Res. Commun.* **37**, 204.
42. HOUSMAN, D., PEMBERTON, R., and TABER, R. (1971). Synthesis of α and β chains of rabbit hemoglobin in a cell-free extract of Krebs II ascites cells. *Proc. natn. Acad. Sci. U.S.A.* **68**, 2716.
43. RHOADS, R. E., McKNIGHT, G. S., and SCHIMKE, R. T. (1971). Synthesis of ovalbumin in a rabbit reticulocyte cell-free system programmed with hen oviduct ribonucleic acid. *J. biol. Chem.* **246**, 7407.
44. GURDON, J. B., LANE, C. D., WOODLAND, H. R., and MARBAIX, G. (1971). Use of frog eggs and oocytes for the study of messenger RNA and its translation in living cells. *Nature, Lond.* **233**, 177.
45. DEÁK, I., SIDEBOTTOM, E., and HARRIS, H. (1972). Further experiments on the role of the nucleolus in the expression of structural genes. *J. Cell Sci.* **11**, 379.
46. SIDEBOTTOM, E. and HARRIS, H. (1969). The role of the nucleolus in the transfer of RNA from nucleus to cytoplasm. *J. Cell Sci.* **5**, 351.
47. DEÁK, I. I. (1973). Further experiments on the role of the nucleolus in the transfer of RNA from nucleus to cytoplasm. *J. Cell Sci.* **13**, 395.

48. HARRIS, H. (1963). Nuclear ribonucleic acid. *Prog. nucl. Acid Res.* **2**, 20. Academic Press, New York.

49. HARRIS, H. (1959). Turnover of nuclear and cytoplasmic ribonucleic acid in two types of animal cell, with some further observation on the nucleolus. *Biochem. J.* **73**, 362.

50. BRUNS, G. P., FISCHER, S., and LOWY, B. A. (1965). A study of the synthesis and interrelationships of ribonucleic acids in duck erythrocytes. *Biochim. biophys. Acta* **95**, 280.

51. IZAWA, M. and KAWASHINA, K. (1969). Incorporation of L-[^{14}C]-leucine into the nucleoli of mouse ascites tumor cells. *Biochim. biophys. Acta* **190**, 139.

52. KAWASHINA, K., IZAWA, M., and SATO, S. (1971). Studies on the origin of proteins in the nucleoli of mouse ascites tumour cells: a test for protein transfer to the nucleoli. *Biochim. biophys. Acta* **232**, 192.

53. RINGBORG, U., DANEHOLT, B., EDSTRÖM, J.-E., EGYHÁZI, E., and RYD-LANDER, L. (1970). Evidence for transport of preribosomal RNA from the nucleolus to the chromosomes in *Chironomus tentans* salivary gland cells. *J molec. Biol.* **51**, 679.

54. RINGBORG, U. and RYDLANDER, L. (1971). Nucleolar-derived ribonucleic acid in chromosomes, nuclear sap, and cytoplasm of *Chironomus tentans* salivary gland cells. *J. Cell Biol.* **51**, 355.

55. BARONDES, S. H. and NIRENBERG, M. W. (1962). Fate of a synthetic poly-nucleotide directing cell-free protein synthesis. I Characteristics of degradation. *Science, N.Y.* **138**, 810.

56. BARONDES, S. H. and NIRENBERG, M. W. (1962). Fate of a synthetic poly-nucleotide directing cell-free synthesis. II. Association with ribosomes. *Science, N.Y.* **138**, 813.

57. TATA, J. R. (1970). Hormonal control of metamorphosis. *Control processes in multicellular organisms* Ciba Foundation Symposium, p. 131. Churchill, London.

58. COCCUCI, S. M. and SUSSMAN, M. (1970). RNA in cytoplasmic and nuclear fractions of cellular slime mold amoebae. *J. Cell Biol.* **45**, 399.

59. MOORE, R. J. and HAMILTON, T. H. (1964). Estrogen-induced formation of uterine ribosomes. *Proc. natn. Acad. Sci. U.S.A.* **52**, 439.

60. COMSTOCK, J. P., ROSENFELD, G. C., O'MALLEY, B. W., and MEANS, A. R. (1972). Estrogen-induced changes in translation, and specific messenger RNA levels during oviduct differentiation. *Proc. natn. Acad. Sci. U.S.A.* **69**, 2377.

6

Differentiation

1. Definitions

WHEN an experimentalist begins to be worried about the way scientific terms are used and attempts restrictive definitions of them, his colleagues are apt to shake their heads and conclude that his days as an experimentalist are numbered. But it seems to me that I cannot fail to increase the confusion that surrounds the use of certain common terms in embryology if I refrain from discussing the ideas that underlie the use of these terms; and I must, in any case, make clear the restrictions that I intend to impose on these terms in this chapter. Differentiation is commonly defined as the process by which, during the development of the individual from the fertilized ovum, specialized cells, tissues, and organs are formed. The word was first, and is still, most commonly used in connection with the growth of multicellular organisms, and thus implies the production from a single cell, the fertilized ovum, of progeny that exhibits increasing heterogeneity as the individual develops. But a biologically equivalent process also takes place in some unicellular organisms. In these a part of the cell may undergo morphological and functional specialization to form a structure that exists also in multicellular organisms, but is composed, in the latter, of large numbers of cells. I propose to use the term differentiation to describe this process of specialization, whether it occurs in unicellular or multicellular organisms. When we come to use the terms 'differentiated', 'undifferentiated', and 'dedifferentiated', it is not so easy to delineate a precise empirical content. If one defines the fertilized ovum as *the* undifferentiated cell, then cells become differentiated as they acquire characters that permit them to be distinguished from the ovum and from each other; but since the two daughters resulting from the first division of the ovum can easily be distinguished from the ovum itself, if only by the difference in size, it is the second feature, that is, the development of recognizable heterogeneity within the progeny of the ovum, that is commonly used to define the onset of cellular differentiation. This is, of course, simply a convention. The sperm and the ovum are themselves the products of complex processes of differentiation and it is perfectly reasonable to argue that there are no undifferentiated cells. If, however, the conventional frame of reference is assumed, undifferentiated cells may be defined as those descendants of the fertilized ovum that have not yet developed recognizable heterogeneity, and differentiated cells may be defined as those that have. 'Dedifferentiation' is more difficult and involves a much vaguer frame of reference. Of course, a differentiated cell does not ever revert to a fertilized ovum, or even to one of its early descendants, so that, *sensu stricto*, the word is a misnomer. But, under certain conditions, differentiated cells that show one or more specialized charactersitics lose these characteristics and may acquire others. In some cases this transformation superficially resembles a partial reversal of the process of differentiation in that a cell that has acquired a specialized characteristic at some stage of differentiation comes to resemble, at least superficially, an earlier ancestor that lacked this particular characteristic. It is not at all clear that this sort of transformation does indeed represent a reversion to an ancestral cell type: we may merely be observing the loss of some easily recognizable properties and their replacement by others that are less striking. I shall therefore use the word 'dedifferentiation' sparingly, and simply to describe the loss of some easily recognizable feature or features in a differentiated cell, without necessarily implying thereby that any reversal of the process of differentiation has taken place.

2. Changes in DNA

The simple observation that some of the changes produced by differentiation were very stable and could persist through many cell generations suggested to early investigators of this problem that differentiation might be the result of progressive alterations in the genetic material of the cell. This view gained some support from the fact that differentiation in some cells was accompanied by obvious morphological changes in the nucleus and the chromosomes. A more contemporary and more precise statement of this position would be that the events that determine the process of differentiation are changes in the nucleotide sequences of the DNA of the cell. In the case of one special form of differentiation, the formation of antibodies by cells of the lymphoid series, the view is commonly held that some form of variation in the nucleotide sequences of the DNA determines the specificity of the antibody; but the general theory that differentiation as a whole is determined by changes in the nucleotide sequences of the DNA now has few adherents. It is, of course, common knowledge that many plants can be propagated vegetatively by cuttings from different parts of the plant. In some cases, small fragments from almost any part of the plant will regenerate a whole new plant. It is thus at once clear that completely differentiated tissues in these plants contain at least some cells which under appropriate conditions can give rise to progeny showing all the forms of differentiation that characterize the complete plant. In more recent years this has been demonstrated also for small groups of cells[2-4] and, in certain cases, for single cells,[5-7] cultivated *in vitro*. These small groups of cells or single cells produce a callus from which the whole plant can sometimes be grown. In some of the experiments in which whole plants were grown from single cells, these were originally differentiated cells in that they showed morphological features characteristic of their tissue of origin.[5,6] In animals the evidence is perhaps less decisive, but it leads to the same conclusion. Nuclei isolated from cells of a renal tumour of the adult frog (the Lucké carcinoma) can be transplanted into enucleated frog eggs, where they will support development to the stage of the feeding tadpole;[8-10] and nuclei from cells of the intestinal epithelium of the tadpole have been shown to support the development of mature and even fertile frogs.[11,12] We may therefore conclude that if differentiation depends upon changes in the nucleotide sequences of the DNA of the cell, these changes are not irreversible. We must then envisage an elaborate and directed progression of changes in DNA nucleotide sequence during the course of differentiation and their accurate reversal when differentiated cells resume activities in which they were engaged earlier in their development. Nothing that we know about changes involving DNA in biological material provides any ground for believing that a process of this sort exists. In the current state of our knowledge, the ability of the nuclei of some differentiated cells to support the development of a whole plant or a whole animal must be regarded as strong evidence that differentiation is not achieved by progressive changes in the nucleotide sequences of DNA.

3. Differentiation and regulation

We are then left, in principle, with three other possibilities: differentiation might be produced by selective transcription of different parts of the DNA at different times, so that some messenger ribonucleic acids are made available at one time and others at another; or it might be produced by selective translation of different messengers at different times; or it might be produced by both of these mechanisms. Now this is ground that I have already covered in Chapters 3 and 4, when I discussed the regulation of protein synthesis; but, although differentiation clearly involves such regulation, it poses two additional problems that I have not yet mentioned. Most studies that have been made in recent years on the regulation of protein synthesis have involved the use of systems in which the maintenance of a change in protein synthesis is dependent upon the continued presence of the stimulus that induced the change. For example, a particular small molecule may induce the synthesis of a particular protein, but the synthesis of this protein stops when the small molecule is removed; or another small molecule may repress the synthesis of the protein, but synthesis is resumed when this small molecule is removed. Although differentiation obviously includes changes of this sort, it also involves changes that persist after the stimulus or stimuli that initiated them have been removed. In some cases, the initial stimulus sets in train a complex chain of reactions in which the synthesis of a specific protein is a terminal event occurring many hours or days after the original stimulus has ceased to exist. The second characteristic feature of differentiation is that phenotypic changes produced in the cell by a particular stimulus may be maintained through many cell generations after the stimulus has been removed; and, in some cases, these changes may be maintained indefinitely.

I should like to illustrate these two special features of differentiation with some examples. If a dorsal pancreatic rudiment, containing both epithelium and mesenchyme, is dissected from an 11-day mouse embryo and then cultivated *in vitro* on a porous membrane, the cells of the rudiment will differentiate into typical pancreatic tissue showing both the structural and functional characteristics of normal pancreas. By the second day after explanation ultrastructural changes indicative of differentiation can be observed in the epithelial cells; by the third day the amylase activity of the explants is about 100 times that present initially; and between the fourth and fifth day typical zymogen granules appear.[13] If the mesenchyme is removed from the fragment prior to explanation, then the remaining epithelium fails to differentiate in this way. But if the mesenchyme is maintained in contact with, or in close proximity to, the epithelium for the first 48 h after explanation, all subsequent stages of differentiation proceed normally even when the mesenchyme is removed.[13,14] It is clear that the mesenchyme in this case provides a stimulus to differentiation, but, once the chain of events has been initiated, it goes to completion even if the stimulus is no longer present. Suspensions of presumptive muscle cells (myoblasts) can be made from chick embryo muscle tissue, and these cells can then be grown as a monolayer on a glass surface. They have initially a morphology resembling that of fibroblasts and do not show the characteristic striations or enzymatic reactions of muscle; nor do they undergo contractions. The cells grow on the glass without undergoing any morphological change until the monolayer becomes confluent, at which stage fusion takes place between adjacent cells to give rise to multinucleate cells. These then develop striations, acquire enzymatic activities characteristic of muscle and undergo vigorous contraction.[15,16] In this case, an initial stimulus to muscle formation has occurred in the embryo, but overt differentiation is held in abeyance through several cell generations until appropriate cultural conditions for complete differentiation are achieved.

On the other hand, it is a common observation that differentiated cells showing certain specialized morphological or biochemical features may undergo 'dedifferentiation', that is, the loss of these specialized features, when they are explanted and grown in artificial culture. The prevalence of observations of this sort at one time gave rise to the idea that the differentiated state could not be maintained in prolonged culture outside the body. Recent investigations have made it clear that in at least some cases the failure to propagate differentiated cells *in vitro* was due to the fact that in artificial culture these cells were at a selective disadvantage relative to other cells in the population, and were consequently overgrown.[17] When steps were taken to overcome this selective disadvantage, it became possible to grow differentiated cells, showing specific biochemical and morphological features, for many months, and in some cases indefinitely, *in vitro*. The cells lines that appear capable of indefinite multiplication without loss of the differentiated state have all so far been derived from differentiated tumours;[17-21] but muscle cells, cells that form pigment and cells that form cartilage have been continuously propagated for many months from diploid cells isolated directly from the embryo.[22-24] It is thus clear that, in principle, a highly differentiated state can be maintained not only through many generations of cells in the body, where it could at a pinch be argued that the cells remain subject to continuous inductive stimuli, but also *in vitro* where, at least under certain conditions of culture, such stimuli cannot be present.

4. Genetic activity and differentiation

Having thus delineated these two cardinal features of differentiation, I should like now to examine what fragmentary data we have on these problems, to see whether they throw any light on the underlying mechanisms that might be involved. To my mind, the most illuminating experiments on differentiation have been carried out in unicellular organisms; and, for the most decisive observations, we must return once again the giant unicellular alga, *Acetabularia* (see Chapter 1). You will recall that this cell grows for many weeks by elongation of its stalk, and then, under appropriate conditions, undergoes differentiation to form a fruiting body or cap by means of which its spores are disseminated. The formation of the cap is a classical example of differentiation involving dramatic morphological and biochemical changes; it is in every way comparable to the formation of similar fruiting bodies in related multicellular organisms. Now I have already pointed out that in *Acetabularia* growth of the stalk and complete differentiation of the species-specific cap can take place long after the cell nucleus has been removed. We therefore conclude at once that in this organism the *overt* stages of differentiation do not result from differential transcription of the genetic material. The stalk is not formed at a particular time because at that time stalk-forming genes are being transcribed; and the cap is not formed at another time because at that time cap-forming genes are being transcribed. The genes involved in forming both the stalk and the cap are obviously transcribed long before the overt events themselves take place. Experiments that I have already described on the induction of premature caps indicate that all the genes necessary for cap formation must be transcribed in some species of *Acetabularia* at least 70 days before the cap is normally formed;[25] and experiments on the accumulation and storage of information in the cell cytoplasm indicate that, for a large part of the period of growth of the cell, the templates for both stalk formation and cap formation are delivered to the cytoplasm continuously.[26] Moreover, formation of the cap can be held in abeyance indefinitely if the cells are maintained at low levels of illumination. This permits continued growth of the stalk, which may thus become very much longer than normal. Such grossly elongated stalks can be induced to form caps by an increase in the level of illumination, even after they have been enucleated.[27] These observations make it quite clear that in *Acetabularia* the overt act of differentiation is elaborated by the cytoplasm of the cell on the basis of pre-existing messenger RNA, and that this elaboration does not require the presence of the relevant genes.

This state of affairs, as I have pointed out before, is not limited to *Acetabularia*. Most unicellular organisms which survive enucleation for any length of time appear to be capable of at least some measure of differentiation. Where differentiation involves the co-operation of a number of cells, enucleation of the differentiating tissue is obviously not possible, so that we have no observations in multicellular organisms as decisive as those that have been made on *Acetabularia* or *Stentor*.[28] But the experiments that demonstrate the failure of high concentrations of actinomycin to inhibit critical overt events in the differentiation of colonial myxamoebae,[29] of pancreatic cells in the mouse embryo,[30,31] and of haemoglobin-forming cells in the chick embryo,[32] argue strongly in favour of the view that in multicellular organisms also the actual expression of a particular differentiated trait does not require the concomitant transcription of the relevant genes.

The most extreme example of 'pre-programming' of the cell cytoplasm is perhaps to be seen in the ovum itself. A frame of reference in which the ovum is regarded as *the* undifferentiated cell has the disadvantage that it tends to encourage an underestimate of its structural and functional complexity. If one is accustomed to thinking of the ovum as undifferentiated, one tends to assume that the progressive imposition of diversity in the progeny of the ovum must require an elaborate sequence of highly specific signals and a correspondingly elaborate system of specific genetic switches. Indeed, some optimistic molecular biologists have even suggested that to explain differentiation one has simply to determine which genes are switched on and when. At least as far as the early steps in differentiation are concerned, this idea appears to be very improbable: the evidence does not at present encourage the belief that specific genetic switches are important determinants in the observed sequence of events. Although the data so far available are rather preliminary, they lead one to suppose that in a wide range of biological material all the organization necessary for the early stages of embryonic development is present in the cytoplasm of the ovum before it is fertilized. The only decisive test that we have at present for detecting when new genetic instructions are given in the developing embryo is to determine when markers of paternal origin make their appearance. Many enzymes show species or strain specificities that are revealed by differences in electrophoretic mobility, heat stability, or other physical properties. When sperm and ovum are derived from species that show such differences in a particular enzyme, analysis of the nature of the enzyme synthesized in the zygote will reveal when new genetic information for that enzyme passes to the cytoplasm and is translated; for, when this occurs, paternal as well as maternal enzyme will be synthesized. While the number of such studies is so far very limited, they concur in showing that paternal enzymes become detectable only at relatively advanced stages of embryonic development. In the sea-urchin egg, the enzymes responsible for digestion of the coat during hatching of the embryo are still apparently entirely of maternal type.[33] In amphibia paternal enzymes do not appear until development of the embryo has proceeded to the stages of muscle movement and heart beat;[34] and in interspecific fish and bird hybrids, paternal enzymes also appear only at a late stage of embryonic development.[35] No doubt more sensitive methods will reveal the presence of paternal markers somewhat earlier, but it seems very likely that the development of the embryo to a relatively advanced stage is achieved essentially on a basis of maternal information, that is, information that was delivered to the cytoplasm of the egg before formation of the heterozygotic nucleus. In the case of ascidians, not only do the embryos of interspecific crosses show an entirely maternal character,[36] but, at least in some species, the embryos appear to develop to the stage of swimming tadpoles without synthesizing any detectable amount of RNA.[37] During these early stages of development it is therefore very likely that differentiation is achieved not by switches that initiate the transcription of structural genes in the nucleus, but by switches that initiate the expression of a programme that is already present in the egg cytoplasm.

In considering the immediate determinants of overt events in differentiation we are therefore thrown back once again on the problem of how cytoplasmic regulatory mechanisms might operate, and, more especially, how a genetic programme delivered to the cytoplasm at an earlier stage is elaborated in an ordered sequence of subsequent

events. We have glimpses of this kind of organization in the phenomenon of 'sequential induction' (induction *en chaîne*) of enzymes in
bacteria.[38] Here, members of a group of related enzymes are formed
sequentially when the first enzyme of the series has been induced;
and it is generally thought that the end product of each enzyme, or
some related compound, is the inducer for each subsequent enzyme.[39]
While such phenomena may well be involved in differentiation, the
analogy cannot, however, be pressed too closely. The persistence of
an induced sequence of enzymes in bacteria remains dependent on
the presence of the initial inducer, whereas differentiation is
characterized by progressive independence of the initial stimulus.
Moreover, differentiation characteristically produces structural
changes in the cell and may involve many very different groups of
proteins. Structural changes often appear to be at the heart of the
process, and the electron microscope may reveal reorganization of
the pattern of ribosomal particles in the cytoplasm, or the development of ordered membrane systems, some time before the overt
features of the differentiated state make their appearance.[40,41] The
only processes in bacteria that are at all analogous to differentiation
in higher cells are sporulation and germination. I have already
discussed in Chapter 2 the close similarity between sporulation and
germination in bacteria and the corresponding processes in eukaryotic
organisms; and I have reviewed the evidence indicating that sporulation and germination, once initiated, become progressively independent of continued genetic activity. We may therefore hope that
the continued study of these processes in bacteria will contribute to
our knowledge of differentiation in higher cells, even if the genetic
regulatory mechanisms that have been best studied in vegetative
bacterial cells appear at present to be only marginally relevant.

5. Co-ordination in multicellular organisms

In one respect differentiation in multicellular organisms poses a
special problem. While it is altogether probable that the fundamental
biochemical basis of any particular type of differentiation will be the
same whether it occurs in a unicellular or multicellular organism, in
the latter case we have also to explain how co-operation between a
large number of individual cells is actually achieved. There are two
ways in which this might be done: either all the cells are individually
exposed to the same stimuli at the same time in the same say; or the
cells interact with each other to ensure a corporate response to any

given stimulus. The second alternative is, of course, intrinsically more probable; and there is now convincing experimental evidence that interaction between cells is not only a means of achieving a corporate response, but is, in some cases, an essential requirement for the process of differentiation itself. For example, I have described how a pancreatic rudiment from the mouse embryo, explanted into artificial culture under appropriate conditions, will differentiate into functional pancreatic tissue,[13,14] If this rudiment is cut into smaller pieces, which are then cultivated separately, differentiation of the epithelium into pancreatic cells does not take place. But if these fragments are grown close together, so that they fuse again into a single mass, then differentiation will proceed.[13,42] Similar effects are also seen with other epithelia.[43] It is clear that differentiation in these cases requires large scale co-operative activity between cells, and that single cells, or small groups of cells, cannot achieve the conditions necessary to permit the differentiation to occur.

Recent experiments, initiated by Loewenstein and his colleagues,[44-47] have greatly illuminated our understanding of how this co-operative activity might be achieved. These authors, using micro-electrodes to measure the voltage drop across individual cell membranes, have established that there is virtually free passage of electrolytes from cell to cell in epithelia from a wide range of different sources: salivary glands and renal tubules of diptera, sensory epithelium in the ampullae of Lorenzini (large sense organs) of elasmobranchs, urinary bladder of the toad, larval skin of urodeles, and both normal and regenerating liver parenchyma of the rat. Similar systems of intercellular communication have also been found in plant tissues.[48] The flow of electrolytes appears to take place through specialized regions of contact between adjacent cell membranes.[49] These regions are known variously as 'tight-junctions' 'gap junctions' or 'junctional complexes', and, under the electron microscope, they show differences in both form and number in different tissues. It has, moreover, been demonstrated that these junctions permit the passage not only of small ions, but also of much larger dye molecules and perhaps even of macromolecules of the dimensions of proteins and nucleic acids.[50] These intercommunicating cells may therefore be regarded as functionally unified systems; and it is possible that the essentially regional character of each successive step in the differentiation of multicellular organisms may be determined by the range over which any particular system of intercellular communication extends. Some recent observations on the development of systems of intercellular communication in embryos lend some support to this suggestion.[51-55]

6. Heritable differentiation

While we do not yet have a clear understanding in molecular terms of how cells initially become differentiated, it seems probable that the solution of this problem will be found in terms with which we are already familiar—the transcription of DNA, the translation of RNA, the interaction of substrate with enzyme, the production of a specific end-product. But when we come to consider how a particular differentiated state becomes heritable, we seem to be confronted with problems of a quite novel kind for which there is at present no satisfactory conceptual framework. In a sense, the fact that a phenotypic change produced by differentiation can be inherited, and in some cases inherited apparently indefinitely, is an observation that has a rather Lamarckian flavour, for here, although we are only dealing with cellular inheritance, we are none the less dealing with the inheritance of acquired traits. What mechanisms might be involved in ensuring the indefinite inheritance of a phenotypic change imposed on a cell by the process of differentiation?

There appear, in principle, to be three possibilities: 1. Specific changes might be produced in the cytoplasm by stimuli acting at one particular time, and these changes could become self-generating, and hence independent of the stimuli that originally produced them, through the agency of self-replicating cytoplasmic structures. 2. Changes might be produced at specific sites in the chromosomes, and these could be faithfully reproduced in the daughter chromosomes even though the initial determinants were no longer operative. 3. Self-generating states could be set up by continuing interaction between the chromosomes and the cytoplasm of the cell.

1. When we consider mechanisms of heritability, we now think naturally in terms of self-replicating molecules, and since nucleic acids are the only molecules for which self-replication has so far been decisively demonstrated, it is not surprising that the idea has been proposed, in various forms at different times, that RNA carrying instructions for the synthesis of specific proteins might undergo self-replication in the cell cytoplasm and thus provide a basis for the inheritance of differentiated traits. That messenger ribonucleic acids can be replicated is clear from the study of RNA viruses; but there

has never been much support for the idea that cellular messenger ribonucleic acids might be replicated, even though recent studies have revealed the existence of enzymes that appear to be capable of doing this. But even if mechanisms that replicate cellular messenger ribonucleic acids could be shown to be operative in uninfected cells, this would not in itself provide an adequate solution to the problem of differentiation. We should still have to explain why some messenger ribonucleic acids undergo self-replication, whereas others do not, and why different cellular messengers are replicated in different cell types; and we should still have to provide some mechanism for the accurate reversal of the differentiated state when, for example, a differentiated plant cell was called upon to generate a whole new plant. Under these circumstances self-replication of RNA would have to stop and the replicated RNA molecules, but not others, would have to be eliminated.

Recent studies with hybrid somatic cells in fact make it very improbable that heritability of differentiated traits can be maintained by self-generating cytoplasmic entities that operate completely independently of the chromosomes. Since mononucleate hybrid cells may initally contain the chromosome sets of both parent cells, they readily tolerate chromosome losses that in strictly diploid cells would be lethal. In hybrid cells, the retention or loss of phenotypic markers can therefore be correlated with the retention or loss of specific parental chromosomes; and such correlations form the basis of a rudimentary kind of somatic cell genetics that permits the assignation of markers to specific chromosomes.[56-59] Hybrids between various kinds of differentiated parent cells have also been used to study the chromosomal determinants of certain heritable differentiated states. I shall have more to say presently about the experiments that have been done with this kind of hybrid cell; but at this point it is enough to say that these experiments make it highly improbable that heritability of differentiated traits can be determined by self-replicating cytoplasmic entities that operate independently of the chromosomes. All the observations that have so far been made concur in demonstrating that the persistence or loss of a heritable phenotypic trait does depend on the retention or loss of specific chromosomes;[60-69] and certainly a pattern of differentiation initially present in a hybrid cell can be lost when certain chromosomes are eliminated.[69]

2. It seems then that chromosomes are in some way involved in determining the heritability of differentiated traits. I have already

presented reasons for rejecting the idea that differentiation results from induced changes in the nucleotide sequences of DNA. The main objection to this idea is the difficulty of envisaging mechanisms for the accurate reversal of such changes when the nucleus of a differentiated cell supports the development of a whole plant or a whole animal. This difficulty also confronts a theory, recently proposed, in which replication of RNA and modification of DNA are, in a sense, combined.[70] This theory postulates that specific cytoplasmic messenger ribonucleic acids are transcribed into DNA copies by the 'reverse transcriptase' enzymes that have now been characterized,[71–74] and that these DNA transcripts are then integrated into the cellular DNA. The requirement for reversibility applies to this proposal no less than to any other than invokes changes in the nucleotide sequences of DNA: under regenerative conditions the interpolated DNA sequences, but not others that are identical, or virtually so, would need to be accurately excised. It is in any case difficult to see how differentiation could be satisfactorily explained by a process that simply increases the dosage of certain genes, which is essentially all that reverse transcription of ribonucleic acids can be expected to achieve.

Another model that invokes induced changes in DNA, but one that overcomes, at least in part, the difficulty posed by the requirement for reversibility, has been put forward.[75] This model postulates that heritability of differentiation has its basis in specific alterations in the tertiary and higher order configuration of the DNA. It is suggested that these alterations in 'gene superstructure' might determine a specific pattern of gene transcription which could be stably inherited because the gene superstructure might be faithfully replicated. The imposed changes in gene superstructure might require only minimal, or no, changes in the primary nucleotide sequences, so that reversal of the imposed changes need not present special problems. There are two difficulties with this model. First, it seems improbable that the higher order configuration of DNA alone (for example, supercoiling) could contain information of the required degree of specificity; and second, it is difficult to see how a complex superstructure of the kind envisaged could be maintained through the DNA replication cycle without the co-operation of other molecules to stabilize the structure. But once one invokes cooperative effects in which the structural changes that determine selective transcription in the chromatin are produced by interaction between the DNA and other molecules, one is, of course, proposing a model of the third category, that is, a model in which the self-generating state requires continuous interaction between the chromosomes and other cellular constituents.

3. Self-generating states can be induced in cells without the imposition of any structural change on the genetic material itself. A well known example of this is seen in the induced synthesis of β-galactosidase in *E. coli*, which I have discussed in detail in previous chapters. This enzyme, once induced, continues to be synthesized at a maximal rate so long as exogenous inducers are present in the medium, but ceases to be synthesized as soon as the inducers are removed or exhausted. Induction of the enzyme normally involves induction of a 'permease' system in the cell membrane, which serves to maintain an adequate concentration of inducer within the cell. If the enzyme and the 'permease' system are once induced in a cell by an inducer, the concentration of inducer in the medium can then be reduced to levels well below those normally required to initiate induction, but the cells remain induced and the enzyme continues to be synthesized at the maximal rate for many generations.[76] The induction of the 'permease' system provides an intracellular concentration of inducer sufficient to determine continued maximal synthesis of the enzyme even when the external concentration of the inducer is inadequate. In this case we have an example of a self-generating cytoplasmic change, involving synthesis of a specific enzyme, imposed by the establishment of a new equilibrium in an existing metabolic pathway. Another example of this sort of phenomenon is seen in the formation of the cell wall in *B. subtilis*. If these organisms are treated with the enzyme lysozyme, their cell walls are dissolved and 'protoplasts', bounded simply by the cell membrane, are formed. In suitable media these protoplasts can be cultivated indefinitely, or at least for very long periods, as 'L-forms' that lack the normal wall. When, however, the L-forms are transferred to a solid medium containing hard agar or gelatin, they will revert, virtually quantitively, to the usual bacillary forms producing a normal cell wall.[77-80] These heritable phenotypic changes are not mutational in character and there is no evidence that they involve structural changes in the bacillary DNA.

In eukaryotic cells, however, it seems probable that heritable patterns of differentiation will involve structural changes in the chromatin, if only because structural changes, such as condensation and dispersion, seem to determine whether the genes in a particular region are transcribed or not. The imposition of this kind of structural change does not require alteration of the primary DNA nucleotide sequence, although it might involve secondary modification of the DNA, for example, by methylation. I have already discussed, especially in connection with the polytene chromosomes of insects, how a specific pattern of regional condensation and dispersion of the chromatin, determining a pattern of differential gene transcription, could be imposed. It is not so easy to see how such a pattern could become heritable. It is commonly suggested that the pattern could be maintained by a continuous flow of specific cytoplasmic signals, specific in the sense that they permit the transcription of one set of genes and not another; but this suggestion is not very helpful, for it simply transposes the question. How, then, is the system of specific cytoplasmic signals maintained from one cell generation to the next? If it is to be maintained by the selective activity of other genes, the argument, of course, becomes circular. This circularity seems to me to be an insuperable difficulty of all models for heritable differentiation that require the continuous generation of a system of specific cytoplasmic signals; and it is my view that this dilemma can only be resolved by consideration of models in which the imposed pattern of structural changes in the chromatin, whatever the specificity of the stimuli that originally imposed it, is maintained by non-specific factors that are generated continuously in all cells. If one supposes, for example, that those regions of the chromatin that have undergone a particular kind of structural change have an affinity for a protein that stabilizes the induced structure, and that other regions of the chromatin do not have this affinity, then a regional pattern of structural changes could be maintained in the chromatin indefinitely so long as the postulated protein continues to be synthesized. A specific pattern of differential gene transcription could then become heritable without the continued intervention of a system of specific cytoplasmic signals, provided that the structural changes imposed on the chromosomes could be replicated in the daughter chromosomes.

Somatic cell heterokaryons and mononucleate hybrid cells provide systems in which models of this kind can be tested. If, for example, the inheritance of a particular differentiated trait requires the continuous production of specific cytoplasmic signals, then the fusion of cells that express this marker with others that do not might be expected to result in interaction between the two set of genes; for example, both sets might now express the marker, or it may cease to be expressed altogether. If, however, the inheritance of a differentiated trait is due to the faithful replication of a structural change in the chromatin, stabilized by a factor produced by both parent cells, then the two sets of genes in the hybrid cell would not be expected to interact. A number of experiments of this kind have now been done, and some interesting, if preliminary, findings have emerged. As I have mentioned previously, it has not proved possible to reactivate an inactive X chromosome in any form of hybrid cell, even when selective conditions are imposed in which the survival of the hybrid cell requires the reactivation of the inactive X.[81] The inactive X generates an inactive X on replication; but, whatever structural changes might be responsible for this genetic inactivity, they are apparently insensitive to any factors that might be produced by a cell that does not contain an inactive X. For the synthesis of albumin, melanin, the hepatic enzyme tyrosine aminotransferase, and a few other proteins characteristic of the differentiated state, interactions between the two sets of parental genes have been observed. When the cells that express the marker are fused with cells of a completely different type, synthesis of the marker commonly stops in the hybrid cell;[60–68; 82–88] but in some cases synthesis of the marker increases, or the parent cell that does not synthesize the marker may be induced to synthesize it.[62,63; 89,90] For other markers of differentiation, the two sets of parental genes appear to operate independently, and no interactions resulting in suppression or initiation of the synthesis of the marker are observed.[91,92] Hybrids made by fusing immunoglobulin-producing myeloma cells with cells of fibroblastic type synthesize little, if any, immunoglobulin;[93,94] but when the two parents are both cells of lymphoid type and differ only in that one synthesizes immunoglobulin and the other does not, then synthesis of immunoglobulin is not suppressed in the hybrid.[95] When myelomas producing different immunoglobulin chains are fused together, the hybrid cells synthesize both parental immunoglobulins.[96] In the case of albumin synthesis, interactions seen in mononucleate hybrid cells[90] are not seen in heterokaryons where the two parental nuclei remain discrete.[97] The variability of these findings reflects not so much the complexity of the problem as the complexity of the chromosome constitution of most of the mononucleate hybrid cells that have been studied. In almost all cases the hybrids have been constructed from aneuploid cell lines, so that their initial chromosome constitution is highly variable. This variability is subsequently complicated not only by loss of chromosomes, but also by translocations and other structural rearrangments which make a precise definition of the chromosome constitution at any one time extremely difficult. None the less, there is reason to hope that the analysis of appropriately constructed hybrid cells will help to clarify the problem of heritable differentiation, at the very least by reducing the number of models that are now thought to be plausible.

7. Determination

I should like finally to say a few words about the subject of determination. Although views to the contrary have recently been expressed,[98] I think it is not difficult to distinguish operationally between determination and differentiation, although differentiation, when it becomes heritable, and determination, when it is expressed, clearly overlap. The term 'determination' arises from a body of experiment that demonstrates that there are heritable restrictions on the ability of cells in the embryo to undergo, or take part in, subsequent morphological development. It is, in general, the case that the immediate progeny of the fertilized ovum are totipotent, that is, each of the daughter cells is capable of generating a complete individual. This totipotency is maintained for a number of cell divisions which varies from one organism to another; but, as the embryo develops, cells are soon generated that can no longer support the development of a whole individual but show a more limited range of developmental capacities.[99] The restrictions on developmental capacity are extended as the embryo matures, and, eventually, populations of cells are generated that can only support development within a specific narrow morphological range. These restrictions on developmental capacity may be heritable, and, in some experimental situations, they can be maintained indefinitely through successive generations of cell culture. What is inherited here is not the overt differentiated state, but the ability to generate a particular differentiated state and, at the same time, the inability to generate others. Determination is the word used to describe the series of events that results in the generation of cells that show specific heritable restrictions on developmental capacity.

The problem of determination has been studied in greatest detail in the 'imaginal discs' of the larvae of holometabolous insects,

PLATE 17

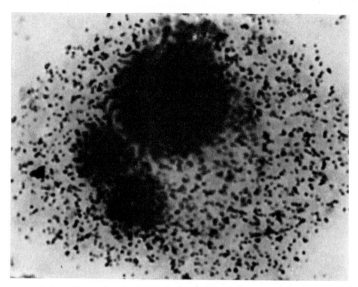

a. Autoradiograph of a heterokaryon containing a mouse nucleus and 2 chick erythrocyte nuclei, exposed for 6 h to a tritiated RNA precursor. The mouse nucleus and the 2 erythrocyte nuclei are very heavily labelled, and there is substantial cytoplasmic labelling.

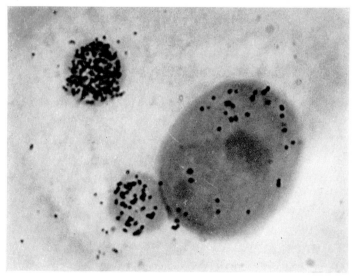

b. Autoradiograph of another heterokaryon from the same preparation as the cell shown in Plate 17*a*. The mouse nucleus has been inactivated by a microbeam of ultraviolet light. The erythrocyte nuclei, which have not yet developed nucleoli, are heavily labelled, but the cytoplasm contains almost no radioactivity.

PLATE 18

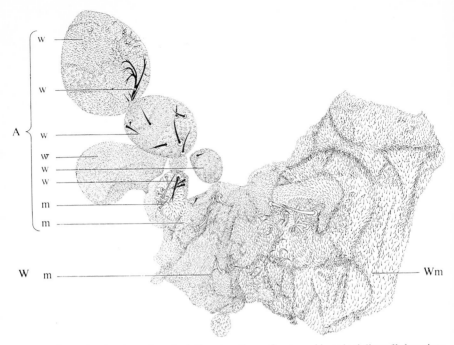

A

W

W

W

W

W

W

m

m

W   m

Wm

a. Transdetermination in an imaginal disc. A culture of antennal imaginal disc cells has given rise to a wing. Most of the antennal components (A) have normal wild type coloration (w), but two areas (the palpus and rostral membrane) have mutant coloration (m). These regions represent a clone of mutant cells. From this clone transdetermination has given rise to a wing (W) which also has mutant coloration. (By courtesy of Dr. W. Gehring.)

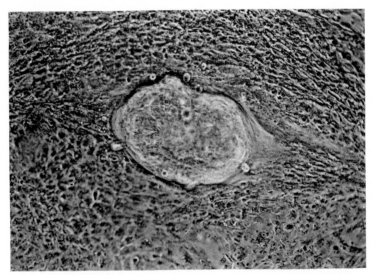

b. 'Transdifferentiation' in cell culture. A clonal population of pigmented retinal cells has given rise to a subcolony of cells that produce lens proteins and organize themselves into a 'lentoid' body. (By courtesy of Drs. G. Eguchi and T. S. Okada.)

especially *Drosophila*.[100] These 'discs' are collections of cells in the larva from which the various structures of the adult organism (the imago) develop. The bulk of the larva undergoes dissolution during metamorphosis. Each disc is destined to support the development of the whole, or a part, of a particular adult structure (for example, 3 pairs of discs form the head, 3 pairs the legs and the ventral part of the thorax, and 3 pairs the wings, halteres and the dorsal part of the thorax). The imaginal discs may be explanted from the larva into the abdominal cavity of the adult fly where the cells in the disc continue to multiply but where they do not undergo morphological differentiation. The disc cells may be subcultivated from adult fly to adult fly indefinitely without differentiating, but when they are returned to the larva, and thus exposed to the hormonal influences associated with morphogenesis, they will undergo the precise form of development that characterizes the original imaginal disc from which the cell cultures were derived. The ability to undergo a specific pattern of development, and the restrictions that prevent the execution of other patterns of development, can thus be inherited indefinitely in a cryptic form. It is this crypticity that distinguishes determination from heritable differentiation in which overt markers characteristic of the differentiated state continue to be expressed from one cell generation to the next.

If we know very little about the basis of heritable differentiation, we know even less about the basis of determination. It seems clear that the determined state is carried in the individual cell and not in the organization of a collection of cells;[101] and it is also clear that, like heritable differentiation, determination is not carried by self-generating cytoplasmic entities that operate independently of the chromosomes. Occasionally, a cell, or a very small group of cells, within an imaginal disc culture will, when returned to the larva, execute not the programme of development characteristic of the imaginal disc from which the culture was obtained, but the programme characteristic of another imaginal disc (Plate 18*a*). This event is known as 'transdetermination' and it has been the subject of intensive study, although no clear picture of the underlying mechanism has yet emerged.[101] Transdetermination can be mimicked by certain mutations called homeotic mutations which seem to be single cellular events. As in the case of heritable differentiation, it is difficult to construct plausible models of determination that do not involve inheritance of imposed patterns in the chromosomes, patterns which, in this case, can be modified by mutational events. It seems possible that some information about the mechanisms responsible for determination might be obtained if cell fusion could be applied to imaginal disc cells and the resulting hybrid cells analysed. This might, however, prove a formidable undertaking. In the meantime, an interesting opening for experiment appears to have presented itself in a phenomenon very close to transdetermination that has recently been described in cell cultures derived from the retina of the chick embryo. It has been shown that clonal populations of these cells, which are pigmented, generate occasional cells that produce lens proteins and organize themelves into 'lentoid' bodies[102] (Plate 18b). We have here 'transdifferentiation', if not 'transdetermination', *in vitro;* and I think it is not unduly optimistic to hope that the analysis of this system, or systems like it, by cell fusion might shed some light on what remains one of the most obscure, but one of the most interesting, problems in modern biology.

REFERENCES

1. *Antibodies: Cold Spring Harb. Symp. quant. Biol.* (1967). **32**, *passim.*
2. STEWARD, F. C., MAPES, M. O., and SMITH, J. (1958). Growth and organized development of cultured cells. I. Growth and division of freely suspended cells. *Am. J. Bot.* **45**, 693.
3. STEWARD, F. C., MAPES, M. O., and MEARS, K. (1958). Growth and organized development of cultured cells. II. Organization in cultures grown from freely suspended cells. *Am. J. Bot.* **45**, 705.
4. STEWARD, F. C. (1958). Growth and organized development of cultured cells. III. Interpretations of the growth from free cell to carrot plant. *Am. J. Bot.* **45**, 709.
5. VASIL, V. and HILDEBRANDT, H. C. (1965). Differentiation of tobacco plants from single isolated cells in microcultures. *Science, N.Y.* **150**, 889.
6. JOSHI, P. C. and BALL, E. (1968). Growth of isolated palisade cells of *Arachis hypogaea in vitro. Devl. Biol.* **17**, 308.
7. REINERT, J. (1968). Morphogenese in Gewebe- und Zellkulturen. *Naturwissenschaften* **55**, 170.
8. KING, T. J. and MCKINNELL, R. G. (1960). An attempt to determine the developmental potentialities of a cancer cell nucleus by means of transplantation. *Cell physiology neoplasia*, p. 591. University of Texas Press.
9. MCKINNELL, R. G. (1962). Development of *Rana pipiens* eggs transplanted with Lucké tumor cells. *Am. Zool.* **2**, 430.
10. MCKINNELL, R. G., DEGGINS, B. A., and LABAT, D. D. (1969). Transplantation of pluripotential nuclei from triploid frog tumours. *Science, N.Y.* **165**, 394.
11. GURDON, J. B. (1962). The developmental capacity of nuclei taken from intestinal epithelium cells of feeding tadpoles. *J. Embryol. exp. Morph.* **10**, 622.

12. GURDON, J. B. and UEHLINGER, V. (1966). 'Fertile' intestine nuclei. *Nature, Lond.* **210**, 1240.

13. GROBSTEIN, C. (1964). Cytodifferentiation and its controls. *Science, N.Y.* **143**, 643.

14. FELL, P. E. and GROBSTEIN, C. (1968). The influence of extra-epithelial factors on the growth of embryonic mouse pancreatic epithelium. *Expl. Cell Res.* **53**, 301.

15. KONIGSBERG, I. R. (1960). The differentiation of cross-striated myofibrils in short-term cell structure. *Expl. Cell Res.* **21**, 414.

16. KONIGSBERG, I. R. (1961). Some aspects of myogenesis *in vitro. Circulation* **24**, 447.

17. YASUMURA, Y., TASHJIAN, A. H., and SATO, G. H. (1966). Establishment of four functional, clonal strains of animal cells in culture. *Science, N.Y.* **154**, 1186.

18. MOORE, G. E. (1964). *In vitro* cultures of a pigmented hamster melanoma cell line. *Expl. Cell Res.* **36**, 422.

19. STEVENS, L. C. (1960). Embryonic potency of embryoid bodies derived from a transplantable testicular teratoma of the mouse. *Devl. Biol.* **2**, 285.

20. RICHARDSON, U. I., TASHJIAN, A. H., and LEVINE, L. (1969). Establishment of a clonal strain of hepatoma cells which secrete albumin. *J. Cell Biol.* **40**, 236.

21. AUGUSTI-TOCCO, G. and SATO, G. (1969). Establishment of functional clonal lines of neurons from mouse neuroblastoma. *Proc. natn. Acad. Sci. U.S.A.* **64**, 311.

22. CAHN, R. D. and CAHN, M. B. (1966). Heritability of cellular differentiation: clonal growth and expression of differentiation in retinal pigment cells *in vitro. Proc. natn. Acad. Sci. U.S.A.* **55**, 106.

23. COON,. H. G. (1966). Clonal stability and phenotypic expression of chick cartilage cells *in vitro. Proc. natn. Acad. Sci. U.S.A.* **55**, 66.

24. YAFFE, D. (1968). Retention of differentiation potentialities during prolonged cultivation of myogenic cells. *Proc. natn. Acad. Sci. U.S.A.* **61**, 477.

25. WERZ, G. (1965). Determination and realization of morphogenesis in *Acetabularia. Brookhaven Symp. Biol.,* No. 18, p. 185.

26. HÄMMERLING, J. and ZETSCHE, K. (1966). Zeitliche Steuerung der Formbildung von *Acetabularia. Umschau.* **15**, 489.

27. HÄMMERLING, J. (1963). Nucleo-cytoplasmic interactions in *Acetabularia* and other cells. *A. Rev. Pl. Physiol.* **14**, 65.

28. TARTAR, V. (1961). *The Biology of* Stentor, p. 297. Pergamon Press, Oxford.

29. NEWELL, P. C. (1971). The development of the cellular slime mould *Dictyostelium discoideum:* a model system for the study of cellular differentiation. *Essays Biochem.* **7**, 87.

30. WESSELLS, N. K. and WILT, F. H. (1965). Action of actinomycin D on exocrine pancreas cell differentiation. *J. molec. Biol.* **13**, 767.

31. RUTTER, W. J., WESSELLS, N. K., and GROBSTEIN, C. (1964). Control of specific synthesis in the developing pancreas. *J. nat. Cancer Inst. Monogr.* No. 13, p. 51.

32. WILT, F. H. (1965). Regulation of the initiation of chick embryo hemoglobin synthesis. *J. molec. Biol.* **12**, 331.

33. BARRETT, D. and ANGELO, G. M. (1969). Maternal characteristics of hatching enzymes in hybrid sea urchin embryos. *Expl. Cell Res* **57**, 159.

34. WRIGHT, D. A. and SUBTELNY, S. (1969). Expression of genes controlling enzymes in diploid and androgenetic haploid hybrid frog embryos. *J. Cell Biol.* **43**, 160a.

35. OHNO, S. (1969). The preferential activation of maternally derived alleles in development of interspecific hybrids. *Heterospecific genome interaction. Wistar Institute Symposium Monograph No.* 9, p. 137. Wistar Institute Press, Philadelphia.

36. FARINELLA-FERRUZZA, N. and REVERBERI, G. (1972). Hybrids from fused gigantic ascidian eggs. *Expl. Cell Res.* **73**, 503.

37. LAMBERT, C. C. (1971). Genetic transcription during the development and metamorphosis of the tunicate *Ascidia callosa*. *Expl. Cell Res.* **66**, 401.

38. STANIER, R. Y. (1951). Enzymic adaptation in bacteria. *A. Rev. Microbiol.* **5**, 35.

39. MANDLESTAM, J. and JACOBY, G. A. (1964). Induction and multisensitive end-product repression in the enzymic pathway degrading mandelate in *Pseudomonas fluorescens*. *Biochem. J.* **94**, 569.

40. KALLMAN, F. and GROBSTEIN, C. (1964). Fine structure of differentiating mouse pancreatic exocrine cells in transfilter culture. *J. Cell Biol.* **28**, 399.

41. WESSELLS, N. K. and EVANS, J. (1968). Ultrastructural studies of early morphogenesis and cytodifferentiation in the embryonic mammalian pancreas. *Devl. Biol.* **17**, 413.

42. WESSELLS, N. K. and COHEN, J. H. (1967). Early pancreas organogenesis: morphogenesis, tissue interactions and mass effects. *Devl. Biol.* **15**, 237.

43. DEUCHAR, E. M. (1970). Effect of cell number on the type and stability of differentiation in amphibian ectoderm. *Expl. Cell Res.* **59**, 341.

44. LOEWENSTEIN, W. R. and KANNO, Y. (1964). Studies on an epithelial (gland) cell junction. I. Modifications of surface membrane permeability. *J. Cell Biol.* **22**, 565.

45. LOEWENSTEIN, W. R., SOCOLAR, S. J., HIGASHINO, S., KANNO, Y., and DAVIDSON, N. (1965). Intercellular communication: renal, urinary bladder, sensory, and salivary gland cells. *Science, N.Y.* **149**, 295.

46. LOEWENSTEIN, W. R. and KANNO, Y. (1967). Intercellular communication and tissue growth. I. Cancerous growth. *J. Cell Biol.* **33**, 225.

47. LOEWENSTEIN, W. R. and PENN, R. D. (1967). Intercellular communication and tissue growth. II. Tissue regeneration. *J. Cell Biol.* **33**, 235.

48. SPITZER, N. C. (1970). Low resistance connections between cells in the developing anther of the lily. *J. Cell Biol.* **45**, 565.

49. REVEL, J. P., YEE, A. G., and HUDSPETH, A. J. (1971). Gap junctions between electronically coupled cells in tissue culture and in brown fat. *Proc. natn. Acad. Sci. U.S.A.* **68**, 2924.

50. KANNO, Y. and LOEWENSTEIN, W. R. (1966). Cell-to-cell passage of large molecules. *Nature, Lond.* **212**, 629.

51. SHERIDAN, J. D. (1968). Electrophysiological evidence for low-resistance intercellular junctions in the early chick embryo. *J. Cell Biol.* **37**, 650.

52. ITO, S. and LOEWENSTEIN, W. R. (1969). Ionic communication between early embryonic cells. *Devl. Biol.* **19**, 228.

53. LOEWENSTEIN, W. R. (1968). Emergence of order in tissues and organs. *Devl. Biol. Suppl.* **2**, p. 151.

54. TUPPER, J., SAUNDERS, J. W., and EDWARDS, C. (1970). The onset of electrical communication between cells in the developing starfish embryo. *J. Cell Biol.* **46**, 187.

55. LENTZ, T. L. and TRINKAUS, J. P. (1971). Differentiation of the junctional complex of surface cells in the developing *Fundulus* blastoderm. *J. Cell Biol.* **48**, 455.

56. WEISS, M. C. and GREEN, H. (1967). Human-mouse hybrid cell lines containing partial complements of human chromosomes and functioning human genes. *Proc. natn. Acad. Sci. U.S.A.* **58**, 1104.
57. MIGEON, B. R. and MILLER, C. S. (1968). Human-mouse somatic cell hybrids with single human chromosome (group E): link with thymidine kinase activity. *Science, N.Y.* **162**, 1005.
58. MILLER, O. J., ALLDERDICE, P. W., MILLER, D. A., BREG, W. R., and MIGEON, B. R. (1971). Assignment of human thymidine kinase gene locus to chromosome 17 by identification of its distinctive quinacrine fluorescence in a man-mouse somatic hybrid. *Science, N.Y.* **173**, 244.
59. RUDDLE, F. H., CHAPMAN, V. M., RICCIUTI, F., MURNANE, M., KLEBE, R. and MEERA KAHN, P. (1971). Linkage relationships of seventeen human gene loci as determined by man-mouse somatic cell hybrids. *Nature, Lond. New Biol.* **232**, 69.
60. DAVIDSON, R., EPHRUSSI, B., and YAMAMOTO, K. (1968). Regulation of melanin synthesis in mammalian cells, as studied by somatic hybridization. I. Evidence for negative control. *J. cell. Physiol.* **72**, 115.
61. DAVIDSON, R. and YAMAMOTO, K. (1968). Regulation of melanin synthesis in mammalian cells, as studied by somatic hybridization. II. The level of regulation of 3, 4-dihydroxyphenylalanine oxidase. *Proc. natn. Acad. Sci. U.S.A.* **60**, 894.
62. DAVIDSON, R. L. (1972). Regulation of melanin synthesis in mammalian cells: effect of gene dosage on the expression of differentiation. *Proc. natn. Acad. Sci. U.S.A.* **69**, 951.
63. FOUGÈRE, C., RUIZ, F., and EPHRUSSI, B. (1972). Gene dosage dependence of pigment synthesis in melanoma x fibroblast hybrids. *Proc. natn. Acad. Sci. U.S.A.* **69**, 330.
64. WEISS, M. C. and CHAPLAIN, M. (1971). Expression of differentiated functions in hepatoma cell hybrids: reappearance of tyrosine aminotransferase inducibility after the loss of chromosomes. *Proc. natn. Acad. Sci. U.S.A.* **68**, 3026.
65. WEISS, M. C., BERTOLOTTI, R., and PETERSON, J. A. (1972). Expression and re-expression of tissue specific functions in hepatoma cell hybrids. *Molecular genetics and developmental biology* (ed. M. SUSSMAN), p. 425. Prentice-Hall, New Jersey.
66. BERTOLOTTI, R. and WEISS, M. C. (1972). Expression of differentiated functions in hepatoma cell hybrids. VI. Extinction and re-expression of liver alcohol dehydrogenase. *Biochimie*, **54**, 195.
67. SPARKES, R. S. and WEISS, M. C. (1973). Expression of differentiated functions in hepatoma cell hybrids: alanine amino transferase. *Proc. natn. Acad. Sci. U.S.A.* **70**, 377.
68. KLEBE, R. J., CHEN, T., and RUDDLE, F. H. (1970). Mapping of a human genetic regulator element by somatic cell genetic analysis. *Proc. natn. Acad. Sci. U.S.A.* **66**, 1220.
69. WIENER, F., COCHRAN, A., KLEIN, G., and HARRIS, H. (1972). Genetic determinants of morphological differentiation in hybrid tumors. *J. natn. Cancer Inst.* **48**, 465.
70. TEMIN, H. W. (1971). The protovirus hypothesis: speculations on the significance of RNA-directed DNA synthesis for normal development and for carcinogenesis. *J. natn. Cancer Inst.* **46**, 111 (Feb.).
71. FRIDLENDER, B., FRY, M., BOLDEN, A., and WEISSBACH, A. (1972). A new synthetic RNA-dependent DNA polymerase from human tissue culture cells. *Proc. natn. Acad. Sci. U.S.A.* **69**, 452.

72. WARD, D. C., HUMPHRYES, K. C., and WEINSTEIN, J. B. (1972). Synthetic RNA-dependent DNA polymerase activity in normal rat liver and hepatomas. *Nature, Lond.* 237, 499.

73. BOBROW, S. N., GRAHAM SMITH, R., REITZ, M. S., and GALLO, R. C. (1972). Stimulated normal lymphocytes contain a ribonuclease-sensitive DNA polymerase distinct from viral RNA-directed polymerase. *Proc. natn. Acad. Sci. U.S.A.* 69, 3228.

74. KANG, C.-Y. and TEMIN, H. W. (1973). Early DNA-RNA complex from the endogenous RNA-directed DNA polymerase activity of uninfected chicken embryos. *Nature, Lond. New Biol.* 242, 206.

75. COOK, P. R. (1973). Hypothesis on differentiation and the inheritance of gene superstructure. *Nature, Lond.* 245, 23.

76. NOVICK, A. and WEINER, M. (1957). Enzyme induction as an all-or-none phenomenon. *Proc. natn. Acad. Sci. U.S.A.* 43, 553.

77. LANDMAN, O. E. and HALLE, S. (1963). Enzymically and physically induced inheritance changes in *Bacillus subtilis. J. molec. Biol.* 7, 721.

78. MILLER, I. L., ZSIGRAY, R. M., and LANDMAN, O. E. (1967). The formation of protoplasts and quasi spheroplasts in normal and chloramphenicol-pretreated *Bacillus subtilis. J. gen. Microbiol.* 49, 513.

79. TICHY, P. and LANDMAN, O. E. (1969). Transformation in quasi spheroplasts of *Bacillus subtilis. J. Bact.* 97, 42.

80. MILLER, I. L., WIEBE, W., and LANDMAN, O. E. (1968). Gelatin-induced reversion of protoplasts of *Bacillus subtilis* to the bacillary form: photomicrographic study. *J. Bact.* 96, 2171.

81. MIGEON, B. R. (1972). Stability of X chromosomal inactivation in human somatic cells. *Nature, Lond.* 239, 87.

82. SCHNEIDER, J. A. and WEISS, M. C. (1971). Expression of differentiated functions in hepatoma cell hybrids. I. Tyrosine aminotransferase in hepatoma-fibroblast hybrids. *Proc. natn. Acad. Sci. U.S.A.* 68, 127.

83. BERTOLOTTI, R. and WEISS, M. C. (1972). Expression of differentiated functions in hepatoma cell hybrids. II. Aldolase. *J. cell. Physiol.* 79, 211.

84. DAVIDSON, R. L. and BENDA, P. (1970). Regulation of specific functions of glial cells in somatic hybrids. II. Control of inducibility of glycerol-3-phosphate dehydrogenase. *Proc. natn. Acad. Sci. U.S.A.* 67, 1870.

85. BENDA, P. and DAVIDSON, R. L. (1971). Regulation of specific functions of glial cells in somatic hybrids. I. Control of S100 protein. *J. cell. Physiol.* 78, 209.

86. BENEDICT, W. F., NEBERT, D. W., and THOMPSON, E. B. (1972). Expression of aryl hydrocarbon hydroxylase induction and suppression of tyrosine aminotransferase induction in somatic cell hybrids. *Proc. natn. Acad. Sci. U.S.A.* 69, 2179.

87. SONNENSCHEIN, C., RICHARDSON, U. I., and TASHJIAN, A. H. (1971). Loss of growth hormone production following hybridization of a functional rat pituitary cell strain with a mouse fibroblast line. *Expl. Cell Res.* 69, 336.

88. JAMI, J., FAILLY, C., and RITZ, E. (1973). Lack of expression of differentiation in mouse teratoma–fibroblast somatic cell hybrids. *Expl. Cell Res.* 76, 191.

89. KOYAMA, H. and ONO, T. (1970). Initiation of a differentiated function (hyaluronic acid synthesis) by hybrid formation in culture. *Biochim. biophys. Acta* 217, 477.

90. PETERSON, J. A. and WEISS, M. C. (1972). Expression of differentiated functions in hepatoma cell hybrids: induction of mouse albumin production

in rat hepatoma-mouse fibroblast hybrids. *Proc. natn. Acad. Sci. U.S.A.* **69,** 571.

91. GREEN, H., EPHRUSSI, B., YOSHIDA, M., and HAMERMAN, D. (1966). Synthesis of collagen and hyaluronic acid by fibroblast hybrids. *Proc. natn. Acad. Sci. U.S.A.* **55,** 41.

92. MINNA, J., NELSON, P., PEACOCK, J., GLAZER, D., and NIRENBERG, M. (1971). Genes for neuronal properties expressed in neuroblastoma X L cell hybrids. *Proc. natn. Acad. Sci. U.S.A.* **68,** 234.

93. PERIMAN, P. (1970). IgG synthesis in hybrid cells from an antibody-producing mouse myeloma and a L cell substrain. *Nature, Lond.* **228,** 1086.

94. COFFINO, P., KNOWLES, B., NATHENSON, S. G., and SCHARFF, M. D. (1971). Suppression of immunoglobulin synthesis by cellular hybridization. *Nature, New Biol.* **231,** 87.

95. MOHIT, B. (1971). Immunoglobulin G and free kappa-chain synthesis in different clones of a hybrid cell line. *Proc. natn. Acad. Sci. U.S.A.* **68,** 3045.

96. COTTON, R. G. H. and MILSTEIN, C. (1973). Fusion of two immunoglobulin-producing myeloma cells. *Nature, Lond.* **244,** 42.

97. SZPIRER, C. (1973). Reactivation of chick erythrocyte nuclei in heterokaryons with rat hepatoma cells. *Expl. Cell Res.* (In press.)

98. GROSS, P. R. (1967). The control of protein synthesis in embryonic development and differentiation. *Curr. Top. develop. Biol.* **2,** 1.

99. BOVERI, T. (1901). Über die Polarität des Seeigeleies. *Verh. phys.-med. Ges. Würzb.* **34,** 145.

100. URSPRUNG, H. and NÖTHIGER, R. (eds). (1972). *The biology of imaginal discs.* Springer Verlag, Berlin, Heidelberg, New York.

101. GEHRING, W. (1972). The stability of the determined state in cultures of imaginal discs in *Drosophila.* In *The Biology of imaginal discs* (eds. H. URSPRIUNG and R. NÖTHIGER), p. 35. Springer Verlag, Berlin, Heidelberg, New York.

102. EGUCHI, G. and OKADA, T. S. (1973). Differentiation of lens tissue from the progeny of chick retinal pigment cells cultured *in vitro*: a demonstration of a switch of cell types in clonal cell culture. *Proc. natn. Acad. Sci. U.S.A.* **70,** 1495.

Author index

Aaij, C., 72
Abercrombie, M., 102
Aboud, M., 44
Abrams, R., 75
Abrass, J. B., 76
Acs, G., 18, 69
Adams, D. H., 71
Adesnik, M., 76
Adhya, S., 43
Adler, K., 41
Agsteribbe, E., 72
Allderdice, P. W., 140, 163
Allfrey, V. G., 101, 104
Aloj, S. M., 101
Alpers, D. H., 40
Ames, B. N., 100
Anderson, F., 73
Anderson, W., 41–2
Angelo, G. M., 161
Apel, K., 16
Appel, S. H., 40
Arditti, R., 42
Arnold, E. A., 104
Aronow, A., 72
Aronson, A. I., 45, 68, 72
Artman, M., 69
Asano, K., 69
Ashburner, M., 102
Ashworth, J. M., 44
Astrachan, L., 72
Attardi, B., 70–1, 107
Attardi, G., 70–1, 76, 107
Augusti-Tocco, G., 161
Auricchio, F., 108
Avadham, G., 76
Aviv, H., 74

Bacon, D. F., 44
Baglioni, C., 75
Balhorn, R., 104
Ball, E., 160
Ballesteros, A. O., 100
Ballesteros-Olmo, A., 100
Baltus, E., 16
Barondes, S. H., 141

Barrett, D., 161
Barros, C., 18
Barton, R. W., 100
Bartoov, B., 73
Bass, R. E., 40
Baudisch, W., 102
Baxter, J. D., 18, 99
Beato, M., 75
Beckwith, J. R., 40, 42
Bedford, D., 139
Been, A. C., 103
Beermann, W., 102
Bellamy, A. R., 68
Belozersky, A. N., 68
Benda, P., 164
Benedict, W. F., 164
Benson, C. E., 42
Benzer, S., 39
Béraud, G., 19
Berberich, M. A., 43
Berendes, H. O., 106
Berg, P., 106
Berger, S., 16
Bergstrand, A., 69
Berissi, H., 100
Berlin, C. M., 20, 107
Berlin, I., 15
Berlowitz, L., 101, 104
Bernardi, A., 43
Bernhard, W., 72, 106
Berns, A. J. M., 75
Bertolotti, R., 163–4
Beuzard, Y., 100
Beyreuther, K., 40–1
Billing, R. J., 72
Birnboim, H. C., 70–1
Bladen, H. A., 106
Blasi, F., 100–1
Bloemendal, H., 75
Blundell, M. R., 44
Bobrow, S. N., 17, 164
Bock, R. M., 43, 100
Bodmer, W. F., 44
Boeker, F. A., 71
Bolden, A., 16, 163

Bolton, E. T., 68
Bolund, L., 104–6, 139
Bonner, J., 70
Boone, C., 140
Borst, P., 72
Borun, T. W., 75
Bosmann, H. B., 108
Bourgeois, S., 41
Boyadjiev, S. I., 72
Boyd, J., 102
Boyd, Y. L., 140
Brachet, J., 17
Bramwell, M. E., 40, 70, 72, 139–40
Brandhorst, B. P., 72
Brawerman, G., 75
Breckenridge, B., 71
Breg, W. R., 140, 163
Brehmeyer, B. A., 42
Bremer, H. J., 16
Brenner, M., 100
Brenner, S., 68
Brimacombe, R., 73
Britten, R. J., 68–9
Brown, D. G., 104
Brown, D. M., 43
Brown, J. L., 43
Brown, S. W., 101–2
Brownlee, G. G., 75
Bruns, G. P., 17, 71, 107, 141
Brunt, J. V., 69
Bryson, V., 16
Bultmann, H., 103
Burger, M., 44
Burns, R. O., 100
Burny, A., 72
Burr, H. E., 74, 76
Bussard, B., 40
Butcher, F. R., 18
Butcher, R. W., 41
Byrne, R., 106

Cahn, M. B., 161
Cahn, R. D., 161
Cailleau, R., 17
Callan, H. G., 102
Cameron, I. L., 102, 139
Campagne, R. N., 101
Campbell, G. le M., 139
Canellakis, E. S., 75
Capecchi, M. R., 43
Carlsson, S.-A., 139
Caro, L. G., 70
Cartwright, E. M., 75
Caskey, T., 73
Cattanach, B. M., 103
Cavicchi, P., 19
Chalkley, R., 104
Chantrenne, H., 72
Chaplain, M., 163
Chapman, V. M., 163

Chargaff, E., 68
Chen, B., 41–2
Chen, D., 45
Chen, T., 163
Chen, T.-R., 140
Cheng, P.-Y., 70
Chet, I., 19
Chong-Cheng, C., 100
Clauss, H., 15
Clement, A. C., 17
Clements, G. B., 140
Clemetson, K., 42
Clever, U., 102–4, 107
Cline, A. L., 43, 100
Coccuci, S. M., 141
Cochran, A., 163
Coffey, D. S., 104
Coffino, P., 165
Cohen, J. H., 162
Cohen, S. S., 39, 69
Cohn, M., 39, 41, 107
Collins, F., 103
Colot, H. V., 17
Comings, D. E., 101, 104
Comstock, J. P., 74, 141
Connaway, S., 42
Conway, T. W., 44
Cook, P. R., 140, 164
Coombs, R. R. A., 139
Coon, H. G., 161
Cooper, H. K., 105
Cooper, H. L., 72
Coote, J. G., 44
Cortese, R., 100
Cousineau, G. H., 18
Cowan, N. J., 75
Cowen, D. M., 139
Cowie, D. B., 68
Cozzone, A., 69
Craig, E., 76
Crawley, J. C. W., 70, 106
Crick, F. H. C., 102
Crocker, T. T., 17
Crouse, H. V., 101
Curtiss, R., 44

Da Cunha, A. B., 103
Dalgarno, L., 69
Daneholt, B., 72, 103, 141
Danon, D., 102
Darnell, J. E., 70–2, 75–6
Darrow, J. M., 103
Darzynkiewicz, Z., 105–6, 139
Davern, C. I., 40, 68
Davidson, N., 162
Davidson, R., 163
Davidson, R. L., 163–4
Deák, I. I., 140
DeAngelo, A. B., 99
De Crombrugghe, B., 41–3

Deggins, B. A., 160
De Hauwer, G., 44, 76
Dehlinger, P. J., 108
De Kloet, S. R., 70
De Maggio, A. E., 19, 45
Denamur, R., 75
Dendy, P. R., 140
Dennis, D., 75
Dessev, G. N., 72
Dethlefsen, L., 18, 99
Deuchar, E. M., 162
Dewey, H. K., 18
Dickson, E., 102
Dieckmann, M., 106
Dillard, W. L., 16
Dingman, C. W., 72
Doctor, B., 73
Dolapchiev, L. B., 72
Doyle, D., 103, 107
Drysdale, J. W., 18
Dubin, D. T., 73
Duckworth, D. H., 40
Duerksen, J. D., 68
Dure, L. S., 19, 45
Dworkin, M., 45

Eagle, H., 107
Ebel, J. P., 73
Ecker, R. E., 17
Edmonds, M., 75–6
Edström, J.-E., 71, 102, 141
Edwards, C., 162
Eggen, K., 43
Ege, T., 139
Egyházi, E., 141
Ehresmann, C., 73
Eliasson, N. A., 69
Eliceiri, G. L., 140
Ellem, K. A. O., 72
Ellgaard, E. G., 104
Emerson, C. P., 71
Emmer, M., 41–2
Engelberg, H., 69
Engelsberg, E., 42–3
Ephrussi, B., 163, 165
Eron, L., 42
Espmark, J. H., 139
Evans, E. P., 139
Evans, H. J., 101
Evans, J., 162

Fabricant, R., 40
Fagraeus, A., 139
Failly, C., 164
Fakan, S., 72
Fanning, E., 41
Farber, F. E., 16, 69
Farinella-Ferruzza, N., 162
Faust, C., 74
Feigelson, P., 75

Feldherr, C. M., 107
Fell, P. E., 161
Fellner, P., 73
Fenichel, I. R., 106
Fenwick, M. L., 70
Ference, M., 43, 100
Fetherolf, K., 40
Ficq, A., 17
Fiers, W., 75
Filner, P., 108
Fischer, S., 71, 107, 141
Fisher, H. W., 70, 140
Fitt, P. S., 17
Fleischman, R., 107
Ford, C. E., 101, 103, 138–9
Forro, F., 70
Forschhammer, J., 76
Fougère, C., 163
Fraccaro, M., 103
Francke, U., 104
Freeman, K. B., 73
French, R. C., 40
Frenster, J. H., 101
Fridlender, B., 16, 163
Fry, M., 16, 69, 163
Fryer, A., 103
Fujimoto, G. I., 99
Fujimura, R., 40
Fukamachi, S., 73

Gall, J. G., 102
Gallo, R. C., 17, 164
Gallwitz, D., 71
Garrido, M. C., 103
Gauthier, M., 19
Gaye, P., 75
Geisler, N., 41
Geller, B. D., 20
Genchev, D. D., 72
Giannelli, F., 103
Gibor, A., 16
Gielow, L., 43
Gierer, A., 69, 73
Gierer, L., 69
Gilbert, L. I., 105
Gilbert, W., 40, 68
Girard, M., 70
Glass, R. D., 107
Glazer, D., 165
Gledhill, B. L., 105
Goldberg, I. H., 19
Goldberger, R. F., 43, 100–1
Goldstein, L., 17, 70
Goodman, H. M., 73
Goodridge, A. G., 108
Gordon, M., 18
Gorovsky, M. A., 104
Gorski, J., 75
Gots, J. S., 42
Gottesman, M. E., 41–3

Gowans, J. L., 139
Grace, D. M., 139
Graham, A. F., 68
Graham Smith, R., 17, 164
Grand, R. J., 19
Granner, D., 104
Granner, D. K., 18, 99
Gray, J., 101
Green, H., 140, 163, 165
Greenberg, J. R., 76
Greenblatt, J., 43
Greengard, O., 18
Greenhouse, G. A., 18
Grieninger, G. E., 16
Grobstein, C., 19, 161–2
Gronenborn, B., 41
Groner, Y., 100
Gros, F., 39–40, 68–9, 70–1
Gross, M., 17, 99
Gross, P. R., 17–19
Grossbach, U., 102–3
Gruber, M., 101
Gurdon, J. B., 74, 76, 106, 140, 160–1
Gustavsson, J., 103
Gutnick, D. L., 43

Hadjiolov, A. A., 72–3
Haegeman, G., 75
Hall, C., 73
Halle, S., 164
Hallett, J., 103
Hamerman, D., 165
Hamerton, J. L., 101, 103
Hamilton, T. H., 141
Hamlin, J., 101
Hammarsten, E., 69
Hämmerling, J., 15–17, 161
Handmaker, S. D., 140
Hannover, R., 105
Harris, H., 16, 44, 68–73, 106–7, 138–41
Harvey, E. B., 17
Hatfield, D., 42, 73
Hatfield, G. W., 100
Haxo, F. T., 99
Hayes, D., 69, 73
Hayes, F., 69, 73
Hayman, D. L., 101
Heard, J. G., 19
Hershey, A. D., 68
Hess, R., 69
Heywood, S. M., 75
Hiatt, H. H., 68, 70
Higa, A., 68
Higashino, S., 162
Hildebrandt, H. C., 160
Hirvonen, A. P., 44
Hnilica, L. S., 106
Hofnung, M., 42
Hogness, D. S., 107
Holder, J. W., 74

Holtzman, E., 106
Horowitz, J., 40
Horowitz, S. B., 106
Hosick, H., 103
Houdebine, L., 75
Housman, D., 140
Houssais, J.-F., 71
Howell, R. R., 71
Hsu, T. C., 101
Huang, R.-C., 70
Hudspeth, A. J., 162
Huez, G., 72
Human, M. L., 39
Humphryes, K. C., 17, 164
Humphreys, T., 72
Hunt, T., 18
Hwang, M., 70, 107
Hynes, R. O., 18

Ilan, J., 101
Ihle, J. N., 19, 45
Inglis, A. M., 72
Ippen, K., 41
Irr, J., 42
Isaacson, J. H., 103
Ishihama, A., 69
Israeli-Reches, M., 69
Ito, S., 106, 162
Itzhaki, R. F., 105
Ivanyi, J., 73
Izawa, M., 16, 141

Jackson, E. N., 76
Jacob, F., 39–40, 68
Jacobs-Lorena, M., 75
Jacoby, G. A., 162
Jainchill, J., 101
Jakes, K., 44
Jami, J., 164
Jarvis, J. M., 75
Johns, E. W., 104
Johnson, R. T., 139
Jones, K. W., 102
Jones, O. W., 106
Jones, R. F., 74
Jones-Mortimer, M. C., 42
Joshi, P. C., 160
Jost, J.-P., 18

Kaempfer, R., 100
Kafatos, F. C., 19
Kahn, P., 163
Kakefuda, T., 72
Kallman, F., 162
Kaltreider, H. B., 71
Kang, C.-Y., 164
Kanno, Y,. 106, 162
Katchalski, E., 45
Katoh, A., 19
Katz, L., 42

Kaufman, J., 100
Kawashina, K., 141
Kay, J. E., 72
Keck, K., 15
Kelley, D. E., 73, 76, 107
Kellogg, D., 73
Kemp, J. D., 107
Kennell, D., 40, 69, 76
Keynan, A., 68
Khairallah, E. A., 18
Kidson, C., 70
Kiely, M. L., 74
Kijima, S., 72
Killander, D., 104–5
King, T. J., 160
Kinoshita, J. H., 19
Kirby, K. S., 70
Kirk, D. L., 19
Kitazume, Y., 68
Klebe, R., 163
Klein, G., 163
Klemm, A., 41
Klevecz, R. R., 107
Kloppstech, K., 16
Knight, E. J., 139
Knopf, P. M., 73
Knowles, B., 165
Koch, A. L., 107
Koehn, P. V., 19
Kohen, C., 106
Kohen, E., 106
Kohlmeier, V., 40
Konigsberg, I. R., 161
Kovach, J. S., 43, 100
Koyama, H., 164
Krause, M. O., 105
Kroeger, H., 105–6
Kuan, M., 76
Kurland, C. G., 68
Kuwano, M., 44

Labat, D. D., 160
Labaw, L. W., 68
Labrie, F., 19
LaCour, L. F., 70
Laird, C. D., 102
Lambert, C. C., 162
Lamfrom, H., 73
Landman, O. E., 164
Landy, A., 69
Lane, B. G., 70
Lane, C. D., 74–5, 140
Langendorf, H., 105
Langhans, T., 139
LaTorre, J., 76
Laufer, H., 103
Laux, B. E., 75
Lavallé, R., 44, 76
Lazarus, H. M., 71, 107
Leder, P., 74

Lee, N., 42
Lee, S. Y., 75
Lee-Huang, S., 100
Lele, K. P., 104
Lemay, A., 19
Lentz, T. L., 162
Letourneau, N. W., 71
Levin, J. G., 73, 106
Levine, L., 161
Levinson, B. B., 18, 99
Levinthal, C., 40, 68
Levy, H. R., 107
Lezzi, M., 105
Lim, L., 75
Lin, S., 41
Lindsten, J., 103
Lingrel, J. B., 74–6, 140
Lipmann, F., 44
Littau, V. C., 101
Little, E. P., 107
Littlefield, J. W., 140
Lockard, R. E., 74, 140
Lodish, H. F., 43, 75, 101
Loeb, J. N., 71
Loewenstein, W. R., 106, 162
London, I. M., 17, 18, 70, 100
Longlands, M., 45
Loomis, W. F., 45
Louis, B. G., 17
Lowy, B. A., 71, 107, 141
Luria, S. E., 39
Lyon, A., 40
Lyon, M. F., 101, 103–4

McCarl, R. L., 18
McCarthy, B. J., 68
McClure, F. T., 69
McFall, E., 40
McGregor, D. D., 139
McGuire, V. M., 103
McKibbin, J. B., 18
McKinnell, R. G., 160
McKnight, G. S., 74, 99, 140
McLellan, W. L., 44
McLeish, J., 106
McQuillen, K., 68
Mach, B., 74
Magasanik, B., 68
Maheshwari, N., 70
Malamy, M. H., 44
Malkin, L. I., 18
Mandelstam, J., 44–5, 107, 162
Mapes, M. O., 160
Marbaix, G., 72, 74, 76, 140
Marcaud, L., 70–1
Marchis-Mouren, G., 69
Margolies, M. N., 43
Markov, G. G., 72
Marks, J., 139
Marrs, B. L., 76

Marshall, R., 73
Martin, D., 108
Martin, P. G., 101
Martin, R. G., 43, 100
Martin, T. E., 19
Marvaldi, J., 69
Master, R. W. P., 17
Matsubara, K., 40
Matthaei, J. H., 73
Matthews, M. B., 74, 75
Mayo, V. S., 70
Mazia, D., 17
McKnight, G. S., 74, 99
Means, A. R., 74, 141
Mears, K., 160
Mendecki, J., 75
Meronk, F., 42
Meselson, M., 68
Meyers, M., 100
Micou, J., 17
Midgley, J. E. M., 68
Migeon, B. R., 104, 140, 163, 164
Miller, C. S., 140, 163
Miller, D. A., 163
Miller, G. J., 104
Miller, I. L., 164
Miller, J. H., 41
Miller, O. J., 140, 163
Milstein, C., 75
Min Jou, W., 75
Minna, J., 165
Mirsky, A. E., 101, 104
Mittwoch, U., 102, 104
Mizuno, N., 69
Molloy, G. R., 76, 107
Monier, R., 69
Monneron, A., 106
Monod, J., 39–40, 68, 107
Monroy, A., 18
Moore, C., 105
Moore, G. E., 161
Moore, R. J., 141
Morgante, J. S., 103
Morrison, M. R., 75
Morrison, T. G., 44
Mosley, V. M., 68
Moulé, Y., 106
Moyer, A. N., 19
Moyer, W. A., 18
Muir, C., 106
Müller-Hill, B., 40–1
Munro, H. N., 18
Murnane, M., 163
Murphy, W., 76

Nakada, D., 43
Nakase, Y., 103
Nakazato, H., 76
Naono, S., 39–40, 69
Nathans, D., 43, 73–4

Nathenson, S. G., 165
Nebert, D. W., 164
Nelson, P., 165
Nesbitt, M., 104
Newell, P. C., 18, 45, 161
Nirenberg, M. W., 73, 106, 141, 165
Nissley, S. P., 41, 42
Nitz-Litzow, D., 105
Nomura, M., 40
Norberg, B., 69
Notani, G., 73
Novick, A., 164

Ochoa, S., 100
Oeschger, M. P., 43
Ohno, S., 101, 103, 162
Oka, T., 19
Okada, Y., 139
Okamoto, K., 40
Oldmixon, E., 69
Olins, A. L., 105
Olins, D. E., 105
Oliver, D., 104
Oliver, I. T., 100
O'Malley, B. W., 74, 141
Ono, T., 164
Ord, M. G., 104
Osawa, S., 69
Osborn, M., 74–5
Osborne, D. J., 45
Otaka, E., 69
Owen, M., 71
Oyama, V. I., 107

Paine, P. L., 107
Palacios, R., 74
Palade, P., 69
Pallotta, D., 104
Palmiter, R. D., 19, 99–100
Panitz, R., 102–3
Papaconstantinou, J., 19
Pardee, A. B., 39
Pardue, M. L., 102
Parks, J. S., 41–2
Parnas, H., 70–1, 107
Parsons, P. A., 44
Pastan, I., 41–3
Patel, J., 105
Patel, N., 101
Pavan, C., 103
Peacock, J., 165
Pederson, T., 105
Pelling, C., 101
Pemberton, R., 140
Penman, S., 76, 106
Penn, R. D., 162
Periman, P., 165
Perkins, L. A., 76
Perlman, R. L., 41–2
Perry, R. P., 70, 73, 76, 107

Pestka, S., 73
Peterkin, P. I., 17
Peterson, J. A., 163–4
Pfahl, M., 41
Phang, J. M., 43, 100
Philipson, L., 76
Piez, K. A., 107
Pirrotta, V., 41
Pitot, H. C., 18
Plagemann, P. G. W., 73
Plaut, W., 70
Pogo, B. G. T., 104
Pollack, Y., 100
Potter, V. R., 18
Power, J., 42
Prescott, D. M., 17, 102, 139
Pressman, B. C., 105
Prestidge, L. S., 39
Primakoff, P., 69
Ptashne, M., 41, 241

Rabinowitz, M., 17, 99
Raff, R. A., 17
Raghavan, V., 19, 45
Ralph, R. K., 70
Rasch, E. M., 103
Rechler, M. M., 43
Regelson, W., 104
Reichard, P., 69
Reich, E., 18, 69
Reich, J., 19
Reif-Lehrer, L., 19
Reinert, J., 160
Reitz, M. S., 17, 164
Reuter, W., 17
Revel, J. P., 162
Revel, M., 100
Reverberi, G., 161
Rhoads, R. E., 74, 99, 140
Ricciuti, F., 163
Rich, A., 73
Richardson, V. I., 161, 164
Richter, G., 15
Riggs, A. D., 41
Righetti, P., 107
Rigler, R., 104, 105
Riley, M., 39
Riley, W. T., 70
Ringborg, U., 141
Ringertz, N. R., 104–6, 139
Risebrough, R. W., 68
Ritz, E., 164
Robbins, E., 105
Robert, M., 105
Roberts, R. B., 68
Roberts, W. K., 70
Robison, G. A., 41
Rodgers, A., 70
Rodriguez, L., 104
Rodvien, R., 100

Rogers, M. E., 106
Romball, C. G., 103
Rosas del Valle, M., 45
Rosenfeld, G. C., 74, 141
Rosenfeld, M. G., 76
Rotman, B., 107
Roth, R., 44
Rottman, F., 73
Rothman-Denes, L., 43, 100
Rourke, A. W., 75
Rubin, R. H., 99
Rubinstein, L., 107
Ruddle, F. H., 140, 163
Rudkin, G. T., 102
Ruebush, T. K., 69
Ruiz, F., 163
Rusch, H. P., 19
Rutter, W. J., 19, 161
Rutman, R. J., 76
Rydlander, L., 141

Sabath, L. D., 44
Sager, R., 16
Salditt, M., 76
Santer, M., 69
Santi, D. V., 42
Sarid, S., 45
Sato, G. H., 161
Sato, S., 141
Saunders, G. I., 40
Saunders, J. W., 162
Saunders, P. P., 40
Scharff, M. D., 165
Scherrer, K., 70–1
Schimke, R. T., 19–20, 74, 99, 107, 140
Schin, K. S., 103
Schleif, R., 43
Schlessinger, D., 44
Schmitz, A., 41
Schneeberger, E. E., 139
Schneider, A. B., 42
Schneider, J. A., 164
Schoefl, G. I., 138
Schultz, G. A., 40
Schütz, G., 71, 75
Schwartz, A. G., 140
Schwartz, J. H., 73
Schwartz, M., 42
Schwartz, T., 76
Schweiger, E., 99
Schweiger, H.-G., 15–17, 99
Scott, J. F., 71
Scott Ramsey, W., 45
Searle, A. G., 103
Seed, R. W., 19
Sekeris, C. E., 71
Selvig, S. E., 17
Sedat, J., 40
Serfling, E., 103
Shafiq, A., 18, 69

Shaler, R. C., 18
Sheridan, J. D., 162
Shimada, K., 41
Sheppard, D., 42
Sheridan, J. W., 72
Shimura, Y., 43
Short, R. V., 103
Sidebottom, E., 139–40
Siebert, G., 105–6
Signer, E. R., 40
Silman, N., 69
Silpananta, P., 108
Siminovitch, L. S., 39–40, 68
Singer, C. E., 100
Singer, R. H., 76
Sinsheimer, R. L., 40, 69
Skutelsky, E., 102
Smellie, R. M. S., 72
Smiley, J. D., 19
Smith, G. R., 100
Smith, I., 106
Smith, J., 160
Smith, L. D., 17
Smith, M. A., 18
Socolar, S. J., 162
Soeiro, R., 70–2
Sonnenschein, C., 164
Soria, M., 100
Spahr, P.-F., 43
Sparkes, R. S., 163
Spector, A., 19
Spelsberg, T. C., 106
Spencer, T., 16, 70, 72
Spiegelman, S., 69, 107
Spiers, R. S., 20
Spirin, A. S., 68
Spitzer, N. C., 162
Sporn, M. B., 71, 76, 107
Squires, C., 42
Stanier, R. Y., 162
Steens-Lievens, A., 16
Steinberg, R. A., 41
Stellwagen, R. H., 99
Stenius, C., 101
Stent, G. S., 106
Stephenson, E. M., 102
Sterlini, J. M., 45
Stevely, V. S., 104
Stevens, L. C., 161
Stevens, R. H., 74–5, 108
Steward, F. C., 160
Stewart, G. H., 69
Stewart, J. A., 19
Stiegler, P., 73
Stocken, L. A., 104
Storbeck, I., 103
Strous, G. J. A. M., 75
Subtelny, S., 17, 161
Sugiyama, T., 43
Sullivan, D., 74

Summers, N. M., 74
Summers, W. C., 44
Sussman, M., 44–5, 141
Sussman, R. R., 44–5
Sutherland, E. W., 41
Sutton, D. W., 107
Suzuki, H., 41
Svedhem, L., 72
Swan, D., 74
Swanson, C. P., 101
Sweeney, B. M., 99
Sweeney, E. W., 20, 108

Taber, R., 140
Taft, E. B., 71
Takai, M., 69
Tamaoki, T., 70
Tamm, S. L., 17
Tartar, V., 17, 161
Tashjian, A. H., 161, 164
Tata, J. R., 141
Temin, H. W., 163–4
Tencer, R., 17
Terman, S. A., 18
Thomas, R., 43
Thomas, W., 76
Thompson, E. B., 18, 99, 164
Tichy, P., 164
Tiedemann, H., 17
Tiepolo, L., 103
Tomkins, G. M., 18, 40, 71, 99, 108
Trinkaus, J. P., 162
Triplett, E. L., 16
Tsanev, R. G., 72
Tuffli, C. F., 99
Tupper, J., 162
Tushinski, R. J., 75
Tyler, A., 17

Uehlinger, V., 161

Valanju, S., 69
Vanderhoff,, G., 18
Vander Lign, P., 76
van Kraaikamp, M., 75
Varmus, H. E., 41–2
Vasil, V., 160
Vassalli, P., 74
Vaughan, M. H., 72, 76
Venetianer, P., 43
Venkov, P. V., 72
Villarejo, M., 101
Vincent, W. S., 68
Vogel, H. J., 16, 44
Vogel, R. H., 44
Vogel, T., 100
Voll, M. J., 43
Volkin, E., 72
von Ubisch, H., 69

Walker, P. M. B., 102
Wall, R., 75–6
Waller, P. F., 101
Wallraff, H. G., 99
Ward, D. C., 17, 164
Warner, J. R., 70, 72–3
Waters, L. C., 45
Watkins, J. F., 138–9
Watson, J. D., 68
Watts, J. W., 70–1, 107, 139
Weber, M. J., 71
Webster, W. S., 104
Weiner, M., 164
Weinstein, J. B., 17, 164
Weisberg, R. A., 41
Weiss, M. C., 140, 163–4
Weissbach, A., 16, 163
Werz, G., 15–17, 161
Wessells, N. K., 19, 161–2
White, H. B., 75
Whitfield, H. J., 43
Whitley, J. E., 106
Whitten, J. M., 101
Wiebe, W., 164
Wiener, F., 163
Wiesner, R., 18, 69
Wilcox, G., 42
Wilcox, M., 73
Wild, D. G., 44
Wilde, C. E., 17
Wilhelm, J. A., 106
Wilks, W. D., 18
Williamson, A. R., 74–5, 108
Wilt, F. H., 19, 72, 161
Wobus, U., 103
Wolf, G., 107

Wollman, E., 39
Wong, K.-Y., 105
Wood, D. A., 44
Woodard, J., 104
Woodland, H. R., 74, 140
Wool, I. G., 19
Wright, B. E., 99
Wright, D. A., 161
Wyckoff, R. W. G., 68
Wyllie, R. C., 104

Yaffe, D., 161
Yamamoto, K., 163
Yanofsky, C., 76
Yasmineh, W. G., 102
Yasumura, Y., 161
Yawn, D. H., 104
Yčas, M., 68
Yee, A. G., 162
Yoshida, A., 100
Yoshida, K., 19
Yoshida, M., 165
Young, F. G., 19
Ysebaert, M., 75
Yunis, J. J., 102

Zabin, I., 43, 101
Zajdela, F., 70–1
Zamenhof, P. J., 101
Zasloff, M., 100
Zetsche, K., 15–16, 161
Zielke, H. R., 108
Ziff, M., 19
Zinder, N. D., 73
Zsigray, R. M., 164
Zubay, G., 42–3

Subject index

A$_9$ cell, 126–9, 131–2
abscisic acid, 38
Acetabularia, 2, 3, 7, 9, 10, 38, 76, 147–8
  chloroplasts in, 7
  cliftonii, 4
  crenulata, 5
  cytoplasm, 6, 7
    stability of, 9
  genes in, 9
  phosphatase in, 4 (fig.)
acetylation, 91
acetylornithinase, 35
acridine orange, 92
actinomycin D, 12–14, 35, 38, 50, 66, 77–8, 89, 92, 121, 148
activator, 30, 31, 82, 88, 94
adaptation, 37
adenosine 3′,5′-monophosphate (cyclic AMP), 31
adenylic acid, 47, 64, 127
agar, 155
aggregation, 56
albumin, 89, 157
  synthesis, 157
  methylated, 50, 60–1
alkali hydrolysis, 56
alkaline phosphatase, 23, 24, 26, 28
alpha globin, 81
amino acids
  pools of, 53
  sequence of, 1
amoeba, 12
amphibia, 84, 149
ampullae of Lorenzini, 151
amylase synthesis, 14, 145
aneuploid cell lines, 158
animals, 37
anthranilate synthetase, 35
antibody, 14, 80
  anamnestic formation, 14
  specificity of, 144
antigen, 120, 122, 133
  chick, 122–5, 132
  disappearance, 122
  elimination, 123
  human, 122
  mouse, 122
  reappearance, 123–4
  stimuli, 113
antiglobulin reaction, 122
arabinose, 31–3
Arbacia, 11
arg operon, 35
arginase, 98
arginine
  biosynthesis, 36
  repression by, 35
ascidians, 149
autolysis, 88
autoregulation, 33
autosome, 90
avidin, 63

bacillary forms, 155
bacteria, 36
  chromosomes in, 22, 55
  integrity of DNA, 23
  messenger RNA in, 66–8
  nucleus of, 55
  ribosomes in, 54
  spheroplasts in, 50
  spores of, 38
  synthesis of RNA in, 52
bacteriophage, 52, 62
  λ, 30
  φ1, 34
  φ11, 23
  MS2, 33, 64
  T3, 34
  T7, 34
  T-even, 52
  transducing, 67
  translational controls in, 34
  virulent, 67
Balbiani ring, 89
base composition
  DNA-like, 59, 66
  mean, 60
  of RNA, 47, 49
benzoylated DEAE-cellulose, 51

beta globin, 81
birds, 84, 149
Bradysia, 89
B. subtilis cells, 35, 155

caesium chloride, 53
callus, 144
cap,
  development of, 38
  formation of, 3–5, 147
  forming enzymes, 8
  polysaccharides, 4
  species-specific, 4
  wall of, 3
carbon
  metabolizable source of, 26
carcinoma, 144
cartilage, 146
α_s casein, 63
catabolism, 98
catabolite repression, 26, 28, 30, 36
  of β-galactosidase synthesis, 31
cation
  binding, 95
  concentration, 60
  divalent, 92, 121
  intranuclear, 93
  monovalent, 92
cell,
  A9, 126–8, 131–2
  co-operative activity between, 151
  cytoplasm in, 60
  from different species, 112–13
  differentiated, 146
  Ehrlich ascites, 110
  'end', 113
  enucleate, 2, 5, 5 (fig.), 8–10, 12, 77
    cytoplasm in, 11, 12
    fragments of, 12
    growth of, 9
  eukaryotic, 36, 89
  female, 34
  fractionation of, 61
  fusion of, 90, 109, 111–13, 160
  giant, 2, 88, 116
    nucleus, 10
    polytene chromosomes, 83
  heart, 14
  heavy, 53
  HeLa, 58 (fig.), 65 (fig.), 110, 114–15
  hepatoma, 14, 78
  heterozygotic, 149
  higher, 66, 77, 82, 94
  homogenates, 126
  hybrid, 6, 109, 111, 118, 153, 156–7
  incompatability of, 112
  lymphoid, 157
  mononucleate, 111–12, 153, 156
  multinucleate, 109–11, 146
  multiplication of, 112

  in muscle, 146
  myeloma, 157
  nucleus, 10, 54–5, 59, 61, 93, 96
  pancreatic, 14, 148
  permease system in membrane of, 155
  pulse-labelled, 61
  red, 84, 117, 122
  single, 144
  somatic, 153, 156
  systems free of, 33, 62
  undifferentiated, 143
centromeres, 85
chain,
  alpha globin, 81
  beta globin, 81
  elongation of, 79
  immunoglobulin heavy, 79
  incomplete, 80
  length of, 56
  polypeptide, 79–80
  release of, 79
changes
  in chromosomes, 143, 152
  in configuration, 80
  in enzyme level, 37
  phenotypic, 145
  structural, 150, 156
chick
  embryo, 148
    fibroblasts, 116
    muscle tissue, 146
    retina, 160
  erythrocytes, 124–5 (fig.), 127–9 (fig.), 131
  specific
    antigens, 124–5 (fig.), 132
    markers, 131
  surface antigens, 122–4
Chironomus tentans, 86–7, 89
  pallidivittatus, 89
chloramphenicol, 77
chloroplasts
  of *Acetabularia*, 7
  DNA of, 6, 8
  function of, 7
  ribosomes of, 77
  transplantation of, 7
chromatin, 84, 91–2, 95, 119, 155
  condensed, 84
  dispersion of, 19–21
  melting profile of, 91, 121
  protein content of, 93
  sensitivity of, 92
  structure of, 156
chromocentres, 84–5
chromosomes, 37, 55, 89
  bacterial
    integrity of, 23
  changes in, 143, 152
  condensed, 86

chromosomes—*contd*
  deletions from, 87
  disintegration of, 23
  giant polytene, 83, 86
  haploid set of, 90
  homologous, 84
  human, 130
  in hybrid cells, 157
  inactivation of, 83–4, 90
  isolated, 93
  loss of, 153
  maternal, 83, 90
  paternal, 83, 90
  patterns in, 85, 159
  polytene, 89, 92–3, 156
  ribosomal RNA on, 138
  sex, 83
  structure of, 88, 158
  X, 83–4, 90, 157
cilia, 11
circadian rhythm, 77
cocoonase, 14
coding,
  function, 87
  sequences, 85
coenocytic organisms, 11
colonial myxamoebae, 148
condensation, 83–4, 86, 91, 155
constitutive, heterochromatin, 29, 85–6
control, 33, 35, 94, 137
  dual systems, 31
  negative systems, 28–9
  positive systems, 32
  of transcription, 82
  of translation, 32–5, 78, 81–2
cotton seeds, 38
crypticity, 159
β-crystallins, 63
cuticle, 88
cyclic
  adenosine monophosphate, 14, 31, 36
cyst, 38
cytidine, 53
cytidylic acid, 46
cytoplasm, 61, 95, 121
  bridges, 110
  DNA in, 6, 7
  in egg, 149
  foreign, 118
  hybrid, 118
  labelling of RNA in, 55, 60, 133, 135, 136
  mechanisms in, 8, 9, 15
  to nucleus flow, 95, 119
  RNA in, 6, 7, 10, 66, 88
  signals in, 90, 117, 119, 156
  stimuli in, 113

Dasycladaceae, 2
decay, 22, 25–6, 67
dedifferentiation, 146

degradation, 13, 15, 54, 59, 81, 96, 98, 138
deletions, 87
density gradient centrifugation, 46, 53
deoxyribonuclease, 55
depolymerization, 23
  of bacterial DNA, 26
detergent, 60–1
determination, 158–9
development capacity, 158
Dictyostelium, 14, 38
diethylstilboestrol, 14
differentiation, 142, 145–6
  heritable, 152, 159
  markers of, 157
  nuclear, 84
dimethyl sulphoxide, 51
Diptera, 86
diphtheria toxin, 127, 132
dispersion, 91, 119–20, 155
DNA,
  adenylic acid in, 47
  bacterial, 23, 47
  bacteriophages, 34
  changes in, 143
  of chloroplasts, 6, 8
  in chromocentres, 85
  coding sequences of, 1, 85
  configuration of
    higher-order, 154
    tertiary, 154
  content in bands, 83, 87–8
  cytoplasmic, 6, 7
  depolymerization of, 23, 26
  diploid amount of, 86
  in *lac* region, 30
  of mitochondria, 6, 8
  nucleotides in, 1, 143–4, 154
  phosphate groups of, 92
  ratio to RNA, 95
  RNA hybridization, 67
  satellite, 85
  secondary modification of, 156
  synthesis, 30, 111, 113
  transcription of 1, 12–14, 26, 82, 145, 154
dorsal pancreatic rudiment, 145
Drosophila, 87, 159

egg
  anucleate halves of, 11
  cytoplasm in, 149
  enucleated, 11
  frog, 11
  sea-urchin, 149
  unfertilized, 83
Ehrlich ascites, 110, 114
elasmobranchs, 151
electrolyte
  composition, 92
  environment, 121

electrolyte—*contd*
  flow of, 151
  interactions, 92
electrophoresis, 56, 126, 149
embryo, 152
  chick, 116, 146, 148
  hatching of, 149
  mouse, 14, 145, 148, 151
  wheat, 38
end-cells, 113
end product, 80–1
engagement, 96
enucleation, 12
  physiological, 13
enzymes,
  abnormal, 24
  activity, 78
  assay of, 126
  cap-forming, 8
  changes in level of, 37
  degradative, 98
  first, 79
  intracellular concentration of, 98
  lag phase in, 25
  maternal, 149
  molar amounts of, 32
  multi complex, 36
  mutant forms of, 80
  paternal, 149
  protein, 10
  polymeric, 28
  polysaccharide forming, 14
  regulation of, 22
  related sequences of, 37
  sequential induction of, 150
  stabilization by substrate, 99
epinephrine, 14
episomic F sex factor, 34
epithelium, 145, 151
erythrocyte, 116, 124, 126–9
  ghosts, 117, 121
  hen, 113, 115
  mammal, 113
  nucleated, 113
  nucleus of, 118–19, 121, 123, 128–34
Escherichia coli, 21, 29, 36, 51–2, 56, 155
  male cells of, 34
  mutants of, 31
  pulse labelling of, 47
  radiation sensitive strain, 26
euchromatic regions, 34
eukaryotic cells, 36, 89
exonuclease, 56, 98, 138
extranucleolar region, 136

feed-back, 79–80
female cells
  permissive, 34
F factor
  episome, 34

  mutants, 34
fibrocyte, 84
fish hybrids
  interspecific, 149
flagella, 12
5-fluorouracil, 23, 26, 28
fly
  foot pad, 88
foreignness, 115, 118
fragmentation, 50, 151
frog
  eggs, 66
  enucleated eggs, 12, 144
  erythrocyte nuclei, 118
  oocytes, 12, 63, 66, 95
fructose pathway, 31
fruiting body
  formation of, 38, 147
fungi, 36
fungus gnat, 83

galactose operon, 30–1
galactoside, 29
  permease, 28
  transacetylase, 28
β-galactosidase, 21, 27–8, 32, 155
  antibodies to, 24, 80
  catabolite repression of, 31
  constitutive, 27
  gene, 24–5
  inactive form, 24
  induced synthesis, 23 (fig.)
  inducible, 22, 29
  structural gene, 22
  synthesis of, 25–6
gametes, 11
gelatin, 155
genes, 33, 38, 87, 90
  for cap formation, 147
  clustering of, 37
  dispersed, 36
  dosage of, 154
  duplication of, 7
  β-galactosidase, 24
  independent operation, 157
  information in, 9
  interaction between, 157
  lac, 32
  mutations in, 33
  polymerase, 33
  regulation, 21
  related, 22, 33, 36–7
  removal of, 22, 25
  signals, 90
  specific repressors, 91, 94
  structural, 22, 28, 33, 82
  superstructure, 154
    switches, 148
  transcription of, 38
  tryp, 34

germination, 14, 37–8, 150
gibberellic acid, 38
glandular tissue, 86
globin, 12
glutamine synthetase, 14
glycerokinase, 31
glycerol, 26
glycerophosphate permease, 31
glycol, 26
Gram negative bacteria, 22
growth
    hormone, 14
    logarithmic, 97
    under restricted illumination, 5
G translocation factor, 36
guanosine monophosphate reductase, 31
guanosine triphosphate, 36
guanylic acid, 47

haem, 12
haemadsorption, 122–3
haemoglobin, 12
    messenger RNA, 62–4, 66
    synthesis of, 14, 78, 81
haemolymph, 89
haemolysis, 117
heat stability, 149
heart
    beat, 149
    cells, 14
    muscle, 14
heavy
    cells, 53
    isotopes, 43
    nitrogen, 46
    ribosomes, 53
HeLa cells, 58 (fig.), 65 (fig.), 110, 114–15
hen
    erythrocyte, 113, 115
hepatoma cells, 14, 78
heritability of differentiated traits, 153,
    159
heterochromatin, 85–6
heterochromatic regions, 83–4, 86
heterogeneous giant nuclear RNA, 56
    sedimentation behaviour, 48, 51
heterogenotes, 29
heterokaryons, 110–11, 114–16, 124–5
    (fig.), 126–9 (fig.), 131, 133, 156–7
heterozygotic cell, 149
higher cells, 66, 77, 82, 94
histidine
    operon, 32–3
    repression by, 79–80
    synthesis, 79
histone, 63–4, 91
homeotic mutations, 159
homogeneity, 46, 48, 61, 62
human
    antigens, 122

chromosomes, 130
hybrid cells, 130
ribosomes, 130
hybrid
    birds, 149
    cells, 109, 111, 118, 153, 157
hybridization, 51, 67
hyperinducibility, 33
hypoxanthine, 126, 128, 131

i^+, 31
    crosses between organisms, 29
i^-, 29, 32
illumination, 5, 148
i locus
    mutations at, 28–9
Ilyanassa obsoleta, 12
imaginal discs, 158–9
    cells of, 159
    subcultivation, 159
imago, 159
immune
    haemadsorption, 122
    responses, 113
immunoglobulin, 157
    heavy chain, 63, 79
    light chain, 63
inactivation, 24, 83–4, 90–1, 109, 131–2,
    135
inducer, 29, 150
    exogenous, 67, 155
inducibility, 29
    hyper-, 33
induction, 22
    en chaine, 150
    of β-galactosidase, 22
    kinetics of, 22
    of permease system, 155
    sequential, 150
    super, 78
infectivity, 110
information, 37
    for cap production, 6
    expression of, 8
    flow of, 94
    genetic, 9
    transfer of, 1, 6, 121
inheritance
    of acquired traits, 152
    non-mendelian, 7
inhibitor, 35, 78, 81
inosinic acid pyrophosphorylase, 126,
    127 (fig.), 129, 131, 132, 132 (fig.)
insulin, 14
interband, 87–8
intercalating dyes, 92, 121
intercellular communication, 151
    in embryos, 152
interspecific
    hybrids, 149

interspecific—*contd*
  hybrid cells, 109
  integration of cells, 118
interphase, 83–5
intestinal epithelium
  nuclei from, 144
intranuclear regulation, 59, 93, 96, 137
ion concentration, 93
ionic
  effects, 92
  strength, 60
i region, 31
isoenzyme patterns,
  species-specific, 9
isopropyl-thiogalactoside, 30

junctions
  complex, 151
  gap, 151
  tight, 151

kieselguhr, 60
kinetics
  of induced synthesis, 23 (fig.)
K ion, 93

lac
  DNA in, 30
  genes, 32
  operon, 30
  repressor, 30
lactate dehydrogenase, 9
lactose operons, 31
lag phase, 25
Lamarck, 152
Langhans, 116
larvae, 86
  of holometabolous insects, 158–9
  imaginal discs of, 158
lens, 63
lentoid bodies, 160
L-forms, 155
light
  cells, 53
  isotopes, 53
  ribosomes, 53
liver parenchyma
  regeneration of, 151
Lucké carcinoma, 144
lymphocyte, 84, 113–16
lymphoid series, 144
lysis, 35
lysosomes, 89
lysozyme, 155

macrophage, 113–16
magnesium, 48–51, 54
malate dehydrogenase, 9
male cells, 34
  development, 83
  non-permissive, 34

maltose operon, 32
mammals, 83
  erythrocytes of, 113
  eutherian, 90
marsupials, 83
maternal enzyme, 149
mealy bug, 83
melanin, 157
melanoblasts, 12
mesenchyme, 145–6
messenger RNA, 46, 60, 62–7, 81, 83, 89,
    96, 138, 154
  in bacteria, 66–7
  biologically active, 65
  degradation of, 81
  haemoglobin, 62–4, 66
  in higher cells, 66
  histone, 64
  life of, 66, 68
  pre-existing, 148
  replication of, 152
  stability of, 66, 89
  structure of, 81
  translatability of, 63, 81
  transport of, 65
metabolic sequence, 79
metamorphosis, 88–9, 159
metaphase plate, 112
metazoa, 15
methylation, 156
microbeam, 132–3, 136
micro-electrodes, 151
microtubule proteins, 11
microvilli, 110
miracil D, 36
mitochondria, 7, 8, 61
mitosis, 85
  tetrapolar, 112,
  tripolar, 112
molecular weight, 30, 47, 63
mononucleate cells, 111–12, 153, 156
  multiplication of, 112
morphogenic event
  critical variables, 78
morphological changes, 143
moulting periods, 88
  pupal, 88
mouse
  antigens, 122
  embryo of, 14, 145, 148, 151
  hybrid cells of, 130
  ribosomes, 130
MS2 phage, 33
mud snail, 12
multicellular organisms, 142, 150
multi-enzyme complex, 36
muscle
  cells, 146
  movement, 149
  tissue, 146

mutations, 29, 30, 33, 80
myeloma cells, 157
myoblasts, 146
myosin, 63
Myxococcus xanthus, 38
myxoviruses, 110

Na ion, 93
negative control, 28–9, 31
neural
    crest, 12
    retina, 14
nuclear
    antigens, 120
    damage, 61
    differentiation, 84
    division, 10, 11
    fusion, 112
    growth, 11
    labelling, 55
    membrane, 94–6
    pores, 96
    transplantation, 7
    volume, 84, 91
nucleolar antigens, 120
nucleolus, 123, 131–3, 135
    proteins in, 138
    inactivation of, 137
nucleoside permease, 127
nucleotides, 1
    composition of, 86
    in DNA, 1, 88
    repetitive, 88
    sequences, 62–4, 143
    unique, 88
nucleus
    elimination, 84
    erythrocyte, 119, 121, 123, 126, 128–30,
        133–4
    of higher cells, 94
    human, 111
    information transfer from, 121
    interphase, 83–4
    irradiated, 119
    macrophage, 114
    mass of, 119
    murine, 111
    transplanted, 3
nutrient supply, 37

o locus, 28, 29–31
oocytes, 12, 63, 66, 95
operator, 28
operon, 29, 36, 79
    arabinose, 32
    galactose, 31
    histidine, 32–3
    lactose, 31

maltose, 32
rhamnose, 32
organ
    grafts, 112
    specificity, 88
organisms
    coenocytic, 11
    multicellular, 142, 150
    unicellular, 142, 147
ornithine transcarbamylase, 35
ovalbumin, 63
    synthesis, 14, 78
ovum, 143, 148–9
    fertilized, 142–3
    progeny of, 158

pancreatic
    cells, 14, 148
    rudiment, 145, 151
    tissue, 145
parotid gland, 14
parternal enzyme, 149
peptide chain, 79
Peranema trichophorum, 12
permeability characteristics, 95
permease system, 155
phage,
    f2 group, 33
    ghosts of T2, 27
    λ, 23, 26, 32
    messenger RNA, 52
    MS2, 33
    RNA, 33, 52, 54
    T-even, 26
    T4, 47, 52, 54
phenol, 60–1
phenotypic changes, 145
phosphatase, 4–5 (fig.), 26
phosphate, 47
    radioactive, 59
    groups, 91
phosphoribosyl
    pyrophosphate, 126
    transferase, 33–4
phosphorus pulse method, 59
phosphorylation, 91
photosynthesis, 77
    in marine alga, 11
pigment
    cells, 12, 146
    granules, 12
pilocarpine, 89
pinocytosis, 12
pituitary
    gland, 14
    hormones, 11
plants, 37
    cuttings of, 144
    growth of, 144
    hormones in, 5

plasma phosphoprotein, 14
p locus, 28
  mutations at, 30
polyacrylamide gels, 56, 58 (fig.)
polyadenylic acid, 60, 64–5, 65 (fig.), 66, 97, 137
polyanions, 91
polycations, 92
polycistronic RNA, 24
polydispersity, 50, 61, 65
polymerase gene, 33
polymeric enzymes, 28
polynucleotides, 56
polypeptide, 1
  release of, 79
  chain, 80–1
polyribonucleotides, 62
polysaccharide
  in cap, 4
  composition of, 3
polysomes, 61, 65, 65 (fig.)
polytene chromosomes, 83, 86, 88–9, 92–3, 156
polythymidylic acid, 65
  cellulose, 66
positive control, 30–2
post-mitotic reconstitution, 112
p region, 30
proflavine, 36
promoter, 28
prophase, 86
protein, 14, 15, 29, 32, 95
  abnormal, 27
  basic, 91
  catabolism, 98
  in chromatin, 93
  coaptation with RNA, 96
  coat, 33
  cross-reacting, 27
  flow of, 96, 119
  lac, 32
  lens, 14, 160
  membrane, 98
  microtubule, 11
  non-enzyme, 81
  in nucleolus, 138
  PZ, 27
  receptor, 31
  ribosomal, 53
  RNA complexes, 61
  secretory, 88–9
  synthesis, 11, 14, 38, 46
protoplasts, 155
protozoa, 15
Pseudococcus obscurus, 83
puffs, 86–7, 89
  formation of, 88
  pattern of, 88, 92
  tissue-specific, 88
pulse-chase procedures, 97

pulse labelling, 47–9
puromycin, 77
pyrimidine analogue, 23
pyrophosphate phosphoribosyltransferase, 79

rabbit
  haemoglobin, 63
  macrophages, 113–15
  reticulocytes, 63
radioactive
  chromosomes, 25
  decay of phosphorus, 22, 25–6
  nucleus, 119
  phosphorus, 22, 49, 53, 59
  precursors, 57
  zygotes, 26
rat
  diaphragm, 14
  lymphocyte, 113–15
regenerative processes, 8
regulation, 34, 87
  coordinate, 22, 36
  of DNA synthesis, 113, 116
  in higher cells, 77
  intranuclear, 96
  mechanism, 21, 33
  reiteration, 87
  renal tubules, 151
  repressed cultures, 34
repression
  by arginine, 35
  by histidine, 79–80
  of operon, 79
  specific translational, 34
  by tryptophan, 34
repressors, 28, 30, 35, 79
  binding of, 30
  catabolite, 31
  gene-specific, 82–91
  histidine, 79–80
  lac, 30
  specific, 29, 33–4
  of translation, 78
reptiles, 84
reticulocyte, 12, 79
reverse transcriptase, 154
rhamnose, 32
rhizoids, 2
ribonucleases, 6
ribonucleoprotein complex, 98
ribosomal RNA, 8, 46–7, 51, 54–5, 58–9, 62, 130, 138
  life of, 46
  nucleotide sequences in, 62
  precursor of, 48–9
  preformed, 53
  proteins, 53
  sedimentation behaviour of, 47
  sequence analysis of, 62

ribosomal RNA—*contd*
  synthesis of, 133
  18S, 66
  28S, 130
ribosomes, 35, 46, 95
  attachment of, 138
  bacterial, 54
  chloroplast, 77
  cytoplasmic, 61, 77
  heavy, 53
  human, 130
  mouse, 130
  nascent, 138
  particles, 150
  subunits, 138
  30S, 52
  50S, 52
  70S, 48, 51
rifampicin, 35–6, 67
RNA
  bacterial, 52, 66–8
  from bacteriophages, 62
  cellular, 46
  components of, 61
  cytoplasmic, 7, 8, 10, 46, 66, 83
  degradation of, 13, 81, 96, 136
  density of, 46
  in erythrocyte nuclei, 128
  f2, 64
  flow to cytoplasm, 97, 135–7
  fragmentation of, 50, 50, 51 (fig.)
  free, 61
  giant, 56
  half life, 66–7
  heterogeneous, 51
  histidyl transfer, 79–80
  intranuclear, 96–7
  labelling
    cytoplasmic, 133, 135
    pulse, 48–51, 51 (fig.), 56, 58 (fig.)
    rapid, 54–6, 58–61, 96, 129
  leucyl transfer, 79
  life of, 8, 9, 59, 66, 68
  messenger *see* messenger RNA
  metabolism of, 6
  mitochondrial, 65
  molecules of
    size, 24
    weight, 24, 63
  non-ribosomal, 136
  nuclear, 56, 59
  nucleotides in, 1, 62–3
  phages, 33
  polyadenylic acid in, 65–6
  polycistronic, 32
  polydisperse, 65, 96, 129–30
  precursor
    pools, 49, 53
    radioactive, 55, 57, 111
  protein complex, 61

  in puff, 89
  ratio to DNA, 95
  replication of, 7, 8, 152, 154
    cytoplasmic, 8
    self, 153
  sedimentation characteristics of, 24, 47,
    50
  specific activity, 61
  stability of, 66, 81, 89
  synthesis, *see* synthesis
  28S, 130
  16S, 130
  templates, 8, 9, 22
  transfer, 8, 79, 81, 136
  translation, 81, 130
  turnover of, 10, 96–7
  unstable, 48

salivary glands, 86, 88–9, 138, 151
Salmonella typhinurium, 79
satellite, 85
Sciara coprophila, 83, 89
sea
  snail *Triton*, 12
  urchin, 14, 149
secondary
  effects, 12, 26, 35
  modification, 91, 96
  nuclei, 10
  structure, 24, 60, 63–4
secretory proteins, 88–9
sedimentation
  behaviour of RNA, 24, 49, 51 (fig.), 55,
    65 (fig.)
  coefficients, 55–6, 62–3
  heterogeneous, 56, 61, 65
  polydispersity of, 50, 61
  rate of, 56
seeds
  germination of, 14, 38
Sendai virus, 110, 117
sequential induction, 150
serine deaminase, 31
sex chromosomes, 83, 90
sexual conjugation, 22, 24, 29, 36
short-lived intermediates, 25
signals, 90, 117, 119
silk moth, 14
slime mould, 14, 38
species-specific
  cap, 4
  cytoplasmic signals, 119
  isoenzyme patterns, 9
  marker, 127
  restrictions on RNA translation, 130
  surface antigens, 122, 133
specificity, 90
  of antibody, 144
sperm, 143, 149
spindle, 112